es, general relief and a lo

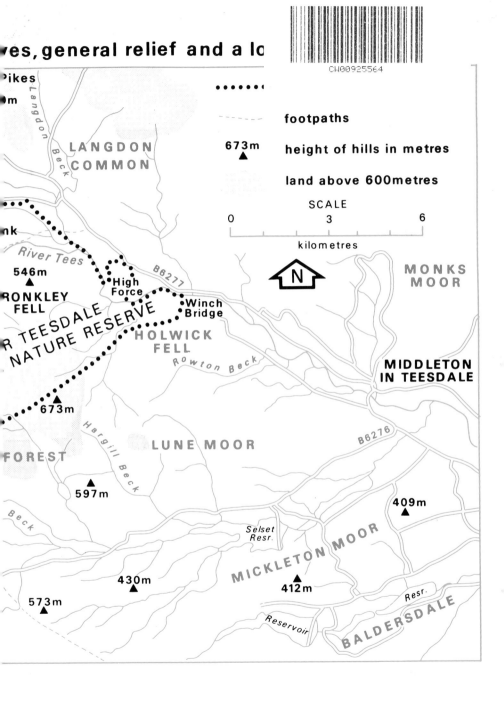

·ikes
·m

Langdon Beck

LANGDON COMMON

·nk

River Tees

546m ▲

RONKLEY FELL

High Force

B6277

Winch Bridge

R TEESDALE NATURE RESERVE

HOLWICK FELL

Rowton Beck

673m ▲

Hargill Beck

LUNE MOOR

B6276

FOREST

597m ▲

Beck

409m ▲

Selset Resr.

MICKLETON MOOR

430m ▲

412m ▲

573m ▲

Reservoir

Resr.

BALDERSDALE

MONKS MOOR

MIDDLETON IN TEESDALE

• • • • • •

- - - - - footpaths

673m ▲ height of hills in metres

land above 600metres

SCALE

0   3   6

kilometres

N

To John   Xmas 1978,

Upper Teesdale

THE AREA AND ITS NATURAL HISTORY

Upper Teesdale

THE AREA AND ITS NATURAL HISTORY

edited by

A. R. CLAPHAM

COLLINS
ST JAMES'S PLACE, LONDON

William Collins Sons & Co Ltd

London · Glasgow · Sydney · Auckland

Toronto · Johannesburg

First published 1978

© The Teesdale Trust 1978

ISBN 0 00 219743 X

Phototypeset by Tradespools Ltd, Frome, Somerset

Made and Printed in Great Britain by
William Collins Sons & Co Ltd Glasgow

Contents

6 CONTENTS

Plates

Figures in the Text

The map inside the front cover is of Upper Teesdale and its immediate surroundings and shows the Upper Teesdale and Moor House National Nature Reserves.

The geological map inside the back cover illustrates the account by Dr G. A. L. Johnson (in Chapter 6) of the geology of Upper Teesdale.

Preface

THIS book gives general readers an account of the natural history of Upper Teesdale and of the vigorous programme of scientific research carried out in the area during the past ten years with the help of the Teesdale Trust and a gift of £100,000 from the Imperial Chemical Industries Limited. Upper Teesdale has long been a field for research sponsored by Universities and the Research Councils, but the Trust was set up in 1967 with the aim of gathering as much as possible of the scientific information that might otherwise have been lost through the coming of the Cow Green reservoir.

Ever since the seventeenth-century naturalist John Ray found the shrubby cinquefoil near Greta Bridge, and particularly since a more detailed botanical exploration was begun towards the end of the eighteenth-century, Upper Teesdale has been renowned for the peculiarity and richness of its flora. Many plant species have been found there which are of special interest because they occur either nowhere else in the British Isles or only in one or two other restricted and often far distant localities, and for this reason Upper Teesdale has for long been hallowed ground for British botanists. Many went there to see what are now recognized as the very locally surviving remnants of vegetation-types once characteristic of parts of the country that escaped the ice-sheets of the final stages of the Pleistocene Ice-Age, spreading more widely as the retreating ice uncovered new ground in northern Britain but shrinking again when forests were once more able to clothe all but the higher slopes of mountains.

It was therefore to have been expected that scientists, and especially botanists, would raise objection from their points of view to the construction of the large reservoir at Cow Green proposed by the Tees Valley and Cleveland Water Board and the Northumbrian River Authority to supply the extra water needed to meet the growing needs of industry and domestic consumers on Teesside. The campaign against the reservoir reached its climax when the Tees Valley and Cleveland Water Bill, which was to authorize the construction of a reservoir at Cow Green, was being considered by the two Houses of Parliament.

Parliament recognized both the scientific importance of the area and the need for extra water. The promoters of the Bill were able to satisfy Parliament that this need was urgent, that they had properly considered all the feasible alternative sites, and that they had the support of the Water Resources Board and had consulted the Natural Environment Research Council. Noting particularly that only a small part of the floristically rich area would be inundated and that steps could be taken to minimize the danger to the remainder, Parliament considered that the balance of advantage was in favour of the reservoir and approved the Bill.

The Imperial Chemical Industries Limited, being major users of water on Teesside, were relieved that the reservoir could now go ahead but concerned about any irretrievable loss to botanical interests which might result. They therefore decided to offer the sum of £10,000 a year for ten years to promote a programme of research. In consultation with the Natural Environment Research Council they set up the Teesdale Trust to administer the scheme. The then Chairman of the Natural Environment Research Council became a member of the Trust.

The Trust proceeded immediately to set up a Scientific Committee to advise it in general and in particular on the merits of the applications for grants for research which it hoped to receive. In the event I.C.I.'s initiative had an enthusiastic response from interested scientists.

The Scientific Committee agreed that priority for the allocation of financial support should be given to research into the causes of the floristic and ecological uniqueness of Upper Teesdale. This implied a detailed specification of the unusual features as well as studies of the past and present climate, geology and soils of the area and of the history of its vegetation since the last retreat of the ice. Some of these studies were clearly more urgent than others and in particular those which involved sites that would be destroyed or seriously modified during the construction of the reservoir or lost through eventual inundation.

Inevitably the presence of the Cow Green Reservoir has made a significant change in this area of Upper Teesdale and some of the floristically rich and scientifically interesting parts of Cow Green have been submerged. One rare sedge, a bog-moss and a mayfly have been lost from the area. On the other hand, a major additional supply of water has been made available for the vital industrial area of Teesside on which so many jobs and so much of our national economy depend. The great care with which the construction of the reservoir was undertaken minimized the danger to the surrounding area of special scientific interest. The Trustees would wish to express their gratitude to all those concerned who did so much to confine the disturbance, and especially to Mr T. G. Buffey who was the Site Research Officer during the period of construction of the dam.

Lord Nugent of Guildford, PC,
Chairman of the Trustees of the Teesdale Trust.

Editorial Foreword

IT falls to me, as editor of this volume on behalf of the Teesdale Scientific Committee, to thank all who have assisted in its production. Our aim has been to show why Upper Teesdale has for so long been an area of outstanding interest to botanists and how recent scientific research, and in particular research carried out during the past decade and much of it with financial aid from the Teesdale Trust Fund, has shed light on the reasons for the concentration of rare plant species on Widdybank and Cronkley Fells.

All those who wrote chapters for the book have been personally involved in the investigations they describe, and their willingness to contribute, busy as they are, has been much appreciated. Thanks are also due to those members of the Committee who have acted as sub-editors for sections of the book: Dr J. C. Coulson, Sir Harry Godwin, the late Mr J. E. Lousley, Professor C. D. Pigott and Professor D. H. Valentine. Mr Lousley's sudden death early in 1975 not only deprived the Committee of the wise counsel and valuable assistance he had been giving us for several years but was a sad loss to all who shared his deep interest in the flora of the British Isles.

We wish further to express our gratitude to those who have provided necessary data for certain chapters, and especially to Mr Frank Green and his assistants for summaries of the meteorological records from the temporary station on Widdybank Fell.

Permission to reproduce photographs has been kindly granted by Dr T. J. Bines, Dr M. E. Bradshaw, Dr J. C. Coulson, Mr J. P. Harding, Professor C. D. Pigott, Rev. H. G. Proctor, Mr A. E. Ramsbottom, Dr D. A. Ratcliffe and Mr G. Wall, as well as by the Freshwater Biological Association and Imperial Chemical Industries Limited. The I.C.I. Photographic Unit at Billingham, under the skilled and experienced direction of Mr H. Mounsey, was always ready to go out into the field or up into the air to take photographs for us, often on occasions which they felt far from ideal but which were the most convenient for us. Above all we are grateful to Dr M. C. F. Proctor, who consented not merely to the reproduction of many of his unsurpassed studies of individual plants and to take additional photographs specially for the book but also to act as our adviser in all matters concerning the plates, and who has been immensely helpful throughout.

Finally we must pay tribute to the valuable services of Dr J. F. D. Frazer, of the Nature Conservancy Council, who has from an early stage acted as Secretary of the Teesdale Scientific Committee and more recently of our editorial sub-committee as well.

Attention should be drawn in this Foreword to two editorial decisions on the form of the book. It was agreed that English names of plants should be used throughout, but that on first mention in any chapter the Latin name should be added in brackets, Latin names to be those in the 1973 and 1975 reprints of the *Excursion Flora of the British Isles*. It was also agreed that there should be no separate lists of cited publications at the end of each chapter but a collected bibliography at the end of the book, and that this might usefully be in two parts. The first would be a general numbered list of *research* publications relating exclusively or at least primarily to Upper Teesdale and appearing within the ten year period 1967–1976. Many of these deal with investigations financed wholly or in part from the Teesdale Trust Fund, and references to them commonly occur in more than one chapter. The second part of the bibliography comprises all other publications that have been cited, most of them dating from before 1967. These are listed, chapter by chapter, on pp. 216-22, those for a given chapter being followed by the list-numbers of the accounts of recent research to which reference has been made in that chapter.

A. R. Clapham
28 August 1976

Introduction

Location and General Features of Upper Teesdale

THE River Tees rises on the east side of the saddle between Cross Fell and Little Dun Fell, in the highest part of the northern Pennines. After flowing eastwards for about eight kilometres it turns towards the south-east and maintains that general direction as far as Barnard Castle before winding south of Darlington and then out to sea just north of Middlesbrough. The Moor House National Nature Reserve, immediately south-east of Cross Fell (see map inside the front cover), is bounded by the young Tees on its northern and eastern sides, but the areas in Upper Teesdale of greatest scientific interest, in particular for the numbers of rare plant species found in them, lie further to the south-east, 10–13km upstream from Middleton-in-Teesdale. Widdybank Fell, on the north-eastern or County Durham side of the river, and Cronkley Fell, opposite to it on the Yorkshire side, are both included in the Upper Teesdale National Nature Reserve, as are such other botanically interesting features as the rocky banks of the Tees and the cliffs above them and also the rich hay-meadows adjoining the river. Through all this upper part of the dale the Tees is a typical upland stream, fast-flowing and still subject, above the reservoir, to rapid changes in width and depth.

Most of the Upper Teesdale N.N.R. lies at altitudes of 500–625m (c. 1500–1900ft) above sea-level, and it reaches 790m (2591ft) on the summit of Mickle Fell in its south-western corner, another area of considerable botanical interest. The Nature Reserve is part of a very large area of high ground through which the headwaters of the Tees, Wear and Tyne and their main tributaries have cut their way and which is highest along its western edge. Here the lofty summit-ridge rises to 893m (2930ft) on Cross Fell and continues in a south-easterly direction through Little Dun Fell and Great Dun Fell, 842 and 847m respectively, falling to 673m on Murton Fell to rise again in the south-facing arc extending from Mickle Fell in the east to Hilton Fell (746m) and Burton Fell (731m), these last two continuing the line of the main summit-ridge. This impressive west-facing wall, whose height and steepness are accentuated by its being a fault-scarp and the western edge of the raised Alston Block of the northern Pennines, is separated from the mountains of the Lake District by the deep trough of the Eden valley. It is the watershed between the east-flowing Pennine streams and the tributaries of the Eden, which flows north-westwards to reach the sea in Solway Firth. No road traverses the summit-ridge between those from Alston to Penrith in the north and from Middleton-in-Teesdale to Brough 30km further south, the average width of the roadless rectangle being about 14.5km.

The considerable altitude of the Upper Teesdale N.N.R. results in low

15

temperatures and a high rainfall with a good deal of snow in winter, and the growing season for plants is appreciably shortened compared with that in the adjoining lowlands (pp. 106–10). Gordon Manley, in *Climate and the British Scene*, quotes a Swiss professor of geology who described the high ground between Upper Teesdale and Upper Weardale as 'tundra', no doubt feeling that the aspect of the moorland vegetation matched the subarctic rigours of the climate. Yet trees once grew over most of the area (pp. 110–12) and there are today plantations of Scots pine and other trees, growing sufficiently well to provide usable timber, at up to 460m (1500ft) on the northern slopes of Cross Fell, and although there is now little arable agriculture except in low-lying or specially sheltered spots, oats were said by Winch (1825) to be cropped in his time at altitudes up to 610m (2000ft).

The high altitude and pronounced upland climate of Upper Teesdale, together with its remoteness and the consequent low level of man's past impact on its natural vegetation, must have played a significant part in the persistence there of many unusual plants and plant-assemblages, matters considered in detail in Chapters 5 and 7 (pp. 102 and 141). Further relevant features are the geology of the area and related aspects of its topography and soils, an account of which will be found in Chapter 6 (p. 122). All that needs to be said here is that the bedrock over most of Widdybank Fell and Cronkley Fell is either of Lower Carboniferous age, some of it limestone, some sandstone or shale, or is quartz-dolerite of the Great Whin Sill. The igneous rock of the Sill, which underlies very large areas in the counties of Northumberland and Durham, and beyond them, and which is exposed at various points between the cliffs of High Cup Nick in the west and the Farne Islands in the east, was injected into older rocks at the very end of the Carboniferous period. The whinstone is mostly fine-grained and very hard, and it is much quarried for road-stone (Plate 20). In many places in Upper Teesdale it is exposed in steep well-jointed faces and cliffs above the Tees, as in Cronkley Scars and Falcon Clints (Plate 3), which form respectively the northern face of Cronkley Fell and the southern face of Widdybank Fell. The Whin Sill also forms the ledge over which the Tees falls in the spectacular and much-visited High Force (Plate 2), and the irregular bed of the steep and turbulent cataract at Cauldron Snout (Plate 2). These four, the darkly menacing north face of Cronkley Fell (Plate 4), the beautifully structured Falcon Clints (Plate 3) and the waterfalls, impressive in their quite different ways, at High Force and Cauldron Snout, all involving the Whin Sill, are the most striking topographical features of Upper Teesdale and give it a scenic character very distinct from that of all other dales in the northern Pennines.

Apart from its scenic importance in Upper Teesdale the Great Whin Sill has provided the cliffs, rocky slopes and screes and the rocky riverside banks that are so important as habitats for many plant species unable to survive competition in closed vegetation. In the Craven Pennines plants requiring habitats of these kinds find them in the limestone cliffs and screes and the limestone pavements of Ingleborough, Pen-y-Ghent, the Malham area and elsewhere, but within the Upper Teesdale N.N.R. limestone forms only low cliffs except on Mickle Fell, where the higher cliffs and more extensive scree-slopes harbour many interesting plants, some of them not found elsewhere in the Reserve. Whinstone carries fewer species than limestone, but there are nevertheless certain plants specially characteristic of it, notably juniper, bear-

berry, alpine cinquefoil and some interesting ferns and mosses. The shrubby cinquefoil, too, flourishes at the foot of its riverside cliffs and boulder-strewn slopes.

The Whin Sill has contributed to the unusual character of Upper Teesdale in yet
another way. When the whinstone was injected, hot and molten, into the more or less
horizontally-bedded rocks of the Reserve, limestone in contact with it was baked for
some distance above and below it into a coarsely crystalline marble. This weathers
readily into a loose aggregate of separate crystals resembling granulated sugar and
for that reason called 'sugar-limestone'. There is a striking concentration of rare
plants on the sugar-limestone, for reasons that are considered in Chapters 3 and 6
(pp. 73–6 and 134–7). Where the Sill passed through other types of rock there was
comparable metamorphosis, shales, for example, being converted into a smooth
porcelain-like 'whetstone'. Botanically, however, the sugar-limestone is far and away
the most important of these modified rocks.

History of Botanical Exploration in Upper Teesdale

In 1805 Nathaniel J. Winch, John Thornhill and Richard Waugh, editors of *The
Botanist's Guide through the Counties of Northumberland and Durham*, wrote in
their Preface that 'they were greatly indebted to the communications of various
botanical friends, particularly to the Rev. J. Harriman of Gainford, for pointing out
such indigenous plants as are worthy of notice on the romantic banks of the Tees . . .
The south and south-west of the county of Durham having long been in the possession of such able naturalists, an evident superiority, not only in number but in rarity of
species, will be noticed by the most cursory observer to predominate in that part of the
district'. They go on to recommend investigation of the west and north-west of
Northumberland as being hitherto but slightly explored. 'They must not however
expect that even Cheviot and its surrounding hills will ever be found to vie with
Teesdale, whose mountains are in great measure composed of extensive limestone
ridges, which are well known to be propitious to the growth of alpine plants'. It must
be concluded that Teesdale was already recognized as an area of special interest for
botanists.

The list in *The Botanist's Guide* shows that most of the famous Teesdale Plants had
been found there by 1805: alpine bartsia (*Bartsia alpina*, Plate 11), alpine bistort
(*Polygonum viviparum*, Plate 13), alpine cinquefoil (*Potentilla crantzii*), alpine
meadow-rue (*Thalictrum alpinum*), alpine penny-cress (*Thlaspi alpestre*), bearberry
(*Arctostaphylos uva-ursi*), bird's-eye primrose (*Primula farinosa*, Plate VI), bog
orchid (*Hammarbya paludosa*), hair sedge (*Carex capillaris*, Plate 13), hoary rock-
rose (*Helianthemum canum*, Plate VIII), hoary whitlow-grass (*Draba incana*), holly
fern (*Polystichum lonchitis*), kobresia (*Kobresia simpliciuscula*, Plate 12), mountain
avens (*Dryas octopetala*, Plate 9), Scottish asphodel (*Tofieldia pusilla*, Plate 13), sea
plantain (*Plantago maritima*), shrubby cinquefoil (*Potentilla fruticosa*, Plate V),
spring gentian (*Gentiana verna*, Plate VI), three-flowered rush (*Juncus triglumis*) and
thrift (*Armeria maritima*) are all included, and several others. For most of these it is
not clear precisely when they were first discovered in Teesdale, but we do know that
John Ray published in 1670 the first record of shrubby cinquefoil from a specimen
collected by T. Willisel on the south bank of the Tees, and that Ray himself, on his last

'simpling voyage' in 1671, found it, again on the south bank of the Tees, near a village called Thorpe and below Eggleston Abbey. This is downstream from Barnard Castle and hardly in Upper Teesdale, but in *The Botanist's Guide* two other localities are given: 'near Winch Bridge, and at the High Force . . . where it was observed in Ray's time by Mr. Lawson'.

In his Flora of Northumberland and Durham (1831) Winch adds to this list alpine willow-herb (*Epilobium anagallidifolium*), chickweed willow-herb (*E. alsinifolium*), horse-shoe vetch (*Hippocrepis comosa*, Plate 9) and variegated horsetail (*Equisetum variegatum*). He also writes of both spring gentian and kobresia that they were first shown to him in 1799 by the Rev. J. Harriman of Gainford, and of yellow marsh saxifrage (*Saxifraga hirculus*) that it was 'Said to have been first found by John Binks, a miner'. We are told much more about this John Binks in a contribution to *The Naturalist* for 1884 by James Backhouse Jr (1825–1890) entitled 'Teesdale Botany: Historical and Personal Recollections'. This begins: 'The original discoverer of most of the botanical rarities of Upper Teesdale was John Binks. He was a miner who worked in the lead mines near Middleton in Teesdale, very early in the present century. Though in humble life, Binks was an "observant and intelligent man" . . . of "gentlemanly appearance" . . . "like a little smart French doctor . . . with a delicately formed and highly intellectual face. . . ." . . . Owing to the unhealthiness of the occupation, four days only in the week were devoted to mining; the remaining two being taken advantage of for recreation, and for obtaining from the adjacent hills any plants the druggists wanted, by which a slight addition could be made to his scanty income. Among these plants, I believe, were the rose-root . . ., the Common Juniper, and the Bear Berry'. The phrases in double inverted commas appear as quotations in *The Phytologist* and may have been taken from papers of James Backhouse Sr (1795–1869) or have been remembered from the father's talk.

Backhouse proceeds to state that Binks 'first found and brought under notice' shrubby cinquefoil, spring gentian, bearberry, yellow marsh saxifrage, hoary rock-rose, bog whortleberry (*Vaccinium uliginosum*), alpine bartsia, three-flowered rush, mountain avens and bog orchid, 'and the other Teesdale rarities which became known to the botanical world previous to the year 1820'. He states further that 'Binks brought down his treasured discoveries to a clergyman and to a doctor, both of whom resided at Middleton (or Barnard Castle). These gentlemen sent up the plants to Sir Jas. E. Smith and (I have always understood) got the personal credit of the discoveries by so doing'.

There are some problems here, though there is no reason to doubt John Binks' prowess as a finder of rare plants. Shrubby cinquefoil, however, was already known in John Ray's time to grow in Upper Teesdale. It is of interest that Smith & Sowerby, in volume 7 of *English Botany* (1798), state that spring gentian was 'gathered in April 1797, in Teesdale Forest, Durham, by Mr. John Binks and sent us by the Rev. Mr. Harriman, the first botanist who has ascertained it in England'. This Rev J. Harriman, who showed spring gentian and kobresia to Winch in 1799 and was named as the source of the records for three-flowered rush, bog whortleberry and bog orchid, may well have been the clergyman to whom Backhouse referred. He seems to have been a very active and knowledgeable field-observer who was in close contact with leading botanists of the day and therefore the kind of acquaintance without whom Binks might not have realized the interest and importance of his finds. And even if Harriman was given credit for discovering plants which were in fact first found by Binks, it may nevertheless be true that he found others independently. Winch also stated that W. C. Trevelyan, of Wallington, added chickweed willow-herb to the English flora. This was supposed by the younger Backhouse, from the date on a specimen in his father's herbarium, to have been pointed out by Binks when, as a lad, James Backhouse Sr stayed for the sake of his health on a farm near Barnard Castle and accompanied Binks on 'many a fine and wearying ramble' during 1810. The story of these years of discovery is, it must be admitted, very imperfectly known, but it is at least clear that much had been effected before 1805 and that work continued actively after that date.

James Backhouse Sr was one of those who continued for many years to look for new plants in Upper Teesdale. His son relates that in 1821, when the first figure of a small and inconspicuous fern – oblong or scaly woodsia (*Woodsia ilvensis*) – was published from a Scottish specimen, Backhouse instantly remembered having seen it in Teesdale and said he would go and fetch it. He did so, and the specimen survives. By now the numerous botanical finds in the area had aroused much interest and many botanists visited Upper Teesdale throughout the rest of the century. The first volume of *The Phytologist* (1844), for example, refers to no fewer than six visits. Samuel Simpson of Lancaster made the journey in August 1838, going by pony from Middleton to Widdybank Fell, where he saw alpine bartsia, Scottish asphodel and spring gentian. He looked for and, 'wet through his Mackintosh cape', eventually found woodsia and other ferns. In July 1840 Samuel King, of Luddenden near Halifax, went with a local guide and was first shown yellow marsh saxifrage on Cotherston Fell and later saw shrubby cinquefoil, Scottish asphodel and many others. Then he too 'cast around many an anxious look for *Woodsia ilvensis*; at length . . . to my great joy I espied two small plants, which were instantly secured'. He searched for more, but without success, so 'was obliged to leave the spot with an impression that one day or other it would be extinct there', a prediction that seems, sadly, to have been fulfilled. It is therefore difficult to avoid mixed feelings about his journey back when, well laden with plants, he had to wait for five hours by Brough Castle for the coach to Kirkby Lonsdale. 'We had scarcely taken our seats when the horses started off without guard or coachman, and upset the coach on a bridge; I was so much injured as to be quite incapable of making further observations, and thus ended my botanical excursion in Teesdale'.

In 1843 John Bell of Middleton-in-Teesdale, a mine inspector, discovered a new locality for yellow marsh saxifrage between Cross Fell and Cauldron Snout and also found Jacob's ladder (*Polemonium caeruleum*, Plate 9) nearby. That same summer James Backhouse Jr accompanied his father on a visit to Teesdale and in his account of their finds listed many of the special Teesdale plants. The next year, 1844, a party consisting of the two Backhouses, Silvanus Thompson of York, John Tatham of Settle and G. S. Gibson of Saffron Walden undertook a lengthy excursion in Yorkshire and James Backhouse Jr again published the account. 'After a walk of about twenty-seven miles we arrived late in the evening at the High Force Inn . . . The next morning we set out for Widdybank Fell, Cauldron Snout and Falcon Clints, which comprehend a district probably the richest in Teesdale for a botanist . . . we found a small plant resembling a *Spergula*, but being unable to identify it with any described

British species, we transmitted a specimen to Sir W. J. Hooker and soon received the gratifying intelligence that it was *Spergula stricta*, a plant not previously found in the British Islands'. This was bog sandwort (*Minuartia stricta*), still known nowhere else in the country. Meadow horsetail (*Equisetum pratense*) was also first found in 1844, and other plants with the discovery of which the younger Backhouse was 'personally associated' were alpine saxifrage (*Saxifraga nivalis*) in High Cup Nick in 1843, alpine forget-me-not (*Myosotis alpestris*) on Mickle Fell and Teesdale violet (*Viola rupestris*, Plate VIII) on Widdybank Fell, both in 1862, and alpine willow-herb (*Epilobium anagallidifolium*) in 1872. He was also first to find the large form of field fleawort (*Senecio integrifolius*) on Mickle Fell.

New species have continued to be discovered in Upper Teesdale up to the present decade. Alpine rush (*Juncus alpinoarticulatus*) was found on Widdybank Fell by G. C. Druce in 1903; rare spring sedge (*Carex ericetorum*) by T. G. Tutin, also on Widdybank Fell, in 1949, and alpine foxtail (*Alopecurus alpinus*) in flushes on the slopes of the Cross Fell range by D. A. Ratcliffe and A. Eddy in 1959 (there is some doubt about a possible earlier record for 1945). In 1965 T. C. Hutchinson made the exciting discovery on Widdybank Fell of a plant of dwarf birch (*Betula nana*, Plate 14), a northern and arctic plant also found in central Europe but previously known in this country only from Scotland: a second English find was made more recently (1974) on the Kielder moors south of the Cheviot. Northern water sedge (*Carex aquatilis*) was found by H. G. Proctor in the Cow Green basin in 1972 and, after it had been lost from there by submergence following the construction of the dam, was refound in the Tees near Middleton by N. T. H. Holmes in 1975, the year in which he was also the first to find the very rare arctic-alpine moss *Grimmia agassizii* on rocks in the Tees (p. 194).

In his *Historical and Personal Recollections* of 1884 James Backhouse Jr lists some hawkweeds (*Hieracium*) with the discovery of which he had been associated. He named six as having been found in 1842 when he and Professor C. C. Babington went into the field together after having met at the High Force Inn. These included the beautiful *H. anglicum* and *H. iricum*, both confined to the north and west of the British Isles, the latter known in England only in Teesdale and the Lake District and with one locality in Wales but otherwise restricted to central and northern Scotland and Ireland. Since that year many other hawkweeds have been found in Teesdale, some of them very rare. The total number is probably between 35 and 40, but this is a difficult group and no comprehensive account of Teesdale hawkweeds has been published in recent times.

Comparable with the hawkweeds in their *apomixis*, or production of good seed without need of pollination, are the common lady's-mantles grouped together in the aggregate species *Alchemilla vulgaris*. There are far fewer of them in this country than the several hundreds of native hawkweeds, but their apomixis gives rise to similar problems of discrimination and identification, there being numbers of true-breeding but often only slightly differing *microspecies*. A general review of the native microspecies appeared in a paper by S. M. Walters in the first volume of *Watsonia* (1949), in which he drew attention to the need for further study of the British representatives of this difficult group. The investigations of Walters himself and of M. E. Bradshaw have shown that nine microspecies occur in Upper Teesdale, six apart from the widespread *A. glabra*, *A. xanthochlora* and *A. filicaulis* ssp. *vestita*. These fall into two sets. The first consists of three mountain species with numerous localities in Scotland and found also in northern England, all first discovered in the Teesdale area by Walters in 1947: *A. glomerulans* (Plate 10) and *A. wichurae*, only in Scotland and northern England, and *A. filicaulis* ssp. *filicaulis*, which has also been found in Wales and in one locality in Ireland. The second set is of three species known in this country only in Teesdale and Weardale, where they grow in meadows and pastures or at the sides of roads and tracks. They are: *A. monticola* (Plate 10), formerly but no longer in a few spots in southern England and first detected in Teesdale material by A. J. Wilmott in 1922; *A. acutiloba* (Plate 10), again recognized first by Wilmott, in 1946, in a Teesdale collection dating from 1933, and *A. subcrenata*, first found by Walters in 1951. Bradshaw has suggested that these three might all have been introduced inadvertently at some time, perhaps in hay used as packing material or as fodder, but no definite information is so far available.

This quite recent increase in our knowledge of the Teesdale Alchemillas, and the interesting situation revealed by it, suggests that other genera might yet yield comparable results. The dandelions (*Taraxacum*), like the hawkweeds, include large numbers of apomictic microspecies, and detailed modern studies of them and of the Teesdale roses, blackberries and willows could prove highly informative, and it is to be hoped that such studies may soon be undertaken.

The Origin of the Teesdale Rarities

It is already clear that Upper Teesdale is remarkable for its large number of plant species with few and widely scattered localities in the British Isles and one, bog sandwort, found nowhere else in the country, its nearest locality being in southern Norway. Some grow no nearer to Teesdale than the central Highlands and spring gentian is only in western Ireland. Others occur in one or more other areas in northern England but with their next nearest localities much more distant.

There are two main ways in which this distribution-pattern might have arisen. Viable seeds of the rare species might have reached the area from distant sources and thus have initiated the present Teesdale populations. This seems unlikely because most of the fruits and seeds lack adaptations for long-distance dispersal, and it is clear from many observations and experiments that successful establishment is very infrequent when the seed-source is so distant. It would be necessary, too, for the present habitats of the rare species to have been continuously available for colonization over a very long period, and this is contrary to present geological opinion (see below).

The other main possibility is that the species in question were at some time more continuously spread over northern England than they are today but have lost ground since then and now survive only as 'relicts' in a few scattered localities of which Upper Teesdale is one.

At the maximum of the last glaciation, ice-sheets covered a large area of north-west Europe including part of northern Russia, the Baltic states, northern Germany, almost the whole of Scandinavia apart from the western half of Jutland, most of Great Britain north of a line from the Severn estuary to the Humber and all Ireland except for a broad coastal strip in the south. The high mountains of central Europe were strongly affected, though there was no continuous ice-cover even over the Alps: to the very centre there was 'only a meshwork of more or less connected ice-streams with ridges between' (W. B. Wright, 1914), but glaciers advanced into the surrounding lowlands. Plant-remains assignable to the long period of the glacial maximum give no evidence of closed forests, even of birch, anywhere north of the Alps, though there may have been a few clumps of birches in specially favourable situations. The general vegetation seems to have consisted of cold-tolerant herbs and dwarf shrubs. Identified species from ice-free areas in Great Britain fall into three main categories. Many are today widespread and abundant plants throughout the British Isles, some growing in water or marshy ground, such as duckweeds, pondweeds, water milfoils, greater and lesser spearwort, marsh marigold, meadowsweet and marsh valerian; others are familiar species of drier grasslands and roadsides, such as the three common buttercups, stinging nettle, dandelion, chickweed and sheep's sorrel. At the other extreme are a few species no longer native in this country, like two further buttercups, the arctic *Ranunculus hyperboreus* and the white-flowered arctic-alpine *R. aconitifolius*. Between these extremes are several species which today are either more or less restricted to northern Britain and to mountains or have markedly discontinuous distributions extending into the southern half of England. Both groups include Teesdale rarities, amongst the former being dwarf birch, mountain avens, shrubby and alpine cinquefoil, alpine meadow-rue, alpine bistort and hoary whitlow-grass, while the latter include hoary rock-rose: bog sandwort has also been tentatively identified. This low-growing vegetation must gradually have replaced taller-growing and more warmth-demanding communities as the climate became colder and have consisted in part of the more cold-tolerant components of the former vegetation and in part of northern and mountain plants in retreat from the advancing ice. The vegetational changes of the early-glacial phase were then reversed during the late-glacial period when the ice was retreating but before the re-establishment of the former mixed oak forests over the lowlands, and plant communities of the kind described above may have persisted for forty thousand years or so in the ice-free parts of the country, essentially similar vegetation-types being present all over those areas in north-west Europe lying between the northern ice-sheet and the Alps.

During the early part of this century geologists published evidence for the view that much of the ground in the northern Pennines lying above about 670m (2200ft) had not been ice-covered during the last glaciation. This led first A. J. Wilmott and then K. B. Blackburn to suggest, nearly fifty years ago, that at least some of the Teesdale rarities had survived that glaciation on permanently ice-free 'nunataks' round the head of the dale. More recently, however, geological opinion has favoured the view that the whole of Upper Teesdale was buried beneath the ice, so that perglacial survival *in situ* is no longer a generally acceptable theory.

In 1949 Sir Harry Godwin drew attention to the growing evidence for the view that the rare plants of Upper Teesdale reached the area during the early stages of retreat of the ice as components of the widespread late-glacial vegetation-types which, 10,000–15,000 years ago, recolonized ground made newly available when the ice melted. The colonizing species and their immediate followers must be supposed to have been living in adjacent unglaciated areas, so that they almost certainly included the rare Teesdale plants listed above as well as others not so far identified as components of that vegetation. It must be supposed, too, that the colonizers were initially able to establish themselves over wide areas but that some of them were later eliminated in competition with more strongly growing later arrivals, better able to take advantage of the warmer climate and maturing soils. Still later, when trees eventually arrived from their more distant glacial refuges and formed closed forests, shade-intolerant species would be more and more at a disadvantage. In these ways many of the original colonists would either be lost completely or would survive only very locally.

If this view of the Teesdale rarities as late-glacial relicts is to be accepted there must be convincing reasons for believing that they did in fact reach the area soon after the retreat of the ice and that they have survived there up to the present day. The available evidence is presented and discussed in Chapter 4 and will be seen to give strong support to the relict theory and to direct attention to the question why the rare species have survived in Upper Teesdale but in so few other places.

Some light is thrown on this aspect of the Teesdale problem by plant communities including many of the Teesdale rarities which occur in the mountains of central Europe. In the Jura Mountains for example, at altitudes of 1500–1700m (c. 5000–5600ft) there are steepish limestone slopes, with much bare rock and with very shallow black soil elsewhere, on which the vegetation is a short open grassland dominated by blue sesleria and a blue-leaved form of sheep's fescue and with some sedges, in particular *Carex sempervirens*. More or less prostrate juniper and bearberry are commonly present, and the most conspicuous of the associated herbs are three yellow-flowered leguminous species: bird's-foot trefoil, kidney vetch and horseshoe vetch, the last a very local plant in northern England but found in Upper Teesdale. Other Teesdale rarities characteristic of these slopes are mountain avens, spring gentian, alpine bartsia, alpine bistort, cat's-foot and hoary rock-rose: Teesdale violet also occurs but only very locally. The slopes are usually open to grazing animals but do not seem to be heavily grazed, cattle presumably being deterred by the difficult terrain and the sparse and low growth of the herbage. They are below the tree-limit but are today either treeless or carry only scattered and dwarfed Scots or mountain pine, and they can never have supported closed forest. In these conditions late-glacial immigrants might well have survived to the present time, and the vegetation is regarded by botanists as consisting largely of such relicts. Elsewhere in the Alps and neighbouring mountains there are woods of Scots pine (or occasionally of mountain pine) at altitudes where forests of beech or spruce are normally found but on slopes so rocky and shallow-soiled or so unstable that these trees cannot establish themselves. Here again many of the Teesdale rarities are components of the ground-flora and help to confirm the view that these are relict pinewoods surviving from late-glacial times.

The main purpose of this book is to attempt to answer questions posed above by reference to the outcome of investigations carried out both before and after the establishment of the Teesdale Trust. The stimulus provided by the Trust Fund undoubtedly led to a greatly increased volume of scientific research in Upper Teesdale during the past decade and has made the publication of this assessment of the present situation particularly timely.

The Plan of the Book

The four chapters that follow this Introduction state significant facts about the flora of Upper Teesdale, and in particular about the rare plants, which the next three chapters attempt to explain. Then come chapters about the terrestrial animals of the upper dale and about the plants and animals of aquatic habitats and the effect on them of the construction of the Cow Green Reservoir. The final chapter summarizes these findings and looks to the future.

In Chapter 1 Dr T. T. Elkington considers the geographical distribution of the rare Teesdale plants both inside and outside the British Isles. He then shows how far the Teesdale populations of these species are distinguishable from others in external features, in number and behaviour of their chromosomes and in other ways, and considers whether the observed differences can be related to the presumed isolation of the Teesdale populations since late-glacial times.

In Chapter 2 Dr Margaret E. Bradshaw and J. P. Doody deal with their investigations into ways in which the rare species maintain their populations from year to year, whether by the production and successful germination of seeds or by vegetative reproduction. They also consider the effects of grazing by sheep and rabbits on the maintenance of numbers of individuals of the rare species.

Dr D. A. Ratcliffe deals in Chapter 3 with the plant sociology of Upper Teesdale, describing the various plant assemblages of the area, including those to which rare species belong. He discusses their relation to environmental and historical factors and draws attention to where similar plant communities can be found elsewhere, in the British Isles and further afield.

Chapter 4, by Dr Judith Turner, describes her investigations of plant remains found in peat deposits in Upper Teesdale and reconstructs the vegetational history of the area since the ice began to retreat from it many millennia ago. She lists finds of remains of the rare species in peat of various ages and shows that they confirm Godwin's theory that these species are 'late-glacial relicts'. Dr Turner also adduces evidence of forest destruction, both natural and through man's agency, that may have had an important bearing on the chances of survival of sun-loving species.

The facts having been stated in these first four chapters, the next three are concerned with seeking explanations for the survival of the rare species for 10,000 years or more since the late-glacial period.

In Chapter 5 Professor C. D. Pigott, whose studies of the ecology of the Teesdale rarities extend over more than twenty years, considers how far the climate of the upper dale can provide a sufficient explanation for their continued presence there. It is an upland climate, and many of the rare plants grow also on mountains in Scotland and elsewhere, but is there any relevant difference in this respect between Upper Teesdale and Upper Weardale or the heads of other dales in northern England?

In Chapter 6 Professor Pigott and Dr J. A. L. Johnson describe the geology and soils and try to assess how far they may have been decisive for the survival of the relict species. They conclude that the presence of the sugar-limestone has undoubtedly been of great importance.

In the final chapter of this section, Chapter 7, Dr Brian Roberts gives an account of the history of settlement and land-use and considers how far the remoteness and low population of Upper Teesdale, together with the restrictions on land-use imposed by altitude, topography, climate and soils, have played a significant part in favouring the survival of the rare plants.

In Chapter 8 Dr J. C. Coulson gives an account of the terrestrial animals of Upper Teesdale with special reference to the insects and birds and to the soil fauna. He discusses the effects of altitude on the various groups and the differences between the faunas of mineral soils and peat. He finds no strong evidence for a concentration of rare animal species comparable with that of rare plants, nor any outstanding faunistic features of the sugar-limestone.

Chapter 9, by Dr D. T. Crisp, considers the physical and chemical changes in the water within the Cow Green basin, and in the river below it, following the construction of the dam and the filling of the reservoir. He shows how these changes have already affected the invertebrate and fish fauna and discusses what further changes may be expected. He concludes with an assessment of the reservoir as a sporting fishery.

The Rev. H. G. Proctor, in the first part of Chapter 10, describes the larger aquatic plants of the Cow Green basin up to the filling of the reservoir, giving interesting details of past changes. He then describes effects of the recent impoundment. In the second part of the chapter Dr N. T. H. Holmes describes the larger aquatic plants of the River Tees between Cauldron Snout and Middleton in the light of his 1975 survey.

Professor D. H. Valentine concludes the book with his summarizing review and a consideration of the problems to be solved in order to conserve the natural history of Upper Teesdale.

CHAPTER 1

Phytogeography, Variation and Evolution

Phytogeography

THE first notable botanical record from Teesdale is probably that of shrubby cin-quefoil (*Potentilla fruticosa*), published by John Ray in 1670. As botanical explora-tion of the region proceeded, particularly by nineteenth-century botanists such as the Backhouses, father and son, it became recognized that Upper Teesdale contained a range of species not duplicated anywhere else in Britain and was a meeting-place for plants of very different distributional types which have been able to survive and flourish within this comparatively small area.

In order to illustrate this diversity a scheme of phytogeographical groups has been adopted which is based on that used by Hultén (1950) for the vascular plants of Scandinavia. The complete flora of Teesdale has never been listed separately, but in the preparation of Perring & Walters' *Atlas of the British Flora* lists were made for each ten-kilometre square of the national grid, and those for the relevant squares have been used in the present analysis. The total number of species listed is 508 and of these 390 are recorded in Hultén's Scandinavian lists, 16 of the 21 phytogeographical ele-ments being represented (Table 1). When one takes into account that some of the Teesdale species not listed by Hultén include plants with very distinctive distribution patterns, such as alpine foxtail (*Alopecurus alpinus*) and spring gentian (*Gentiana verna*), it is clear that the Teesdale flora shows an unusually wide range of distributional types.

The most northerly type of distribution is illustrated by alpine foxtail (Fig. 1), a species with a more or less continuous *arctic circumpolar* distribution, ranging through arctic Eurasia, arctic Canada and Greenland, but entirely absent from Scandinavia. The Teesdale locality is almost the most southern of its world distribu-tion, which extends northwards to the point of land nearest to the North Pole in north Greenland. In Teesdale, its only English locality, it grows in high-level flushes on the slopes of the Cross Fell range. In Scotland it occurs in similar habitats in the Moffat region and in the central Highlands.

Most Teesdale species which extend north into the arctic are also found in the mountains of continental Europe, but within this general pattern there is considerable variation. Alpine forget-me-not (*Myosotis alpestris*, Fig. 2), for example, is in a group of *eurasiatic arctic-montane* species (group 2) with a wide distribution in Eurasia but extending only to the western parts of North America. A number of other species are more widespread, being *circumpolar arctic-montane* (group 3). These include Scottish asphodel (*Tofieldia pusilla*, Plate 13), three-flowered rush (*Juncus triglumis*), mountain avens (*Dryas octopetala*, Plate 10), alpine meadow-rue (*Thalictrum*

TABLE 1. Phytogeographical elements of the flora of N.W. Europe (based on those of Hultén), with the numbers of species recorded in Upper Teesdale.
The species are those listed in the Atlas of the British Flora for 10-kilometre grid squares 35/92, 82, 72, 83 and 73. (These grid squares include small areas of Weardale, Lunedale and the Eden Valley).

Group	Characteristics	Number of Species in Upper Teesdale
1	Arctic circumpolar plants	—
2	European and eurasiatic arctic-montane plants	2
3	Circumpolar arctic-montane plants	15
4	'Amphi-atlantic' plants	8
5	European and eurasiatic boreal-montane plants	15
6	Boreal-circumpolar plants	6
7	European seashore and atlantic plants	18
8	Subatlantic plants	60
9	Circumpolar seashore and suboceanic plants	—
10	Northern eurasiatic and boreal-circumpolar plants missing in central Europe	—
11	European–Siberian plants	125
12	Eurasiatic plants connecting with Scandinavia from both east and south	13
13	Boreal circumpolar plants without large gaps	43
14	Incompletely boreal-circumpolar plants	20
15	European and Siberian continental plants	10
16	Central asiatic continental plants	—
17	Southeast European–South Siberian plants	—
18	Plants with two or more widely separated areas	9
19	South or Central-European and Asiatic plants not indigenous to N.W. Europe but not influenced by man	5
20	American plants	1
21	Plants spread by man	40
		Total 390

alpinum) and alpine bistort (*Polygonum viviparum*, Plate 13). Bog sandwort (*Minuartia stricta*, Plate VI), listed in the same group, is now probably extinct in central Europe. The small sedge *Kobresia simpliciuscula* (Plate 12), holly fern (*Polystichum lonchitis*) and others have a similar distribution but with large gaps in Siberia.

All the species so far mentioned have been able, since the last glaciation, to colonize areas throughout the arctic and montane zones of northern latitudes. Others, however, are less extensively distributed, perhaps because the residual populations, from which recolonization had to take place when the ice finally receded, had been reduced to isolated pockets. Examples are alpine bartsia (*Bartsia alpina*, Plate 11),

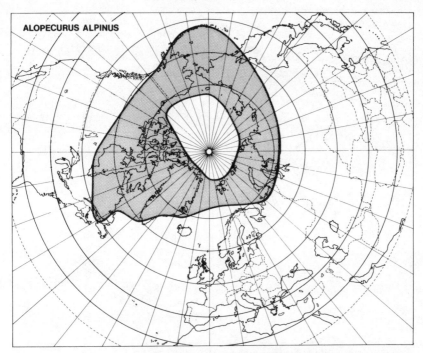

FIG. 1. World distribution of alpine foxtail *(Alopecurus alpinus)*. Dots mark isolated localities in Figs. 1 and 2

hoary whitlow-grass (*Draba incana*), yellow mountain saxifrage (*Saxifraga aizoides*) and alpine cinquefoil (*Potentilla crantzii*), all *amphiatlantic arctic-alpine* species (group 4), typically present in eastern North America, Greenland, Iceland and western Eurasia and confined to mountain areas further south. All are found mainly on mountains and upland areas in Britain. The most restricted is bog sandwort, confined to flushes on Widdybank Fell in Upper Teesdale. Others, such as alpine forget-me-not and kobresia, are present in Teesdale and also in a small number of localities on mica-schist rock in the central Scottish Highlands; and several, including alpine bartsia, are restricted to the northern Pennines and the central Scottish Highlands. Then there is a series of species with progressively wider distributions, amongst them mountain avens (Fig. 6), with a few localities in the Pennines, the Lake District and north Wales, widespread in the central and north-western Highlands and also present in Ireland, particularly in the region round Galway Bay. Finally, there is a group of widely distributed species such as yellow mountain saxifrage and alpine meadow-rue which are relatively common in the Scottish Highlands and present to varying extents further south and often also in Ireland.

Parallel with these is a series of species which, although they may extend almost as far north, have a much wider distribution in more temperate zones and are therefore termed *boreal-montane* species (group 5). Some are more or less circumpolar, such as hair sedge (*Carex capillaris*, Plate 13), dwarf birch (*Betula nana,* Plate 14) and

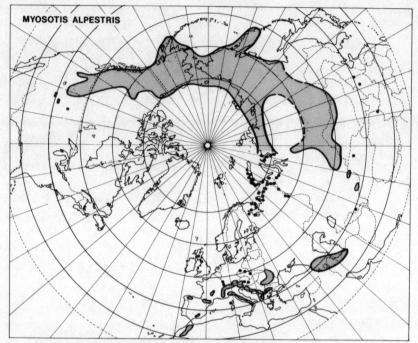

FIG. 2. World distribution of alpine forget-me-not *(Myosotis alpestris).*

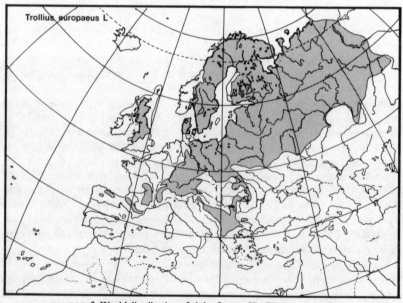

FIG. 3. World distribution of globe-flower *(Trollius europaeus).*

shrubby cinquefoil (Plate V); others, like bird's-eye primrose (*Primula farinosa*, Plate VI) have a wide eurasiatic distribution. Another group, including hoary rock-rose (*Helianthemum canum*, Plate VIII), blue sesleria (*Sesleria albicans*) and globe-flower (*Trollius europaeus*, Fig. 3 and Plate VII) are either restricted to Europe or extend only to western Asia (group 6). The distribution in Britain of some of these boreal-montane species is quite different from that of the arctic–sub-arctic group. The hoary rock-rose, for example, is confined to a number of isolated localities mainly in western Britain, of which Teesdale is the northernmost, and is restricted to open habitats on limestone. Shrubby cinquefoil is extremely localized, being found only in Teesdale, the Lake District and western Ireland. Bird's-eye primrose is only found in base-rich marshes and flushes in northern England, while blue sesleria, with a similar distribution in northern England is also found in the central Scottish Highlands and in western Ireland.

These northern species may be contrasted with those having distributional areas centred in the climatically *continental* parts of Eurasia (group 15) and reaching their northern British limits in northern England, such as horse-shoe vetch (*Hippocrepis comosa*, Fig. 4 and Plate 9). It is widespread on chalk in southern England, becomes rare towards the north and reaches its northernmost locality in Teesdale on the exposed plateau of Cronkley Fell. The bitter milkwort (*Polygala amara**) has a similar distribution, but, unlike horse-shoe vetch, does extend north into Scandinavia. In Britain it is found in four separate areas. Two other species which have comparable distributions but extend eastwards into Siberia are the rare spring sedge (*Carex*

*The British plant referred to is *P. amarella* Crantz in *Flora Europaea* (1968).

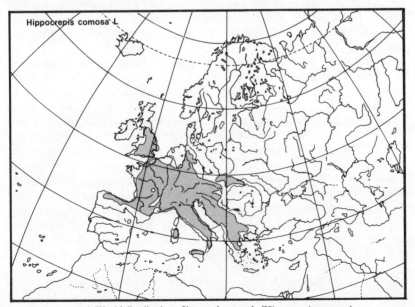

FIG. 4. World distribution of horse-shoe vetch (*Hippocrepis comosa*).

ericetorum, Plate 12) and the Teesdale violet (*Viola rupestris*, Plate VIII). In Britain the Teesdale violet is restricted to a few localities in northern England from Teesdale westwards to Arnside in Cumbria, while the rare spring sedge has a predominantly eastern and mainly lowland distribution, again confined to England and with Teesdale as both its most northerly and its highest locality. The spring gentian is another striking example of a Teesdale plant with its main distribution area in continental Europe and Asia, being particularly common in the Alps but extending west to the Pyrenees and east as far as Lake Baikal in central Asia. In Britain it is found only in Teesdale and around Galway Bay in western Ireland.

The rare species mentioned form, of course, only a minority of the Teesdale flora. Most species belong to one or other of a range of phytogeographical groups which can generally be termed European or Eurasiatic, some having oceanic tendencies in their distribution while others are more continental.

In addition to this range of rare flowering plants there is a considerable number of rare bryophytes and lichens in the Teesdale area; but although it is possible to compare their British distributions with those of flowering plants, information on their world distribution is insufficient to place them in clear phytogeographical groups. Some, however, do have a wide arctic range. For example the moss *Rhytidium rugosum* (Plate 15) has a British distribution which encompasses a range of localities from East Anglia to north Scotland, the lowland localities having a very similar distribution to those of *Carex ericetorum*. In Greenland, however, it extends north to the Thule area at 78° latitude and is described by Holmen as occurring in most parts of the boreal, sub-arctic and arctic zones, and is known to extend south to Austria and Bavaria. Other mosses present in Teesdale, such as *Meesia uliginosa*, *Splachnum vasculosum* (Plate 15) and *Catoscopium nigritum*, have a British distribution similar to that of a number of northern flowering plants restricted to base-rich habitats. Mogensen regards *C. nigritum* as a widespread arctic boreal species and in north-east Greenland it has been recorded as far north as Peary Land.

The reasons for the remarkable phytogeographical diversity of the Teesdale flora have been under discussion for a considerable time. One suggestion, made by Wilmott and others, was that all or part of the Teesdale flora persisted through the final glaciation on nunataks projecting through the ice-sheets. For many reasons this hypothesis is unlikely to be true. Thus it is not likely that southern species would have survived the severe climatic conditions. In any case it now seems almost certain that Upper Teesdale was completely covered by ice during the last advance of the ice-sheets, so that the explanation for the nature and diversity of the present Teesdale flora must be sought in the events which followed the retreat of the ice. The changes in British vegetation from that time to the present day have become known from investigations of pollen and other plant remains preserved in silt and peat; and in 1949 Godwin suggested that localized concentrations of uncommon species such as the Teesdale rarities might be the remnants of a late-glacial vegetation which had migrated northwards as the climate improved and formed open herb-rich communities over much of lowland Britain. Part of the evidence leading to this suggestion is that remains of many of the plants now restricted to the northern uplands have been found in the south of the country. Fruits and leaves of mountain avens, dwarf birch and alpine meadow-rue, for example, are known from a number of localities in

PLATE I. Cow Green dam and partly filled reservoir.

PLATE II. *Above*, waves on Cow Green reservoir, March 1976. *Below*, Holmwath Sike, Widdybank Fell, with Cronkley Scar behind.

southern England, and one fruit of shrubby cinquefoil has been identified from a late-glacial deposit in the Lea Valley in Hertfordshire. Godwin suggested that this shade-intolerant flora disappeared when forests became the dominant vegetation-cover in the post-glacial period and survived only in areas which were never covered by woodland. Later a further restriction of the habitats probably took place as blanket bog developed over much of upland Britain in response to the onset of cool wet conditions. These climatic changes, together with the colonization of the land by man, resulted in the widespread disappearance of the forests and their replacement, particularly in upland areas, by grassland. The very strong evidence that has now accumulated in support of Godwin's view is considered in detail by Dr Turner in Chapter 4 (pp. 88–101).

A number of Teesdale species, particularly those with arctic or sub-arctic distributions, either do not extend south of Teesdale in Britain, like kobresia, alpine foxtail and Scottish asphodel, or do so only in the Craven Pennines and the mountains of the Lake District or in north Wales, such as alpine meadow-rue and mountain avens. Others, like rare spring sedge and horse-shoe vetch, have all or most of their British localities to the south of Teesdale. These contrasted distribution-patterns suggest that there have been both northern and southern sites in which shade-intolerant species could survive through the post-glacial period and that some other factors must limit their British distribution. It seems most likely that these restrictions are climatic in nature. Dahl has suggested that alpine or northern species are restricted to areas of low summer temperature, having observed that alpine plants grown in lowland conditions suffer during spells of hot weather, and Conolly & Dahl have correlated the distribution of a number of northern species in the British flora with isotherms of calculated annual maximum summit temperatures – averages, that is, of the highest annual temperatures recorded over a period of years and extrapolated to the summits of the highest mountains. It is suggested that temperatures reached by some plants in summer may be directly lethal to them (but see p. 117), but others may suffer indirectly through the effects of high temperatures in drying the soil. Another way in which climate may affect survival is illustrated by alpine forget-me-not, the lowest locality for which in Teesdale is at an altitude of 750m, where the ground is frozen for considerable periods in winter. Plants grown at low levels tended to rot in winter because water was held in the leaf-rosettes, a consequence of mild conditions with high rainfall and low evaporation such as are often found by gardeners to be unfavourable for growing 'alpine' plants.

The northern limits of species with a predominantly southern distribution in Britain are probably related to low summer temperatures, but little precise information is available. The very small population of horse-shoe vetch on Cronkley Fell has not been seen to flower since 1930 or even earlier and indeed was thought to be extinct. This may have been due in part to high grazing pressure, but probably to climatic factors as well. Pigott has shown that in Derbyshire, near its northern limit, stemless thistle (*Cirsium acaule*) does flower but fails to produce ripe seed except in favourable summers, even though it is mainly restricted to south-facing slopes.

Teesdale is not the only area in northern England with relict species which were more widespread in the late-glacial and early post-glacial periods. The Craven district of Yorkshire has northern species such as mountain avens, alpine bartsia and hair

sedge and also southern ones like bitter milkwort. Nevertheless Teesdale has a far
wider range of relict species than any other English locality and is rivalled in Great
Britain only by the Ben Lawers range in Scotland. What reasons can be suggested for
this situation?

In the first place Teesdale has a variety of habitats in which relict species grow
today and have presumably grown for much of the post-glacial period. Habitats
important as refugia have been analysed by Pigott & Walters and, of the seven they
identify, five are found in Teesdale.

(i) *Areas above the tree-limit.* M. E. Johnson claims that the tree-limit round the
head of Teesdale has been no higher than about 760m (2500ft) during the post-glacial
period, so that the tops of Mickle Fell, Great and Little Dun Fell and Cross Fell,
where alpine foxtail, alpine forget-me-not and stiff sedge (*Carex bigelowii*) are still
found today, would have been treeless throughout.

(ii) *Inland screes and cliffs.* Cliffs and screes of quartz-dolerite of the Great Whin
Sill are a feature of Upper Teesdale and provide habitats for shrubby and alpine cinquefoil, bearberry (*Arctostaphylos uva-ursi*) and several ferns, including green
spleenwort (*Asplenium viride*) and holly fern, and formerly for oblong woodsia
(*Woodsia ilvensis*).

(iii) *River gorges, eroded river-banks, river shingle and alluvium.* These are
important habitats along the Tees and its tributaries. Shrubby cinquefoil is confined to
sites along the Tees, and the fringing grassland supports northern bedstraw (*Galium
boreale*), sea plantain (*Plantago maritima*), tea-leaved willow (*Salix phylicifolia*) and
many other species. Related habitats are the unstable slopes resulting from the
stream-erosion of calcareous drumlins, described by both Pigott and Bradshaw.
Spring gentian, alpine rush (*Juncus alpinoarticulatus*), alpine bartsia and broad-
leaved cotton-grass (*Eriophorum latifolium*) are amongst the numerous components
of their open vegetation.

(iv) *Marshes and flushes.* These range from very open gravelly flushes, in which
yellow mountain saxifrage, Scottish asphodel, alpine rush, three-flowered rush, spring
sandwort (*Minuartia verna*) and, very locally, bog sandwort grow in an open community (pp. 77–8), with various sedges and grasses, to hummocky marshes prevented
from becoming completely vegetation-covered by a combination of trampling by
cattle and cutting back by springs during very wet spells. Here the abundant sedges
include a small amount of hair sedge and kobresia, and alpine rush is locally abundant
with Scottish asphodel, bird's-eye primrose, alpine bartsia and many bryophytes
amongst the numerous species present.

(v) *Shallow soils over chalk and limestones.* These occur in Upper Teesdale over
both unaltered limestone and the metamorphosed sugar-limestone. The latter carries
a short grassy turf which is readily opened up by trampling and subsequent wind-
erosion, and it is here that many of the rare species are specially concentrated, including mountain avens, hoary rock-rose, spring gentian, Teesdale violet, bitter milkwort
and horse-shoe vetch.

Some of these habitats have carried woodland at times during the post-glacial period (pp. 93–4), but this seems to have been open enough to allow the shade-intolerant flora to survive. An analogous situation is seen today in Southern Norway, where unstable scree-slopes, river gorges and other habitats in the lowland forest zone support a number of shade-intolerant species and in particular mountain avens.

A further feature that seems certainly to have contributed to the survival of so many rare species is the notable lack of luxuriance of much of the vegetation, a consequence in part of the upland climate (pp. 119–21) and in part of a deficiency in the soils of certain plant nutrients (pp. 136–7). This may have prevented the shading out of a number of species of small stature which would otherwise have succumbed in competition with taller and more densely growing associates (pp. 136–7).

It is useful finally to compare Upper Teesdale with other areas with concentrations of species having disjunct distributions. Mountain areas such as Snowdonia, the Lake District, the Craven Pennines and the Scottish Highlands have similar climates and to a large extent similar soils and habitats to those of Upper Teesdale, the habitats including ground above the tree-line, rock-ledges, cliffs and flushes, all with species having arctic, sub-arctic and arctic-montane distributions. Other areas, however, are very different, and perhaps the most remarkable of these is the limestone Burren district of Co. Clare in western Ireland. This, the only other area in the British Isles, apart from Upper Teesdale, where spring gentian grows, has also shrubby cinquefoil, mountain avens and hoary rock-rose and many other species, some with northern and some with southern distributions (including such Mediterranean plants as the orchid *Neotinea intacta*), all of them shade-intolerant. Ivimey-Cook & Proctor, who have described the habitats and vegetation of the Burren, refer to evidence from pollen-analysis that it was completely wooded during much of the post-glacial period. The shade-intolerant relict flora must have survived on cliffs and rock-ledges, in fens and round the edges of the temporary lakes or 'turloughs' which are a feature of the region, spreading more widely when man cleared areas suitable for colonization. It is of particular interest that northern species have been able to survive in the present mild oceanic climate alongside such southern species as maidenhair fern (*Adiantum capillus-veneris*).

Variation and Evolution

INTRODUCTION

The disjunct distribution-patterns of the Teesdale species provide an excellent opportunity to study the effects of isolation on variation in species with different biological characteristics. It is known that the present-day populations of these species have been isolated from one another in the British Isles, and from continental populations, since the spread of forests across lowland Europe some 9000 years ago. What have been the effects of this isolation? Has evolution occurred in response to the varying environmental conditions of the different localities, and if so, can it be related to the ecology and breeding system of the species concerned? The causes of the variation are often impossible to determine with certainty, but a preliminary analysis can be made. Here variation will be discussed under two headings. The first is that of chromosomal variation, especially polyploidy. In the second, patterns of morphological variation will be examined in relation to habitat and geographical distribution.

CHROMOSOMAL VARIATION

Although a full survey of the chromosome numbers of the Teesdale flora has not been made, many of the rarer plants have been examined. These are listed in Table 2, together with the numbers in other populations in Britain and continental Europe. About 40% of the disjunct Teesdale species listed by Pigott are included. Just over half of these are uniform in chromosome number over Europe, while the rest show variation, mainly because of polyploidy. For some species we know little more than that variation exists, but for others we have a reasonably complete picture of its ecological and geographical significance.

TABLE 2. Chromosome numbers of Teesdale plants counted from Teesdale, elsewhere in Britain, and Europe. Somatic numbers are given for all counts irrespective of their being mitotic or meiotic.

	Teesdale	Britain	Europe
Alchemilla filicaulis	$2n = 101{-}106$	—	$2n = 96, 102{-}110$
Alopecurus alpinus	$2n = 100$	$2n = 117$	$2n = > 120, 112, 114$
Armeria maritima	$2n = 18$	$2n = 18$	$2n = 18$
Bartsia alpina	$2n = 24$	$2n = 24$	$2n = 12, 24, 36$
Carex ericetorum	$2n = 30$	$2n = 30$	$2n = 30$
Carex paupercula	$2n = 58$	$2n = 58$	$2n = 58$
Cochlearia alpina	$2n = 12$	$2n = 12, 26$	$2n = 12$
Draba incana	$2n = 32$	$2n = 32$	$2n = 32$
Dryas octopetala	$2n = 18$	$2n = 18$	$2n = 18, 36$
Galium boreale	$2n = 44$	$2n = 44$	$2n = 44, 66$
Gentiana verna	$2n = 28$	$2n = 28$	$2n = 28$
Helianthemum canum	$2n = 22$	$2n = 22$	$2n = 22$
Hippocrepis comosa	$2n = 28$	$2n = 14, 28$	$2n = 14, 28, 42$
Juncus alpinoarticulatus	$2n = 40$	$2n = 40$	$2n = 40, 80$
Minuartia stricta	$2n = 22$	—	$2n = 22, 26, 30$
Myosotis alpestris	$2n = 48$	$2n = 48$	$2n = 24, 48$
Polygala amara	$2n = 34$	$2n = 34$	$2n = 34$
Potentilla crantzii	$2n = 49$	$2n = 42{-}49$	$2n = 28{-}49$
Potentilla fruticosa	$2n = 28$	$2n = 28$	$2n = 14, 28$
Primula farinosa	$2n = 18$	$2n = 18$	$2n = 18, 36$
Saxifraga aizoides	$2n = 26$	$2n = 26$	$2n = 26$
Sesleria albicans	$2n = 28$	$2n = 28$	$2n = 28$
Thalictrum alpinum	$2n = 14$	$2n = 14$	$2n = 14$
Thlaspi alpestre	$2n = 14$	$2n = 14$	$2n = 14$
Tofieldia pusilla	$2n = 30$	$2n = 30$	$2n = 30$
Trollius europaeus	$2n = 16$	$2n = 16$	$2n = 16$
Viola rupestris	$2n = 20$	$2n = 20$	$2n = 20$

One of the best known species is the horse-shoe vetch, studied by G. M. Fearn. This is a frequent plant of calcareous grasslands in southern England, but is less common in the north, where it occurs mainly on limestone cliffs and rocky outcrops. Two chromosome races are present, one diploid ($2n = 14$) and the other tetraploid ($2n = 28$). The tetraploid race occurs over most of the area of the species, and includes the Teesdale population. It grows in a variety of habitats, most commonly in chalk grassland, but also on the oolite of central England and on Carboniferous limestone in the north. The diploid is much more restricted, occurring mainly in south-western England and the Derbyshire dales. It is restricted to the harder limestones and to cliffs and rocky ledges which are inaccessible to grazing animals. Fearn has suggested that one reason for the restriction of the diploid is its intolerance of grazing. She has shown that diploids under both field and experimental conditions produce fewer inflorescences per plant than tetraploids. Reproduction is mainly by seed: grazing will therefore limit the reproductive capacity of the diploids more than that of the tetraploids. In addition, evolution of prostrate forms has taken place in the tetraploid race in grazed situations. Fearn has suggested that both chromosome races were present in England in the late-glacial period but became restricted in the post-glacial to unshaded habitats. When forest clearance on the chalklands of southern England took place only the tetraploids, apparently, were able to colonize them, and the diploids remained on the cliff and rock ledges. The relict tetraploid population in Teesdale fits into this picture, since it grows in sheep-grazed, closed grassland on sugar-limestone. In contrast, in continental Europe, e.g. in France, there appears to be no clear difference in the distribution of the two races. Additionally there is a hexaploid race ($2n = 42$), confined to the Pyrenees, which appears to have evolved comparatively recently.

Most of the species in Table 2 with polyploid series are cytologically uniform in Britain. This is the case in shrubby cinquefoil, where all the British populations are tetraploid ($2n = 28$), as are the populations in Öland. It may be inferred that other populations in northern Europe and in the Ural Mountains are also tetraploid, as all are composed of dioecious plants, a characteristic which appears to be confined to the tetraploids. In southern Europe, populations from the Pyrenees, and one from the Rhodope mountains of Bulgaria, are diploid ($2n = 14$) and characteristically have hermaphrodite flowers. These floral differences make it possible to recognize diploids and tetraploids from herbarium material over the range of the species, although not in central and eastern Asia, where both floral types are found and a complex of forms at three levels of polyploidy is known to exist. It would appear that this species has colonized Europe from the east by two routes. The tetraploids (subsp. *fruticosa*), now represented by isolated populations from the Urals to western Ireland, have followed a northern route. The diploids (subsp. *floribunda*), represented by isolated populations from the Caucasus to the Pyrenees, have followed a southern route. In North America, also perhaps colonized from eastern Asia, only diploids with hermaphrodite flowers are found.

It is not known whether the western movement of diploids and tetraploids into Europe took place at the same time; but in the case of the tetraploids it seems reasonable to suggest that it was in the late or early post-glacial period, since the whole of its Baltic area of distribution was heavily glaciated. Shrubby cinquefoil seems to be intolerant of shade; and as forest became established in the post-glacial period, it must have become extinct over most of its range except for a few places where dense forest never became established. When forest clearance took place shrubby cinquefoil, for some unknown reason, was unable to expand, and it has remained a rare species over the whole of Europe.

There are several other species in Teesdale with polyploid races about which, as yet, comparatively little is known. In the alpine forget-me-not both Teesdale and Perthshire plants are tetraploid ($2n = 48$), but in the Alps counts of both $2n = 24$ (diploid) and $2n = 48$ have been made, while only diploids have been recorded from the Altai and Caucasus mountains and from the Arctic. Little is known of the areas of these two races over the whole distribution of the species, which ranges from western Europe and North Africa, through Asia into western North America. In the Swiss Alps at least, diploids and tetraploids grow within two or three kilometres of one another so that the two races overlap for at least part of their range.

The northern bedstraw is another species which has two polyploid races. It was originally thought that hexaploid plants with $2n = 66$ were restricted to North America and east Asia and tetraploids with $2n = 44$ to Europe and west Asia. More recently, hexaploid counts have been made on this species in Poland, Romania, France and Scandinavia, so that both races seem to be widespread in Europe. So far only the tetraploid has been recorded in Britain, including Teesdale. Although it was at one time suggested that these two races could be separated morphologically, later investigations have shown that none of the characteristics so far studied can be used as distinguishing features.

A rather different situation is illustrated by the alpine foxtail, where the published chromosome numbers range from $2n = 100$ to $2n = 130$. As the basic number of the genus *Alopecurus* is 7 (several diploid species with $2n = 14$ are known), these high numbers probably represent the upper end of a polyploid series. The fact that the numbers are not exact multiples of 7 is probably due to the occasional loss or gain of small numbers of chromosomes. Various authors have reported meiotic irregularities in the development of the pollen grains, such as might lead to change in chromosome number.

Fearn obtained a count of $2n = c.$ 100 from plants in Teesdale (on Little Dun Fell, on the Moor House Reserve), and a count of $2n = 117$ for a plant from Angus, Scotland. The large difference in number is perhaps greater than would be expected in plants drawn relatively recently (in post-glacial time) from the same population; but without some knowledge of variation of chromosome number *within* populations, it is not possible to draw conclusions.

Finally, variation in chromosome number has been recorded from groups which are apomictic, i.e. which produce offspring parthenogenetically, without fertilization. The Teesdale flora is rich in species of lady's-mantle (*Alchemilla*) which have this form of reproduction. They are all high polyploids with variable numbers, though the variation is considerably less than in the alpine foxtail. For example, in *A. filicaulis* from Teesdale, the number varies from $2n = 101$ to 106. The mechanism of chromosome loss and gain is not known but, as in the alpine foxtail, a high polyploid can tolerate variation in chromosome number without deleterious effects and often too, without any visible outward sign.

It is not possible here to give a comprehensive account of chromosomal variation. In particular, the work done on polyploid complexes in the genera *Juncus* and *Cochlearia*, in which the exact affinities of the Teesdale plants are still obscure, has had to be omitted. Nevertheless, the case-studies described show well the value of polyploidy both as an indicator of the direction of evolution, and as a marker which may help to distinguish ecologically distinct populations or to unite populations which are geographically separated.

PATTERNS OF MORPHOLOGICAL VARIATION

In some Teesdale species, no significant variation has yet been detected. Thus, the alpine meadow-rue appears to be uniform throughout its range; and the hair sedge is uniform in Britain, though variable elsewhere. But most of the species are variable, and they will be reviewed under the headings of outbreeders and inbreeders. Those species showing clear ecotypic variation are discussed separately.

Ecotypic variation

The variation pattern in several species seems to be clearly related to the varying ecological conditions in which the species grow. One example is horse-shoe vetch, where both prostrate and erect forms related to the presence or absence of grazing have evolved within the tetraploid race (pp. 36–7). The alpine forget-me-not, which grows in sheep-grazed grassland on several of the high fells in the west of Teesdale, is similar. Plants grown from seed collected in the field are small with prostrate leaf-rosettes and low flowering stems. In Scotland, however, the plants are found mainly on mica-schist rock ledges which are inaccessible to sheep; plants grown from seed collected from this habitat have larger upright leaves and taller flowering stems, differences which reflect the morphology of the plants in the field, and which may be described as ecotypic. Clearly plants with prostrate leaves and shorter flowering stems are at an advantage when the vegetation is being continuously grazed; on the other hand the Scottish plants mainly grow in an ungrazed herb-rich vegetation where taller, less shaded plants will be at an advantage.

Valentine & Harvey have suggested a similar explanation for variation in British populations of the Teesdale violet. After cultivation for one year Teesdale plants were compact with many very short shoots, while a plant from Arnside, Cumbria had a few long shoots and the growth was not compact. The development of these differences after cultivation suggests that they are genetically based. The Teesdale population is restricted to heavily grazed grassland, while that at Arnside is in a relatively inaccessible situation and probably only lightly grazed. It is thus possible that the dwarf nature of the Teesdale plants is the result of a selective response to grazing. Fearn has also noted that when plants of the alpine foxtail from Teesdale and Scotland were grown together in a controlled environment, the Teesdale plants had shorter leaf blades, a difference which may also be related to variation in the intensity of grazing in the original localities.

In the lady's-mantle *Alchemilla filicaulis*, an apomictic species, M. E. Bradshaw has shown, both from transplants and from families raised from seed, that there are genetic differences between plants from high-altitude pastures and low-altitude pastures, hay-meadows and woodlands in Teesdale. The high-altitude plants are shorter, and the leaves are smaller than those from lower altitudes. There are large environmental differences between the two groups of localities and Bradshaw stresses the importance of sheep-grazing in the high-altitude sites, although she points out the difficulties of assessing the relative importance of biotic and altitudinal factors. Incidentally, this is an interesting example of ecotypic variation in an apomictic species.

Geographical variation (outbreeders)

Many variation patterns are more complex and more difficult to understand than those which have just been described. They are usually correlated with geographical factors, and six species showing this kind of variation will now be described.

(i) *Spring gentian* There are differences here between British and continental populations. Thus, the populations from Teesdale, western Ireland and the continent (Alps and Pyrenees) differ both in calyx characters and the shape of the leaves (Fig. 5). Measurements were made on field samples, but other observations indicated that

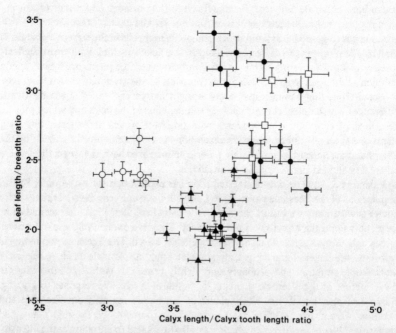

FIG. 5. Spring gentian *(Gentiana verna)*. Scatter diagram of sample means (with their standard errors) for leaf-length/breadth ratio and calyx length/calyx tooth-length ratio, for populations from Britain and the Continent. ○ Irish samples; ▲ Teesdale samples; ● Alpine samples; □ Pyrenean samples.

the differences observed were genotypic. In general, Irish populations tend to have plants with longer, narrower rosette leaves and flowers with more deeply cut calyces than those in Teesdale. The continental and Teesdale populations only differ slightly in calyx characters, but the former show considerable variation in leaf morphology. This is related to altitude, the alpine populations from the highest altitudes (2400–2600m) having relatively short, wide rosette leaves, identical to those of Teesdale plants. Plants from progressively lower altitudes have narrower and longer leaves and those from the lowest altitudes (*c.* 1400–1600m) are more extreme in these features than those from Irish populations. It is clear (Fig. 5) that the Irish populations are the most distinct morphologically, while those from Teesdale are more similar to the continental populations.

Variation of this kind is widespread and often difficult to explain. Frequently it can be regarded as adaptive, though to prove this is often difficult; and the hypothesis is sometimes advanced that the variation is of a random nature, established by genetic drift at a time when their populations were small, and persisting in the population in a neutral way. In this and in examples to follow, these alternative hypotheses will not in every case be discussed, though they must be borne in mind. An explanation in terms of adaptation and natural selection will always be sought.

In the spring gentian, the progressive changes in leaf form can be correlated with altitude in continental Europe, although the adaptive significance of this variation is not clear. One possibility is that it may be related to maintaining an optimal leaf temperature, since it has been suggested that a decrease in leaf width will increase the amount of heat loss from leaves in moving air, and thus at lower altitudes will prevent overheating of the leaves. If this is so it would be reasonable to expect the Teesdale populations, in their upland climate, to be similar to high-altitude continental populations, and the Irish populations, in their oceanic, lowland climate, to be more like low-altitude continental populations. It is difficult to suggest a functional significance for variation in the relative length of calyx teeth; and it is possible that the differences may be linked in some way with the differences in leaf shape and size.

(ii) *Shrubby cinquefoil.* A somewhat similar situation exists in the shrubby cinquefoil, where there is variation both in leaflet shape and floral morphology. The main variation in the leaflets is in their relative width. Table 3 (p. 42) shows the length/breadth ratio of the apical leaflets for samples from plants grown from seed from three British localities, and from hybrids between plants from two localities. The lines link populations which are not significantly different from one another. These measurements correspond to the variation found in field samples, although all plants growing under natural conditions have relatively narrower leaflets. Field samples from teraploid populations in Öland are similar to those from Teesdale; diploid populations from the Pyrenees have relatively wide leaflets. The reason for this kind of variation is not known, but it may be related to environmental factors. All the European habitats (except those in the Lake District) are by rivers and streams or by the sides of lakes, where the plant is often flooded during winter. On the other hand the climates of the European localities vary greatly, ranging from the continental lowland climate of Öland to the oceanic climate of western Ireland and the upland climates of Teesdale and the Lake District; and climatic factors may affect leaflet shape.

TABLE 3. *Mean length/breadth ratios of samples of apical leaflets of shrubby cinquefoil.*

The plants were grown in cultivation from seed collected from wild localities (1, 2 and 4) and from a hybrid derived from them (3).

The lines beneath the ratios link samples which are not significantly different at the 5% level, according to Duncan's multiple range tests.

1	2	3	4
Mullaghmore	Wastwater	Hybrid,	Cronkley Fell
Co. Clare	Cumberland	Mullaghmore x	Teesdale
Ireland	England	Cronkley Fell	England
2.7	2.9	3.2	3.5

Some variation in floral morphology has been noted. In populations grown from seed, the petals of plants of Irish origin are shorter and relatively wider than those from Teesdale. This indicates that the difference is genotypic, though it has not been detected in natural populations; it is possible that the character may be plastically modified by the environment.

(iii) *Hoary rock-rose.* Another species in which the Teesdale plants are distinct from those elsewhere is the hoary rock-rose, studied by Proctor. The British populations fall into three geographical groups, which differ morphologically. The group which most resembles neighbouring continental populations comprises plants from lowland localities on Carboniferous limestone near the coasts of Wales and north-west England. A substantial proportion of the plants in these populations has a felt of stellate hairs on the upper leaf surfaces. The population on Cronkley Fell, the only one in Teesdale, has smaller and narrower leaves, with only a few simple hairs on the upper surfaces and never with a felt of stellate hairs; the plants form much branched, very prostrate mats. In contrast, Irish plants are faster-growing, have large leaves which are sparsely hairy on the upper surfaces, and have taller inflorescences with more flowers than in other British populations; they most resemble plants from the Pyrenees. These differences are maintained in plants grown in cultivation, indicating that they are genotypic. The Teesdale plants are distinct from all others in Europe and have been described as subsp. *levigatum.* It is difficult to relate this variation to environmental factors, although the small leaf size and prostrate nature of the Teesdale plants may be related to grazing as well as to the exposed nature of the area where they grow.

(iv) *Mountain avens.* A somewhat similar situation exists in the mountain avens. There is considerable variation in leaf size between British populations, and cultivation experiments have shown that this character is usually genetically controlled, although some of the variability is due to environmental modification. In Teesdale, for example, exclusion of grazing by sheep and rabbits for four years led to a doubling of the mean leaf area. Observations on cultivated plants show that plants from Teesdale

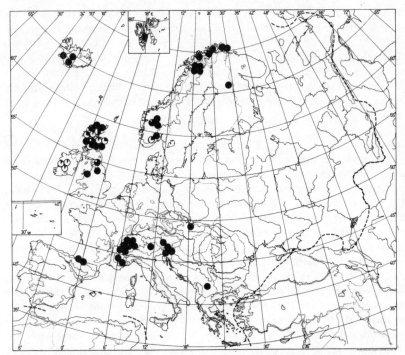

FIG. 6. Mountain avens *(Dryas octopetala).* Distribution of samples, showing the proportion of plants with and without branched hairs on the leaves. Black sectors represent proportions of plants with branched hairs.

and north Scotland have relatively small leaves, and are similar in this respect to populations from exposed, arctic sites. These British populations may thus be unchanged in this respect from those which colonized the sites at the end of the last glacial period. Populations with larger leaves from the central Scottish mica-schist belt and from west Ireland are similar to those in sub-arctic and north temperate, montane areas elsewhere in Europe. In addition, British populations also vary in the number of branched hairs on the veins on the undersides of the leaves (Fig. 6). In some British populations e.g. those from Llyn Idwal, north Wales, all plants have branched hairs. Many others have a mixture of plants with and without hairs, although the relative proportions vary widely, even between populations which are close together. In western Ireland the proportion of plants with branched hairs is low. The only other area outside Britain with a similar polymorphism is south and west Norway; this is in contrast to the general situation in continental Europe where all plants have branched hairs. As with the hoary rock-rose, it is difficult to interpret this situation in relation to environmental variation; polymorphic situations of this kind related to geographical distribution are not uncommon.

(v) *Blue sesleria.* Dale has shown that variation is related to geography in this plant.

44 VARIATION AND EVOLUTION

In the field the lengths of the inflorescence spikes, spikelets and lemmas are generally shorter in the English populations than those from Ireland, Scotland and the Alps. Plants from English and Irish populations grown in cultivation maintained the differences in spike and lemma lengths, indicating that these characters are probably genetically controlled, possibly by the same group of genes. The same type of variation pattern was not detected in any vegetative characters, although transplants from alpine populations had significantly narrower leaves than those from England and Ireland.

(vi) *Thrift.* Also studied by Dale, thrift shows a much more complex variation pattern than blue sesleria. It is a circumpolar species, widely distributed round the coasts of Britain, and also found inland in upland areas. In the Pennines, it is particularly associated with old mine sites, and this is true of two of the three sites in Upper Teesdale. These two have high concentrations of lead and zinc in the soil; the third, on Widdybank Fell (now mostly submerged by the reservoir) has a noticeable amount of zinc in the soil, though much less than in the two mine sites.

Thrift in Britain is represented by two subspecies. Nearly all populations in Britain belong to subsp. *maritima,* and subsp. *elongata* is found only at a single site at Ancaster, Lincs. Subsp. *elongata* differs from *maritima* in having longer ciliate leaves and longer glabrous scapes. These differences are illustrated in Fig. 7, which shows data obtained by Dale from transplant samples for scape length and leaf length. It will be seen that the sample of subsp. *elongata* from Ancaster is quite distinct. It is noteworthy that the only other British population which resembles *elongata* (though it has pubescent scapes) is from Widdybank Fell. All other British populations of

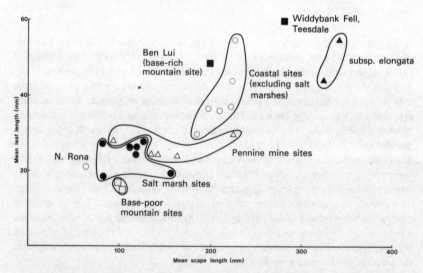

FIG. 7. Thrift *(Armeria maritima).* Scatter diagram of transplant samples (cultivated for one year) showing mean lengths of scape and leaf.

subsp. *maritima* have a variation pattern which is correlated with habitat. Transplants show that the samples with the smallest leaves and scapes come from salt marshes and acidic mountain sites (except for one sample from coastal grassland on North Rona). Cultivated plants from heavy metal mine sites tend to be slightly larger, and those from beach and other rocky coastal sites, larger still. This pattern of variation agrees with that established previously by Baker for coastal and montane populations. Lefèbvre has suggested that plant size is controlled by exposure to wind and to sheep-grazing, and that leaf ciliation is related to the salt content of the soil; Dale's results support these suggestions.

The populations of thrift in Upper Teesdale thus fall into two groups; the heavy metal mine populations, which are similar to other Pennine mine populations, and the Widdybank Fell population, which in cultivation resembles subsp. *elongata* in size.

Dale has also found that hybrids derived from crossing plants from Widdybank Fell with plants from several coastal localities in south-west England have a much reduced pollen viability (35–45%), indicating that genetic barriers to crossing have evolved between the Widdybank Fell and coastal populations. A similar result has been found in experiments with continental populations.

Most of the variable species mentioned so far are outbreeding, the plants normally being cross-pollinated. In most cases the species have biological mechanisms which promote or necessitate this. For example, shrubby cinquefoil is dioecious, thrift is self-incompatible and mountain avens, blue sesleria and hoary rock-rose may also have incompatibility mechanisms. Outbreeding systems tend to produce genetically variable populations, which, if they are close together will be similar to one another. This probably explains why blue sesleria, a wind-pollinated species, is more or less uniform throughout its range in the Pennines. On the other hand thrift is insect-pollinated and the distance between the Widdybank Fell and the nearest mine population, some 11km, is too far for pollen to be transported; this helps to explain why these isolated populations, subject to differing selective pressures, are very different in their morphology.

Inbreeders

In contrast, some of the rare Teesdale species are inbreeding, the plants being predominantly self-pollinated. This has led to the production, in some of these species, of uniform local populations which differ from area to area. Three inbreeding species are discussed here.

(i) *Bitter milkwort*. This species is found in four areas of Britain, viz., Kent, the Craven district of Yorkshire, Teesdale, and Orton in Cumbria. The populations vary in a number of characters, of which the most obvious is flower colour. For many years it was thought that only pink-flowered plants were present in Teesdale (on Cronkley Fell), but the plants rediscovered on Widdybank Fell in 1957 are blue-flowered, and in 1968 two small blue-flowered populations were also found on Cronkley Fell. The plants in the Craven area all have blue flowers, but according to herbarium material collected at the beginning of the century, pink- and white-flowered plants also used to grow there. The populations at Orton have blue flowers. In Kent most plants have flowers with pale greyish-lilac wing sepals and white corollas, although in one population there is a range of colour from white through pink to lilac. Populations with similar greyish-lilac flowers are also known from northern France, although most continental populations are white, blue or pink or a mixture of these colours.

There are also differences in the shapes of the wing sepals and the leaves. The wing sepals are longer in the Craven plants than in those from Kent and Teesdale, but those from Teesdale are relatively broad compared with those from Kent. Plants with the narrowest wing sepals, however, come from grassland sites in the Craven area, while plants from a marsh in the same area are similar to those from Kent. A similar type of variation is shown by the leaves. We thus have distinct races in at least three of the British areas. The most variable is that from the Craven area, plants of which are similar to those in the Alps. Fearn has pointed out that this variability may be due to the diversity of habitats in this area (from grassland to calcareous marsh). Some of the variation, however, may be a reflection of chance differences which existed when the populations were first established and which have been stabilized by inbreeding and isolation.

(ii) *Hoary whitlow-grass.* In this species, a biennial of open habitats, and often in Teesdale on old lead-mine spoil, Fearn has shown a different type of variation. Most British populations have simple hairs on the upper surface only of the leaves of the basal rosette and stellate hairs on the lower surface only. Populations from Widdybank and Cronkley Fells, however, are unique in England in also having some stellate hairs on the upper surface of the leaves; two herbarium specimens from Ben Lawers have the same feature. On the continent all plants examined from the Alps have stellate hairs on both leaf surfaces like those from Teesdale, while those from the Pyrenees have only simple hairs on the upper surface. In Scandinavia the position appears to be similar to that in Britain with most plants having stellate hairs only on the lower leaf surface, and a few having stellate hairs on both surfaces.

Most British plants have glabrous fruits, but a few, including those from two Pennine populations, have fruits with stellate hairs. In the Alps most plants have fruits with stellate hairs, while about 40% of those examined from Scandinavia are of this type; those from the Pyrenees all have glabrous fruits. This pattern of polymorphic variation in Britain is not obviously related to environmental factors, but it has not been experimentally investigated. Like many such polymorphisms e.g. that already described in mountain avens (p. 43), it is difficult to explain in adaptive terms.

(iii) *Alpine penny-cress.* Variation between populations is also well shown in alpine penny-cress, another inbreeding and mainly biennial species, studied by Riley. In Teesdale and elsewhere this plant is largely restricted to old lead mine spoil heaps and there are several populations of this kind near the head of Teesdale. There is also a small population near Winch Bridge on the Whin Sill. Riley showed, by cultivation experiments, that four of the six Teesdale lead mine populations are very similar in size and floral characters; these populations are from sites fairly close together on the same road. The other two, and the Winch Bridge population, are distinct both from the four and from each other. Plants from elsewhere in the Pennines, particularly

Malham and Derbyshire, are distinct from all those in Teesdale, particularly in fruit characters.

CONCLUSION

The second part of this chapter has presented a survey of types of variation in a range of Teesdale species, covering different families, life-forms and breeding systems. Many of the species are variable in Britain and, in some, distinct Teesdale races exist which are genetically unique. Some, described under the heading of ecotypic variation, are clearly related to particular ecological factors, such as grazing. Others, described under the heading of geographical variation, may be the results of responses to climatic factors which are not yet fully understood, e.g. the variation of leaf morphology in hoary rock-rose, spring gentian and shrubby cinquefoil. In other situations chance genetic changes stabilized by inbreeding may be important, e.g. the variation of flower colour in bitter milkwort and of hair characteristics in hoary whitlow-grass. In some cases we can only suggest possibilities and do not know what has been the relative importance of the characteristics of the original, colonizing populations and of the past history of the species in both time and space.

Of course, Upper Teesdale is not the only area in which the evolutionary history of disjunct species and races can be studied. Similar areas, related both floristically and historically to Teesdale, exist elsewhere in north-western Europe, notably in the Burren and in Öland. The studies reported here make it possible to take a first step towards a synthesis of information about the movement and evolution of floras, and relate them to the wider vista of the history of vegetation in Europe during and since the glacial epoch.

CHAPTER 2

Population-dynamics and Biology

Introduction

THE proposal to build a reservoir just above Cauldron Snout made necessary a detailed study of the distribution of individual rare species within the threatened area. With the help of students from the Durham University Extra-Mural Department the distributions of the important plants were recorded on maps (1:2,200) constructed from aerial photographs. In addition suitable habitats on Widdybank Fell were searched for selected rare species including kobresia (*Kobresia simpliciuscula*, Plate 12), spring gentian (*Gentiana verna*, Plate VI), Teesdale violet (*Viola rupestris*, Plate VIII) and its hybrid with the common dog-violet (*V. riviniana*), bog sandwort (*Minuartia stricta*, Plate VI) and rare spring sedge (*Carex ericetorum*, Plate 12). By 1966 the proportions of these populations that were at risk were known with a high degree of certainty: of tall bog sedge (*Carex paupercula*), 100%; of rare spring sedge, 40%; of Teesdale violet, 10%; of the hybrid violet, 5%; and of alpine rush (*Juncus alpinoarticulatus*), 40%. Some 10% of the 220 acres of calcareous dry and flush communities on Widdybank Fell were in the area to be inundated.

The initial survey was followed by intensive mapping of the Teesdale rarities and of such interesting species as creeping willow (*Salix repens*), frog orchid (*Coeloglossum viride*) and alpine cinquefoil (*Potentilla crantzii*) over an area about 1.6 × 0.4km on the dry and wet calcareous soils and flushes on the higher parts of Widdybank Fell (Plate 17). The earlier predictions of the proportional losses of selected rare species were confirmed, and an additional small population of hybrid violet was discovered. These data have formed a starting-point for several projects described in this book.

Method

In 1968 a study was begun of the population dynamics of several of the rare species on Widdybank and Cronkley Fells. The basic questions were asked by Tansley in 1946: 'A knowledge of the means of maintenance of a species in a place where it is already established can often be obtained by direct observation at different times of the year. Do the already established plants persist from year to year? Do any of them die, and, if so, why? Does the species regularly or occasionally produce ripe seed, and do these seeds fall close to the parent plants, germinate, and produce new plants which successfully establish themselves? Sometimes all this information can be obtained by simple observation. A permanent quadrat, charted in succeeding years, will give accurate quantitative information as to the appearance of new plants from seed and the disappearance of the original ones'. A further question of importance

PLATE III. *Above*, limestone grassland on Widdybank Fell, its greenness contrasting with the darker heather-dominated vegetation on acidic soil and peat. *Below*, hay-meadow by the Langdon Beck.

PLATE IV. *Above*, outcrop of sugar-limestone, Cronkley Fell. *Below*, shallow dark-grey or almost black calcareous soil (rendzina) developed over sugar-limestone.

concerns the relative significance of reproduction vegetatively and by seed.

So far this study has been mainly directed to amassing the relevant data on population-structure, including age-composition, mortality and turn-over, reproductive capacity, germination and establishment of seedlings and the extent of vegetative reproduction. The intensive field observations have also yielded much information on the biology of each species. From the data a picture of the structure and dynamics of the populations can be constructed and the life-strategy of each species elucidated. This information is essential if the species are to be conserved, as it enables sound management plans to be devised which can take account not only of the requirement of the vegetation but also of the individual component species.

A first step towards conservation has been a self-imposed restriction on the number and size of samples and a constant watch on the effects of repeated visits to sites, especially where the habitat is fragile and easily altered.

The species studied in detail have been spring gentian, hoary whitlow-grass (*Draba incana*), Teesdale violet, common dog-violet and the hybrid with Teesdale violet, bitter milkwort (*Polygala amara*), rare spring sedge, and purging flax (*Linum catharticum*) which, like the dog-violet, is not rare but is included for comparison. Some records were also made of bird's-eye primrose (*Primula farinosa*, Plate VI), Scottish asphodel (*Tofieldia pusilla*, Plate 13), three-flowered rush (*Juncus triglumis*) and alpine cinquefoil. Using the distribution maps to which mention has already been made, sites were selected where several of the species grew together and at three distances from the margin of the reservoir: 100m, 100-250m, and 500m or more (including Cronkley Fell). All records were made in permanent *plots*, 0.3m wide and varying in length from 0.5m to several metres long, the length depending on the density of the species. Sample *sites*, again of various sizes, were used to give a bigger sample within a permanently marked area. These are the 'plots' and 'sites' mentioned throughout this chapter. All plots and sample sites were marked by sunken pegs, located by reference to surface features. In the permanent plots the individuals were identified by their coordinates, determined from a grid placed over the marker pegs. Fruits and seeds were obtained from the nearby area.

The basis of this study is how the plants behave in their natural habitat. Once the individual, here termed the 'reproductive unit', had been defined for each species, the necessary quantitative data could be obtained from field records of the following: mature reproductive units, inflorescences per unit, flowers per inflorescence or unit, fruits per inflorescence and seeds per fruit, seedlings, juveniles (established seedlings or vegetative shoots which have not flowered) and mature units which have flowered.

In demographic studies it is desirable to know for each species the age-structure of the population, the mean life-span of individuals and the life-expectancy at any particular age. By 1975 figures had been obtained for two species, spring gentian and hoary whitlow-grass, in which the original mixed-age populations had died out. In no case has a reliable method been found of aging plants on morphological features. A useful indication of the life-span is the 'half-life' of the sample populations. The estimates quoted in this chapter are the times taken for half the individuals in an original sample to die.

SPRING GENTIAN

The spring gentian is the best known of the Teesdale rarities. On Widdybank Fell the small populations have a scattered distribution in the *Seslerio-Mesobromion*, the short calcareous grassland dominated by blue sesleria (*Sesleria albicans*), sheep's fescue (*Festuca ovina*) and quaking grass (*Briza media*), and in the variant with crowberry (*Empetrum nigrum*) and heather (*Calluna vulgaris*). Spring gentian also occurs in species-rich bent-fescue grassland of the subalpine pasture Alliance *Ranunculo-Anthoxanthion*, but rarely in acid grasslands or peaty soils. It is present on marshy hummocks in the calcareous flushes of the dwarf sedge communities of the *Tofieldietalia* (names of communities follow Jones (1973) and Shimwell (1971)).

Gentians reproduce vegetatively from slender underground rhizomes, the individual shoots being rosettes with opposite pairs of leaves (Plate 17). These are the reproductive units of this study. On the higher fells they are usually scattered: the really dense clusters seen on central European mountains are very unusual.

Demographic data have been obtained from sample populations on Widdybank and Cronkley Fells. The most surprising discovery was the rapid loss and replacement of the rosettes, so that about one-third of the population was replaced each year. In one particular plot, for example, all 29 units of the original (1969) mixed-age population had died out by autumn 1974, so that the 1975 population consisted entirely of plants of known age. In two more samples only a few of the original plants remained. The three shortest half-lives found were 2.8, 4.1 and 3.0 years, and the longest was 5.6 years on Cronkley Fell. These half-lives are very short compared with values of 50 and 18 years calculated by Harper from Tamm's records in Sweden for wood sanicle (*Sanicula europaea*) and dropwort (*Filipendula vulgaris*) respectively.

Losses are of two kinds: where rosettes are actually seen dead or dying, and where they disappear without trace. Where grazing is prohibited about three-quarters of 38 losses were observed deaths, whereas in grazed areas these were only one-third of all losses. This suggests that sheep and maybe rabbits are responsible for the missing rosettes, though small mammals or soil invertebrates may sever the rhizomes below rosettes. Fairly stable population levels have been maintained by the high rate of production ('birth-rate') of new rosettes. The annual recruitment in 1970 of 98 per 100 was almost twice that of the other years: 43 in 1969, 43 in 1971 and 34 in 1972. In each plot the high total populations of 1970 were maintained in 1971 but then the numbers began to fall back as recruitment-rate declined. Recruitment and mortality vary from sample to sample, and populations in uneven vegetation or terrain seem to have a lower mortality than in more closed or uniform conditions.

The gentian flowers from early May to late June, depending on altitude and the seasonal climate. The duration of flowering seems closely related to climate. Thus in a year with frequent hot sunny days the period is short, while intermittent warm-cold, sunny-dull weather prolongs it. One deep blue flower per rosette is the norm, but three and five have been seen recently and clones of pale blue flowers are known.

The proportions and numbers of rosettes which have flowered each year in recorded plots are as shown in the table on p. 52.

In 1971 a 'haze of blue' was observed from the Birkdale track by both authors, but

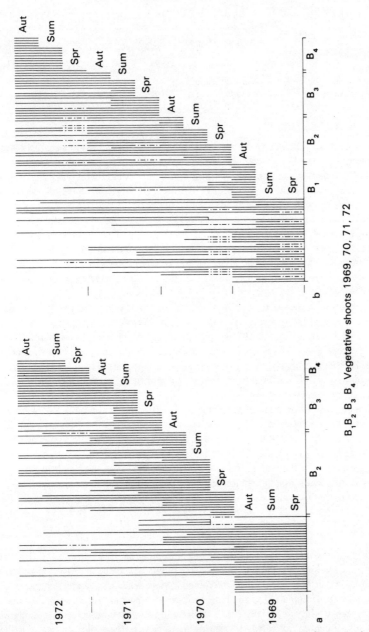

FIG. 8. Behaviour of spring gentian *(Gentiana verna)* in two population samples: *a*, plot 8.3 with few flowers; *b*, plot 8B with many flowers. Each vertical line represents one reproductive unit; a continuous line = vegetative growth; branches = the number of rosettes on one root; dot and dash = flowering; broken line = seedling stage.

	1969	1970	1971	1972	1973	1974	1975
% flowering	8.91	8.30	5.56	7.78	9.45	8.46	1.78
number of plants flowering	67	73	57	64	79	65	14
total summer population	752	881	1026	822	836	780	789

the percentage of flowering rosettes and actual numbers of flowers were the lowest so far recorded. The low percentage can be explained by the presence of a high proportion of juveniles in the population, but the reason for the low total of 57 is not clear, nor is the exceptionally low percentage of flowering rosettes in 1975, only 1.78%. The best flowering year was clearly 1973, when many of the rosettes originating in 1970 reached maturity. The branching lines in Fig. 8 show the behaviour of two populations. In plot 8.3 both the half-life of 2.8 years and the flowering percentage of 2.0% were the lowest in the recorded plots, while plot 8B had a half-life of 3.8 years and the highest flowering rate of 14%. These differences are probably related to the facts that 8.3 is close to a sheep track and 8B in dwarf shrub vegetation of heather and crowberry.

Pollination appears to be by bumble-bees, but they frequently take nectar illegitimately by biting through the base of the flower. Very few capsules are found on the grazed area, though in 1971 a record number of 34 were found in about 4ha of Widdybank Fell. Where grazing is prevented many capsules ripen and contain 150–250 seeds each, so that if all flowers ripened capsules the seed-rain would be very considerable. Two seedlings were found in a plot in 1974, showing that some seed does germinate successfully.

Our records show that the populations of gentian on Widdybank Fell were being successfully maintained by vegetative reproduction under the current land-management regime and throughout a period including the severe winter of 1968/9. This was not so on Cronkley Fell where there is very severe grazing both by sheep and also by rabbits. Successful reproduction by seed is, however, necessary to ensure that genetic variation is maintained to enable the population to survive changing environmental conditions.

HOARY WHITLOW-GRASS

Hoary whitlow-grass has a life-strategy contrasting sharply with that of the spring gentian. Seedlings develop into monocarpic plants which are usually biennial at low altitudes but in Teesdale a protracted juvenile stage leads to an 'extended biennial' or a short-lived perennial. Mature plants have a very compact rosette of leaves and an inflorescence which is initially short, so that they are rarely affected by grazing until the inflorescence elongates. If grazing removes it, then one or more axillary inflorescences may arise.

Hoary whitlow-grass is usually in open communities, especially those where closure is prevented by high levels of lead and barytes in the soil. It grows in shallow skeletal soils of eroded sugar-limestone, especially on Cronkley Fell, and also in a matrix of mosses where higher plants are small or absent. On Widdybank Fell it also grows in communities of blue sesleria where moles have made runs just beneath the sole of the turf and where there are therefore exposed pockets of bare earth. Populations tend to be islated and comparatively small. It is now one of the rarer Teesdale species, the largest population having been lost in the reservoir basin.

Germination is usually in mid-April and gives one main burst of seedlings which are frequently in dense clusters. Self-thinning occurs throughout summer, leaving survivors less than 1cm in diameter in October.

The total number of individuals in each recorded plot varied greatly during the period of study, as can be seen in Fig. 9 which shows the large increase each spring due to the surviving seedlings from the previous year. Mortality is high in the seedling stage and relatively high in the first juvenile year apart from 1970. Only one age-cohort was old enough by 1972 to be seriously reduced by the mortality which follows flowering, that of 1969, of which 15% flowered in 1971, an exceptionally high proportion for two-year-old plants. It may be assumed that these individuals, which experienced good growing conditions in 1969 and 1970, reached the flowering stage sooner than those developing in climatic conditions more usual for Teesdale.

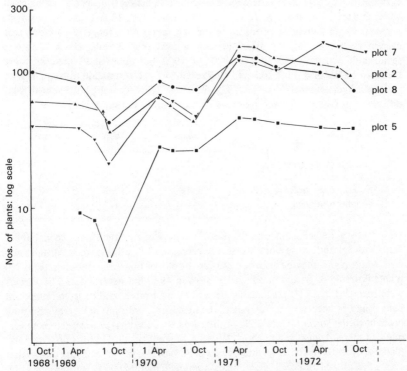

FIG. 9. Total population levels in four plots of hoary whitlow-grass *(Draba incana)*.

The half-lives estimated from three plots of mixed-age populations more than one year old were 2.7, 3.1 and 3.2 years. In only one sample has an age-cohort, originally of 42 juveniles, died out completely. This took seven years, 1969–1975, and included two good growing seasons during the seedling and juvenile stages, so the normal period may prove to be much longer.

The rate of development in Teesdale is slow and flowering does not usually occur until the plants are several years old. In contrast seedlings from seeds germinated in Durham in January, and planted outside in John Innes compost, flowered seven months later, remained alive and flowered again the following season before dying. There is some evidence that plants of a single age-cohort in Teesdale do not mature at the same rate, giving advantage to the species in that a single good seed-year may provide a succession of flowering plants over several years: foxglove (*Digitalis purpurea*) is described by Harper & White (1974) as behaving much the same. Buried seeds will also germinate and mature in different ways.

Hoary whitlow-grass reproduces exclusively by seed. In Teesdale plants rarely flower until they are three or more years old and then they usually die. At the two major sites on Widdybank Fell (2 and 8) very similar proportions, about 12%, of the plants flowered in the period 1969–1972, but on Cronkley, in the sheep enclosure, it was about 22%. It would, however, be unwise to conclude that grazing is the sole or even the major cause of the difference. The mean numbers of fruits per flowering plant were: at site 2, 7.5; at site 8, 10.0; and on Cronkley Fell, 13.5. These are positively correlated with increasing openness of the vegetation. This range of variation was evident each year, but the mean number of seeds per capsule, about 18.5, was remarkably constant at all sites in 1970 and 1972, but values at all three sites were higher in 1971, being 19.5, 20.3 and 19.9 respectively. Germination tests at Durham showed a high percentage viability. The following figures reveal a large year-to-year difference in seed-output and numbers of seedlings in the same plots:

	1969	1970	1971
Number of plants in flower	22	4	34
Total number of fruits	179	68	214
Estimated number of seeds	3379	1292	4034
Number of seedlings	418	227	513

Observations are being made on the role of buried seeds, on the change in viablity of seeds with age and on the mortality of very young seedlings. Some seeds, capsules and even whole plants may be dispersed outside the plot or may enter it from outside. No plants flowered or fruited in one of the plots in 1970 but nevertheless 77 seedlings were recorded in 1971, presumably derived either from buried or from immigrant seed. Light is necessary for germination, so buried seed may not germinate until brought to the surface. Only 15% of the seeds produced in the recorded plots germinated there. Annual values show that 63% of seedlings died in their first year and plants are lost thereafter at an annual rate of 38% of plants over one year old, so that only 1.2% of seeds succeed in producing notionally mature plants at three years old.

A high reproductive capacity is very important for a species which is sensitive to competition and only able to survive in very open or unstable conditions. Hoary whitlow-grass survives well in the open short-herb vegetation of the subalpine tundra today and probably did so in the late-glacial and early post-glacial times in Britain; but survival through the forest maximum may have been limited to open habitats such as exposed rock ledges and eroding sugar-limestone and on soils near naturally exposed veins of lead and barytes.

TEESDALE VIOLET

The Teesdale violet is widespread in the Seslerio-Mesobromion grasslands on Widdybank Fell, on the eroding sugar-limestone outcrops and in turf on shallow soil much disturbed by moles. In these habitats it flowers most profusely, the mean value being 0.21 open flowers per plant; in closed turf very few flowers of any kind are formed. Unlike the gentian it is absent from the heather-grasslands. Although the violet can tolerate partial shade (as under rowan and juniper in arctic Sweden), the shading at low level and the changes in surface soil due to heather and its associates may exclude it. All other habitats of Teesdale violet seen in Britain, Norway, Sweden, Switzerland and southern Slovakia are on limestone or metamorphosed basic rock with very open vegetation, one site being on coarse saccharoidal limestone and almost identical to sites on Widdybank Fell: it also grows on sandy soils. Its whole range is north-continental (p. 31).

Defining the individual in this species was more difficult than with the previous two. A seed produces a plant with a central bud giving rise to a rosette of leaves and axillary flowering branches. The stem may also produce basal branches each with a terminal rosette of a few leaves. These are borne just below the soil-surface but do not produce separate root-systems, and usually the connection with the parent cannot be confirmed without damaging the plant. Each leaf-rosette has accordingly been regarded in this study as a separate individual.

Populations totals were maintained at or above the originally recorded numbers of reproductive units over the period 1968–1972. Some plots showed increases of between 10% and 55% and two decreased initially but recovered their numbers by 1972. As in other species new plants from seed were added to the population totals after their first winter. The risk of mortality seems to be independent of the age of the individual, but there is a seasonal irregularity showing a greater risk of mortality in the growing season.

Survival of the individual plants seems to be adversely affected by inter-specific competition. Where the vegetation is closed, and especially where dominated by a tall course sward of kobresia and blue sesleria, the individuals are widely spaced and few in number, and the half-life values of the recorded populations were only 8, 10 and 11 years respectively. In contrast, in populations on eroding sugar-limestone (and in semi-open communities) the density of individuals is much greater and half-life values of 16 and 14 years were recorded. The survival rate per 100 plants during the April–October period appears to be correlated with the temperature of the previous winter, as shown in the following table:

Year	Feb. mean* air temp.	Survival rate, April–Oct.	Ann. recruitment rate, seedlings
1969	—3.5°C	0.82	0.27
1970	—2.0°C	0.88	0.12
1971	2.2°C	0.94	0.08
1972	0.5°C	0.95	0.09

* = ½ (max. + min.) daily temp.

The extreme climatic conditions of 1969 and 1970 imposed greater stress on weak individuals, rendering them less able to cope with the following growing season. Yet there must be doubt about the significance of these low winter temperatures for survival in Teesdale when they are compared with the severe conditions to which the species is exposed in some of its arctic and central European sites.

Recruitment in Teesdale violet is from seed and by vegetative shoots. The latter were of greater importance overall in maintaining numbers, providing 16 new shoots per 100 plants compared with 13 seedlings. Survival of vegetative shoots and seedl-

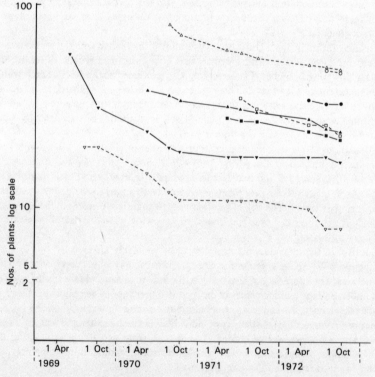

FIG. 10. Survival of Teesdale violet *(Viola rupestris)* seedlings and vegetative shoots 'born' at the same time. Seedlings ——, vegetative shoots - - - -.

ings appears to be independent of age except perhaps the seedlings of 1969 (Fig. 10). Vegetative reproduction varied greatly between plots and years. The rate of recruitment in 1970 of 30 per 100 was more than twice that of the other years – 9 in 1969, 11 in 1971 and 14 in 1972. Seedling recruitment varied more widely between plots than from year to year, the highest annual rate of 23 per 100 occurring where moles created small pockets of loose soil in the turf, while the closed habitats had the very low rates of 2 and 5 per 100. A very open eroding sugar-limestone site had the lowest rate of 1 per 100: even though the production of flowers and capsules was high, only a single seedling was found. Somewhat smaller though still large differences were apparent in year-to-year comparisons, as shown in the table above. It is known that the seed requires chilling before germination can occur, but these figures suggest an increased germination with exposure to lower temperatures. The seeds are heavy (mean weight = 1.20mg) and produce large persistent epigeal cotyledons. Once the seedling is established the risk of mortality is usually no greater than for older plants (Fig. 10).

The production of flowers, fruit and seeds is inversely related to the density of the vegetation in which the populations occur. In the most open site 33% of the individuals flowered each year, producing either open flowers or small flowers that remained closed (cleistogamous). Very few of the former are produced even by the most prolific plants, the mean value per rosette being only 0.21. More closed flowers are produced per rosette and in some sites mean values as high as 1.52 have been recorded. The number of ripe fruits per rosette, with a mean value of 0.54, is considerably higher than the number of open flowers. The mean number of seeds per capsule was 9.98 in 1970, 8.42 in 1971 and 8.26 in 1972, the value for 1970 being again the highest. Seed production is correlated with the openness of the habitat, as shown in the table below.

Nature of site	Total numbers of plants in the recorded area	Number of seeds per 100 plants
Most open	539	133
Semiclosed	1145	86
Disturbed	1321	81
Closed	627	0
Closed	226	0

Similarly the seed production shows much variation from year to year, as is seen in values per 100 individuals: 38 in 1969, 107 in 1970, 95 in 1971 and 52 in 1972. As a result of wastage of seeds only 13 seedlings per 100 rosettes are recorded annually.

Plants usually do not flower until they are at least four years old, though new vegetative rosettes may flower in the second year in favourable conditions. Records show, however, that an individual, once mature, can flower frequently but not always continuously, and can also reproduce vegetatively for many years.

Plants in the more or less open habitats exhibit the highest reproductive capacity and give the appearance today of growing in near-optimal conditions, whereas the survival of the plants in a closed sward is precarious. The success of the Teesdale violet on exposed limestone cliff crevices and crags in the Arctic and in the Alps, and its good reproductive performance on open sugar-limestone sites in Teesdale today, support the likelihood of its survival there from late-glacial times to the present day.

COMMON DOG-VIOLET

The common dog-violet, widespread in Britain and in Europe, has a similar life-strategy in Teesdale to that of the Teesdale violet. Reproduction is by seed and by vegetative shoots produced on the roots, so that both seedlings and root-borne shoots are reproductive units in this study. The annual recruitment of vegetative shoots over four years was twice that of seedlings, 16 and 8 respectively per 100 individuals, more than compensating jointly for the annual mortality of 13 per 100, so that the population totals were all higher in 1972 than in 1968. Mortality in both the originally recorded populations of mixed age and in the known age-cohorts is low compared with gentian, and half-life values for populations first recorded in 1968 were 11, 11 and 14 years. It should be noted that common violet is more frequent in the fescue-matgrass grasslands (*Festuco-Nardetum*) and the closed and damper grasslands of the Seslerio-Mesobromion than in the drier communities favoured by Teesdale violet.

Flowers are of both kinds and again very few open flowers or their capsules were produced. The production of seeds per 100 plants varied greatly in the four years: 29 in 1969, 67 in 1970, 49 in 1971 and 76 in 1972. The high value in 1972 was due to the high number of cleistogamous flowers in one plot (8B). The annual recruitment of seedlings over this period was 8 per 100 individuals. This may seem very low but, in a species where mortality is low, the rate of recruitment need not be high if there is a good rate of survival and as long as environmental conditions remain fairly stable.

THE HYBRID VIOLET

The hybrid violet (*V. rupestris* × *riviniana*) has its only known British locality on Widdybank Fell. The triploid product of a diploid and a tetraploid, it has morphological characteristics intermediate between its parents. It is sterile but has vigorous vegetative reproduction and has given rise to dense clones a few metres in diameter. Numbers of individuals per square metre, calculated from the recorded plots, are 655.5 for the hybrid, 148.9 for Teesdale violet and 174.5 for common dog-violet. Each clone may be derived from a single hybrid seedling or from seedlings from one or more capsules. During the species-mapping project a few very small colonies of five or six reproductive units were recorded. Two of these were included in the population-dynamics studies, but no change in the numbers of rosettes has occurred in three seasons.

In all some ten colonies are known: one other, and some very small clones, were destroyed by the flooding. All were found in disturbed habitats intermediate between the preferred communities of the two parents. Approximately equal numbers of open flowers were produced per flowering individual by the common dog-violet and the hybrid, but fewer by Teesdale violet. The numbers of cleistogamous flowers are variable in the hybrid but tend to be fewer than in either parent type. The survival curves for the two recorded populations indicate that complete replacement of a population sample may take many years, and the clonal genotype should survive almost indefinitely.

This last point raises the question why there should be only ten colonies of hybrid violet. For hybrid seed to be produced plants of both parent species must be within flying range of a pollinator – probably a bumble-bee – and both must have open flowers ready for pollination at the same time. Teesdale violet usually starts to flower one or two weeks earlier than dog-violet, and they will coincide only in occasional years. The weather must also be suitable for potential pollinators to fly, a condition not to be relied on in Upper Teesdale. Very few ripe capsules from open flowers are produced by either parent, so the probability that any of these is the result of hybridization is clearly slight. There is the further point that hybrid seed appears to give rise to established seedlings only in a disturbed habitat of 'intermediate type', so it is perhaps surprising that hybrid colonies occur at all.

BITTER MILKWORT

The bitter milkwort (*Polygala amara*) is a short-lived perennial occurring in a few small populations in Upper Teesdale. In the recorded population there was an annual loss of about one-third of the plants over one year old (Fig. 11). The half-life values of four populations were 6.4, 4.3, 3.6 and 2.7 years. Only the largest population, which had the longest half-life, showed a net increase in numbers by 1972. The percentages of flowering plants in the recorded populations from 1969 to 1975 were: 36.4, 30.7, 30.2, 28.6, 13.8, 10.4 and 16.6. Fruit production per plant varied greatly between populations and between years, ranging from 3.45, the mean for a population with small plants, to 14.95, the mean in 1970, when many plants had several inflorescences. The annual seed production was 377 per 100 plants, although the annual number of recorded seedlings was only 54 per 100 plants. As in hoary whitlow-grass the length of the juvenile stage varied. A relatively high proportion of plants flowered when three to four years old and continued to flower for several years. The annual recruitment of seedlings, 2.22 per plant in 1969, 0.40 in 1970, 0.17 in 1971 and 0.27 in 1972, was highest in 1969, and all populations showed a large increase in 1969, but by 1975 totals had fallen just below the original values in three out of four samples. It is apparent that occasional years good for seeding and ger-mination are essential to maintain viable populations.

ALPINE CINQUEFOIL

On Widdybank Fell alpine cinquefoil is thinly scattered in short calcareous grassland and species-rich heather grassland. Only one population was recorded and this had 26 shoots (reproductive units) in 1969. By 1975 there were 49 shoots, of which 22 were present in 1969, a further 15 were survivors of a big increase of 18 in 1970, and the remaining 12 were survivors of 16 which appeared as annual additions of 2–4 shoots. The increase of over 100% is probably not typical of colonies on the top of the Fell. In the small sample studied there was a higher mortality in the first year (4 units) than in succeeding years up to five years old (1 or 2 a year). In ten years of work on Widdybank Fell only one flower (in 1972) and one inflorescence with a few fruits (29

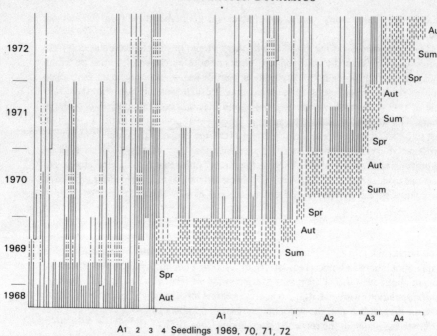

FIG. 11. Behaviour of bitter milkwort *(Polygala amara)*. Each vertical line represents one reproductive unit; a continuous line = vegetative growth; branches = the number of rosettes on one root; dot and dash = flowering; broken line = seedling stage.

July 1966) have been seen. On the Fell top only vegetative reproduction appears to be effective under present conditions, but plants on rock-ledges, at both higher and lower altitudes, flower in most years.

RARE SPRING SEDGE

Rare spring sedge shows variations in habit, life-form and physiology both within and between the populations in the Breckland of East Anglia and Teesdale. The habit can be tufted, dense mat or open mat, but the most striking variation is in the life-form. Teesdale plants (Fig. 12), not very intensively grazed, produce strong shoots which are winter-green, whereas leaves on Breckland plants turn brown in autumn. Moreover new shoots emerge in early autumn in Breckland but remain below ground until May in Teesdale, and Lloyd has shown physiological differences which are advantageous in their respective localities.

In severe weather the winter-green leaves of the Teesdale plants die off at their tips with the most drastic consequences for the flowering shoots, as little as 1.5cm of functional green tissue surviving on each of two or three leaves until spring. The very slender weak inflorescences produced by these starved shoots have no female spike, whereas in good years one male and two or three female spikes are commonly

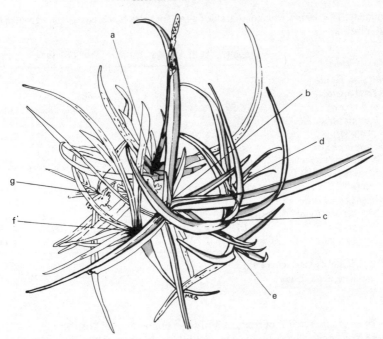

FIG. 12. Reproductive units in rare spring sedge *(Carex ericetorum)*: *a*, fruiting 1975; *b*, shoot born 1973; *c*, shoot born 1974; *d* and *e*, shoots born 1975; *f*, dead shoot 1975; *g*, dead shoot probably fruited 1974.

produced. Fertile fruits are formed in most years, but these are easily detached and the figures given below are almost certainly too low.

	1969	1970	1971	1972	1973	1974	1975
Total population	166	199	204	227	291	271	308
% flowering shoots	9.0	11.0	4.0	7.9	10.0	6.4	5.9
Flowers per infl.	—	13.2	14.3	13.1	11.6	8.3	11.9
Fruits per infl.	6.0	4.3	4.4	1.3	2.5	2.1	1.3

In contrast robust plants protected from grazing for about eight years had 13.0 fruits per inflorescence in 1971. Though no seedlings have been observed on either Widdybank or Cronkley Fell, fruits sown on soil in a warm greenhouse in October 1970 produced 35 seedlings within six weeks.

BIRD'S-EYE PRIMROSE, SCOTTISH ASPHODEL AND THREE-FLOWERED RUSH

Two well-known and attractive species, bird's-eye primrose and Scottish asphodel, have been recorded in permanently marked plots for their potential reproductive capacity. The results, with comparable figures for three-flowered rush, are given in the table below.

	1969	1970	1971	1972	1973	1974	1975
Bird's-eye primrose							
Total rosettes	657	637	654	627	685	753	719
% flowering	*16.50*	*13.19*	*14.80*	*14.51*	*13.60*	*18.28*	*11.96*
Flowers per infl.							
(n≫30)	—	3.30	3.83	3.29	3.34	3.25	2.91
Scottish asphodel							
Number of fl. shoots	—	31*	*85*	56	62	77	53
Flowers per infl.							
(n≫30)	—	*11.49*	*10.93*	*10.90*	*10.61*	*11.19*	*8.81*
Three-flowered rush							
Number of fl. shoots	163	211	—	—	—	52	82
Flowers per infl.	*1.79*	*2.23*	—	—	—	*1.84*	*1.93*
Fruits per infl.**	*1.29*	*1.74*	—	—	—	*1.62*	*1.84*

* 2 plots, not 3 as in later years
** surviving as ripe fruits

There are no records of fruits of bird's-eye primrose or of Scottish asphodel from these plots, none having survived to maturity, but all three species develop some fruit on the Fell.

In 1970 those species which flowered early were adversely affected by very cold weather from mid-April to mid-May, whereas the later-flowering Scottish asphodel and three-flowered rush flowered very well. The high flowering percentage for bird's-eye primrose in 1971 is a reflection of the good growing conditions in the previous summer, when flower-bud initials would have been laid down. Scottish asphodel had the most inflorescences and the highest mean number of flowers per inflorescence in 1971. Both these species, but not the rush, had significantly lower figures in 1975, though it is difficult to believe that the comparatively low rainfall of 1974/5 would have affected them, even the habitats of Scottish asphodel being always damp. On the other hand the reproductive capacity of three-flowered rush was seriously reduced in several successive years by shortage of water in spring in the flushes and stream-beds in which it grows. The last really good year for flowers and fruits was 1970: since then its performance has been poor. In most years the proportion of young fruits reaching maturity was low, though there were many seeds per capsule and their viability proved to be high.

Comment

These studies have provided records of the population flux and life-strategies of several of the rare species of the Upper Teesdale N.N.R. and show the relative importance of reproduction by seed and vegetatively in maintaining the populations. On the higher part of Widdybank Fell most of the investigated species are maintaining themselves successfully in the present conditions. Further observations are needed to determine whether the decreasing populations of hoary whitlow-grass are merely a temporary phase in the rapid oscillations characteristic of short-lived species or a more serious decline. The relative importance of the individual is greatest where the species is seed-dependent and has a short life-span (like hoary whitlow-grass, bird's eye primrose and bitter milkwort) and where life-span is long but with a low recruitment-rate as in the violets. In several species little seed is produced because the flowers and young fruits are destroyed by grazing and trampling. Further observations are needed to determine the importance of this for bird's-eye primrose and others. On Cronkley Fell grazing and burrowing by rabbits and consequential soil-erosion are now intense, and both gentian and bitter milkwort are under heavy pressure in some areas. The milkwort populations are very small and poorly productive, and physical protection of weak plants is necessary to encourage greater seed production. Of the species examined hoary whitlow-grass alone is more productive on Cronkley Fell than on Widdybank Fell. In general it must be said that the successful conservation of the Teesdale rarities demands exact knowledge of their population-dynamics and life strategies derived from records of the kind discussed in this chapter.

CHAPTER 3

The Plant Communities of Upper Teesdale

THE proposal for a reservoir on Cow Green led to a careful evaluation of the whole range of scientific interest within the area that would be affected. Plant ecologists were concerned that the botanical importance of Upper Teesdale should be more widely understood to be not simply the presence or abundance of certain rare species of wild plant, but also the combinations in which these occurred, both with each other and with more common plants. Their interest was in the character of the vegetation as a whole and also in its diversity as expressed in the variety of plant communities present in the area. The presence of particular species makes some of these plant communities unusual or even unique in the British Isles, and certain combinations are not known to be repeated anywhere else in the world. The identification and orderly description of the range of vegetational variation therefore became a major concern for the nature conservationists involved.

The account of the flora of the Yorkshire part of Upper Teesdale, by J. G. Baker in 1863, had an ecological basis in that the rarer species were listed in groups for different main habitats. It was not until 1956, however, that there became available a general account of vegetation types which paid attention to the common as well as the rarer species of the area. C. D. Pigott's paper described the major classes of vegetation in relation to type of habitat and gave detailed lists of species for many of the distinctive plant communities. In 1965 M. E. Bradshaw and W. A. Clark wrote a very readable account of the flora and vegetation, for less specialized readers, in *The Natural History of Upper Teesdale*. That same year the Nature Conservancy needed more information on the precise location and area of important plant communities which would be submerged by the proposed reservoir, and D. A. Ratcliffe surveyed the vegetation of Widdybank Fell, concentrating on the localized areas of sugar-limestone and making comparisons with those on Cronkley Fell. In 1969 D. J. Bellamy and some of his colleagues considered the status of the Teesdale rarities in relation to the floristic composition and biological production of the communities in which they occur, and he later discussed the similarities between certain of the distinctive Upper Teesdale communities and their continental European parallels. The most complete description and classification of the vegetation is that made subsequently by M. E. Bradshaw and A. V. Jones (1976), assisted by a grant from the Teesdale Trust Fund. This refers mainly to Widdybank Fell and includes extremely detailed vegetation maps showing the distribution of the communities described.

These more recent studies have adopted a plant sociological (phytosociological) approach. Basically this involves identifying and describing *types* of plant community

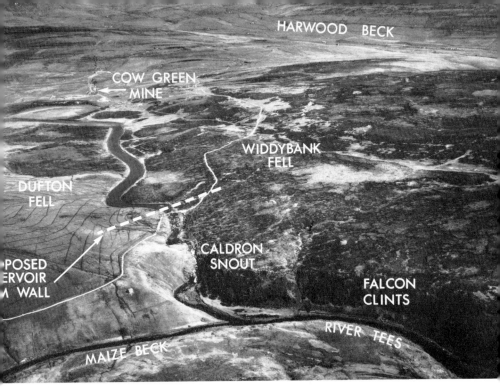

Labels on image: HARWOOD BECK, COW GREEN MINE, WIDDYBANK FELL, DUFTON FELL, CALDRON SNOUT, PROPOSED RESERVOIR DAM WALL, FALCON CLINTS, MAIZE BECK, RIVER TEES

PLATE 1. *Above*, Cow Green basin and its surroundings before construction of the dam. *Below*, vertical aerial view of filled reservoir.

PLATE 2. *Above*, High Force, showing the Whin Sill ledge lying over carboniferous limestone. *Below*, Cauldron Snout.

which together make up the overall vegetational pattern. A hill landscape appears as a mosaic of different shades and textures of colour, sharply separated in some places but merging imperceptibly in others. The range of colour comes from the mantle of vegetation, changing spatially with varying conditions of topography, soil and past land-use, and seasonally according to the stage of growth of the most abundant plants. There is the dark chocolate-brown of the heather moor, greening in late spring and becoming rich purple during flowering-time in August; the bleached straw of mat-grass changing to green in the late spring; the rusty brown of dead bracken-beds turning to deep green by midsummer, and so on. Vertical photographs of the fells taken from an aircraft show a wide range of tone, even on black-and-white film, representing a range of variation in vegetation. The pattern thus revealed can be traced and copied to provide the basis for a vegetation map. But first it is essential to know what the distant pattern of tone or colour actually means on the ground, in terms of real vegetation, so that a truly informative key to the map can be supplied.

Where vegetation appears in the distant view as clear and even in tone or colour, it will often on closer inspection prove to be uniform in the details of its plant cover. Where tone and colour are indistinct or variable, botanical composition will usually show marked diversity. Typical heather moor shows up in the aerial photograph as uniform dark areas, because it is completely dominated by plants of a single species. But the rotational burning to which the moor is usually subjected produces a mosaic of sharply defined patches of varying tone and colour, corresponding to the stages in regeneration of the mature community and involving gradual increase in heather cover and often a temporary abundance of other plant species. By contrast some of the grasslands, especially on limestone, may appear to be uniform but are composed of a large number of different species, with no one clearly dominant. Where there is a wall or fence the vegetation on the two sides may be quite different, but this is an artificial consequence of past management. On the open fell the grassland may be interrupted suddenly by a spring or rill which carries a contrasting group of plants. This is a natural discontinuity, but the water may spread out lower down to flush the slope more diffusely so that there is here only a gradual change in the vegetation as the ground becomes wetter, and no sharp boundary can be discerned.

These examples deal with only a few of the plant communities, the total range of variation in the vegetation of Upper Teesdale being much more complex. The plant sociologist is concerned to describe all the vegetation of a district in terms of vegetational units recognizable by consistently recurring combinations of species. Any one such combination will often include species also present in one or more other combinations, though frequently in different degrees of abundance. The aim is to identify as many of these units as are necessary to depict, adequately for the purpose in hand, the full range of vegetational variation, neither leaving major gaps nor taking account of minute and perhaps irrelevant details of variation. The recognized units of vegetation can be diagnosed and named by their *dominant* species (those with a high ground-cover), by those species which are *constant* (occurring with a high degree of consistency from place to place), or which are otherwise *diagnostic* (neither dominant nor constant but showing a distinct preference for the particular community). Each vegetation-type thus recognized can then be used as a unit for mapping or for vegetational description and will convey immediate meaning to those familiar with the diagnostic botanical features. The following account of types of vegetation in Upper Teesdale will be less formalized than in an orthodox phytosociological treatment but will nevertheless retain essential features of that kind of approach.

The Types of Vegetation

The vegetation of the whole area is essentially of a semi-natural kind, profoundly modified during the last 2000 years by human activity. It is not clear exactly how much of it was wooded during the post-glacial period, but probably much of the drier ground below about 600m carried trees or tall shrubs and has subsequently been denuded during the main phase of deforestation (p. 144). This woodland or scrub cover was evidently discontinuous, opening out on the thin soils of the sugar-limestone outcrops, large block screes and steep rock-faces, and also on the more waterlogged areas of peatland with high *Sphagnum* cover. It has been replaced by the enclosed pastures of the hill farms and by a complex of grassland and heather moor on the unenclosed fells which are managed for both hill sheep and red grouse. The area in which the reservoir lies has, indeed, the appearance at first sight of typical Pennine sheep-walk and grouse-moor, and it is appropriate to describe first the characteristic and widespread vegetation-types of this mainly acidic moorland terrain before dealing with the special limestone communities which add such distinction to Upper Teesdale.

WOODLAND AND SCRUB

Although reduced to mere fragments, the surviving remnants of native woodland have considerable interest. Whilst sessile oak (*Quercus petraea*) was evidently once widespread in the area, very little has survived in Upper Teesdale and the remaining woodland is mainly of birch (Plate 8). Patches and strips of birchwood flank the Tees above and below High Force, the birch being the small northern form of the hairy birch (*Betula pubescens* ssp. *odorata*), notably fragrant after rain and so characteristic of hill woods in north-west Scotland. On acidic soils of the Whin Sill the birchwoods have a rather limited flora, with ferns including broad buckler (*Dryopteris dilatata*), mountain fern (*Thelypteris limbosperma*), beech fern (*T. phegopteris*), oak fern (*Gymnocarpium dryopteris*), and hard fern (*Blechnum spicant*); herbs such as wood sorrel (*Oxalis acetosella*) and common dog-violet (*Viola riviniana*) and, amongst grasses, creeping bent (*Agrostis stolonifera*) and Yorkshire fog (*Holcus lanatus*).

The numerous large blocks in some woods, especially on north-facing slopes, are thickly clothed with green carpets of moss and leafy liverworts, while the gnarled trunks and branches of the birches themselves are also densely grown with mosses and lichens.

Patches of birchwood on base-rich soils derived at least in part from limestone have a different flora. There is a greater variety of trees and shrubs, the birch being accompanied by ash, hazel, alder, bird-cherry and willow. Ferns and mosses are less prominent and the field layer is predominantly herbaceous, with a good variety of species. Grasses such as tufted hair-grass (*Deschampsia caespitosa*) are conspicuous, for these woods are partly grazed, but there is also an abundance of tall herbs including meadow-sweet (*Filipendula ulmaria*), water avens (*Geum rivale*), marsh hawk's-beard (*Crepis paludosa*), common valerian (*Valeriana officinalis*), marsh marigold (*Caltha palustris*) and angelica (*Angelica sylvestris*). In addition there is a characteristically associated group of northern tall herbs, including globe-flower (*Trollius europaeus*, Plate VII), wood cranesbill (*Geranium sylvaticum*, Plate VII) and melancholy thistle (*Cirsium heterophyllum*), which give these richer birchwood fragments a distinct affinity with the extensive mountain birchwoods of south-western Norway. Species of more local and mainly northern occurrence are also present and include giant bellflower (*Campanula latifolia*), the rare soft hawk's-beard (*Crepis mollis*), wood melick grass (*Melica nutans*) and meadow horsetail (*Equisetum pratense*).

The best example of true limestone woodland in the district lies outside the Tees catchment on the terraced scarp-slope of Hillbeck Fell above Brough, and in the adjoining deep rocky glen of Swindale. Here, on slopes with mostly thin limestone soils breaking out into scree and crag, is a quite extensive ashwood with much wych elm, birch, aspen, holly, blackthorn, elder and spindle. This is the most northerly British locality for Midland hawthorn (*Crataegus laevigata*). The field layer communities are mostly those typical of lowland woods on basic soils, with dog's mercury (*Mercurialis perennis*), wild garlic (*Allium ursinum*) and wood false brome (*Brachypodium sylvaticum*). Bluebells (*Endymion non-scriptus*) and nettles (*Urtica dioica*) are dominant in places, and both male fern (*Dryopteris filix-mas*) and lady fern (*Athyrium filix-femina*) are in some quantity. Lesser celandine (*Ranunculus ficaria*), primrose (*Primula vulgaris*), wood anemone (*Anemone nemorosa*), sanicle (*Sanicula europaea*), wild strawberry (*Fragaria vesca*), barren strawberry (*Potentilla sterilis*), herb Robert (*Geranium robertianum*), germander speedwell (*Veronica chamaedrys*), herb bennet (*Geum urbanum*), water avens, bugle (*Ajuga reptans*), wood sedge (*Carex sylvatica*), and rough-stalked meadow-grass (*Poa trivialis*) are all generally abundant. More local species worthy of note include melancholy thistle, wood cranesbill, wood vetch (*Vicia sylvatica*), lily-of-the-valley (*Convallaria majalis*), wood forget-me-not (*Myosotis sylvatica*), giant bellflower, stone bramble (*Rubus saxatilis*), herb Paris (*Paris quadrifolia*), marjoram (*Origanum vulgare*), shining cranesbill (*Geranium lucidum*), wood melick grass and Dutch rush (*Equisetum hyemale*).

This is a more typical lowland wood than the sub-alpine birchwood near High Force and probably represents a type once widespread at lower elevations in the district. Many of its characteristic species are widely distributed now in a variety of non-wooded habitats on the open fells. Fragments of alderwood and willow scrub, sometimes represented by an attenuated fringe or simply by scattered trees and bushes, persist along the lower streamsides and in marshy soaks. The willows include the common grey and eared sallows (*Salix cinerea* and *S. aurita*) but also the rarer and northern tea-leaved willow (*S. phylicifolia*) and dark-leaved willow (*S. nigricans*). Willow scrub was probably once extensive on moist calcareous soils up to considerable altitudes, but has been almost completely eradicated by grazing.

Despite the general loss of tall woody cover, the reach of the Tees between Holwick and Cronkley is notable for the presence of quite large thickets of tall dense juniper on the flats and slopes adjoining the river, where the soils are acidic or only mildly basic (Plate 16). This juniper scrub shows gradual dissection and is represented on the rocky slopes of Cronkley Fell and Falcon Clints by isolated clumps and individual bushes (Plate V). A juniper-covered island in the Tees above Widdybank Farm strongly suggests that the combination of grazing and fire has eradicated the community from much of this higher ground. Yet in the High Force area the dense thickets may have resulted from increase of juniper as woodland itself was destroyed. The junipers are variously associated with grassland, heather and bilberry, and bracken, and though many other species are present their flora is in no way distinctive in the sense of forming a juniper community characterized by other components than the dominant juniper.

THE ACIDIC MOORLANDS AND FELLS

Grasslands and heaths

On dry ground with soils poor in plant-nutrients woodland and scrub have been widely replaced by a dwarf shrub heath dominated by ling or heather (*Calluna vulgaris*). This plant is the staple food of the red grouse and, for well over a hundred years, the heather ground has been managed by a regime of rotational burning so that there are at all times areas of young heather at its most nutritious stage. The operation involves burning strips and rectangles of the oldest heather early each spring, thus giving the familiar mosaic of colours to the moorland as a whole, representing all the various stages from freshly burnt to old heather. During the regeneration of the heather community (*Callunetum*), extending over a period of up to ten years from the last burn, there may be a greater abundance of other species such as bilberry (*Vaccinium myrtillus*), cowberry (*V. vitis-idaea*), bell heather (*Erica cinerea*) and wavy hair-grass (*Deschampsia flexuosa*), but these are gradually reduced to low cover as the ling re-establishes dominance. Crowberry (*Empetrum nigrum*) is also locally abundant. On the Whin Sill outcrops of Widdybank and Cronkley Fells scattered patches of bearberry (*Arctostaphylos uva-ursi*) growing with the heather give a fragmentary representation of a community widespread in the Scottish Highlands. Beneath tall heather on shady slopes there are usually dense carpets of the mosses which grow profusely in rocky birchwoods, such as *Hypnum cupressiforme*, *Pleurozium schreberi*, *Rhytidiadelphus loreus* and certain kinds of bog-moss, *Sphagnum capillaceum* and *S. quinquefarium*. The lesser twayblade (*Listera cordata*), a tiny orchid, is characteristic of this community, and more rarely there is the beautiful feathery moss *Ptilium crista-castrensis*.

Callunetum extends up to 600m or rather higher, on suitable ground, though the heather becomes more dwarfed with increasing altitude, and in places, such as Bellbeaver Rigg on the Tees–Tyne watershed, there is abundance of 'reindeer-moss' lichens (*Cladonia arbuscula*, *C. impexa* and *C. uncialis*) in the community. In many parts of Upper Teesdale, however, and especially on the higher ground, long-continued heavy grazing by sheep, combined with repeated burning, has caused the replacement of heather communities by others more tolerant of the regime. The first stage in the sequence is the rise to dominance of bilberry, which is associated with the same grasses and mosses as the Callunetum. This Vaccinietum is itself replaced by grassland of acidic soils when heavy grazing continues. On dry ground, and this usually means steep slopes, species such as sheep's fescue (*Festuca ovina*), brown and common bent (*Agrostis canina* and *A. tenuis*) and wavy hair-grass usually become dominant, and there is often an abundance of small herbs which include heath bed-straw (*Galium saxatile*), tormentil (*Potentilla erecta*) and field woodrush (*Luzula campestris*). Some of the mosses of the former dwarf shrub heaths persist, but usually in smaller quantity than hitherto. On wetter ground mat-grass (*Nardus stricta*) appears and rises to dominance, and the smaller and less competitive species of the previous community are reduced in abundance. On still more waterlogged and gleyed (p. 131) soils heath rush (*Juncus squarrosus*) typically takes over from the mat-grass, and in places it forms dense stands with its wiry 'bird's-nest' rosettes tightly packed together. Grassland dominated by purple moor grass (*Molinia caerulea*) on shallow peat occurs locally but is not extensive.

These acidic grassland and heath rush communities occur with little change up to the high tops of the Tees catchment at over 790m, as on Mickle Fell and Knock Fell. On drier ground above 600m the replacement of montane *Calluna* heath by bilberry heath and acidic grassland has been almost complete. Locally on the high rocky gritstone slopes there is a mixed grass-heath of bilberry, cowberry, sheep's fescue, mountain fescue (*Festuca vivipara*), brown bent and wavy hair-grass with an abundance of 'reindeer moss' lichens and other lichens such as 'Iceland moss' (*Cetraria islandica*) and *C. aculeata*. The stiff sedge (*Carex bigelowii*) is locally plentiful in this community and is a true montane plant, not descending below about 550m in this area. The northern bog whortleberry (*Vaccinium uliginosum*) was formerly recorded from various parts of the Cross Fell range, and probably included these high-level heaths among its habitats, but it has not been seen recently. Still more surprisingly the northern crowberry (*Empetrum hermaphroditum*), which so typically takes the place of *E. nigrum* in montane dwarf shrub heaths of the Scottish Highlands, is quite unknown in the Pennines, though present sparingly in the Lakeland fells to the west. Clubmosses are less well represented in these Pennine hill grasslands than in those of Lakeland: fir clubmoss (*Lycopodium selago*) is frequent at the higher levels, but both alpine and stag's-horn clubmosses (*L. alpinum* and *L. clavatum*) are uncommon.

Replacement of bilberry and crowberry by grasses has occurred widely within the montane zone, so that short fescue or wavy hair-grass communities are more extensive on dry ground. Sparse and dwarfed shoots of bilberry and cowberry persist, especially in rocky places, lichens remain abundant and heath bedstraw is frequently in profusion. The flora of these high-level grasslands is, however, very poor, stiff sedge and a few inconspicuous lichens being the only montane elements. On the highest tops, especially the large summit-plateau of Cross Fell at 854–885m, the above-mentioned communities merge into a type dominated by woolly fringe-moss (*Rhacomitrium lanuginosum*). Much of the ground here is thrown into low hummocks representing frost-polygons and the fringe-moss occupies the crests of these, whilst the intervening depressions are mostly grass-covered, giving a distinctive vegetational pattern. This community corresponds with the *Rhacomitrium-Carex bigelowii* heaths so extensively and finely developed on the high tops of the Scottish

Highlands but represented in poorer form in northern England. Stiff sedge is abundant in the high Pennine fringe-moss heaths, but least willow (*Salix herbacea*), a characteristic species of the Highland examples, has not been seen recently in its old localities on Cross Fell and Mickle Fell. The Pennine fringe-moss carpets are, moreover, far less luxuriant and continuous and much more mixed with grasses than those in the Highlands, and they are best described as *Rhacomitrium-Festuca* or *Rhacomitrium-Deschampsia flexuosa* communities. The greater amount of grass in the Pennine types evidently results from the heavier grazing by sheep, which by their treading and manuring favour the spread of the fine-leaved grasses in the moss-heath.

The modification of the high-level vegetation through long-continued management for sheep has now obscured the pattern of communities produced by varying length of snow-cover as determined by topography and altitude. This pattern is well represented on the higher mountains of the central Highlands, where prolonged snow-cover is a major factor of the upland environment. With increasing duration of snow-lie there is a change from the prevailing Callunetum to *Vaccinium* heath, *Nardus* grassland and, finally, a range of communities dominated mainly by mosses and liverworts. The sub-montane *Vaccinium* and *Nardus* communities of the Pennines, resulting largely through management for sheep, are so similar to the late snow-bed types in general appearance that it is now hardly possible to separate the two. Whilst this is a warmer region than the Highlands, snow often lies on the high slopes of the Cross Fell range into June, and it is quite likely that there were, formerly, well-defined examples of the less extreme types of vegetation resulting from late snow-cover.

Bogs and flushes

The vegetation so far described belongs to ground ranging from dry to moderately wet. In this district, however, the combination of high rainfall, gentle topography and the prevalence of acidic substrata has led to the extensive development of blanket bog on the moorlands, up to a general level of 750m or so. The prevailing vegetation of these bogs is a type widespread in Britain and, on a European scale, especially characteristic of our strongly Atlantic climate. The least disturbed areas, with a high water-table and more or less continuous *Sphagnum* cover, are probably fairly natural, but there is a series of derived communities resulting from a long period of repeated moor-burning, heavy sheep grazing and, in some instances, deliberate draining of peat. Heather and cotton-grass (*Eriophorum vaginatum*) are usually abundant, but other characteristic vascular plants include crowberry, cowberry, cross-leaved heath (*Erica tetralix*), the other common cotton-grass (*E. angustifolium*), deer-sedge (*Trichophorum caespitosum*), bog asphodel (*Narthecium ossifragum*) and round-leaved sundew (*Drosera rotundifolia*). The western terrace of Widdybank Fell, close to the reservoir, has perhaps the least modified area of blanket bog, dominated by bog-mosses which include *Sphagnum papillosum* and *S. rubellum* on the more pronounced hummocks, *S. cuspidatum* in pools and wet hollows, and occasional hummocks of the rarer *S. imbricatum* (Plate 24) and *S. fuscum*. A typical patch of this kind of *Sphagnum* bog on Widdybank Fell was submerged by the reservoir, but there are still large areas on Foolmire (Fig. 24, p. 143). On the other or western side of the Tees, opposite to Widdybank Fell, a large population of the very local tall bog sedge (*Carex paupercula*), growing in the spongy surface of a similar bog, was completely drowned. It persists, however, in more elevated parts of the Upper Tees catchment. The drier facies of heather-cotton-grass bog have locally abundant cloudberry (*Rubus chamaemorus*), a distinctive montane plant of this habitat which is found in greater profusion in the similar bogs of the high watershed between Wear and Tees. Lichens of the *Cladonia arbuscula-C. uncialis* group show high cover locally in both drier and wetter facies of these bogs.

All stages in degeneration of the blanket bog cover can be seen, from incipient 'haggs' to large ramifying systems of deep gullies and on to the final disintegration of the remaining peat in sheet-erosion. The bog-mosses are gradually lost, the vascular plants become more luxuriant (although the vegetation as a whole becomes more and more reduced and dissected) and some species, such as crowberry, increase along the eroding edges of the peat-haggs. It was in a patch of moderately eroded bog on Widdybank Fell that the interesting discovery of dwarf birch (*Betula nana*, Plate 14) was made in 1966. Although this little northern shrub is growing with the heather, cotton-grass and deer-sedge that are its typical associates in the Scottish Highlands, it has survived on Widdybank Fell, not in an undisturbed bog, but in one which has been strongly modified. No other Pennine localities for dwarf birch have yet been found, but a second English site was discovered in 1974 on the remote Kielder moors of the Cheviot range.

The blanket bogs depend on waterlogging which results essentially from an excess of precipitation over evaporation and run-off. A self-perpetuating system is set up in which anaerobic and strongly acidic conditions resist the decomposition of plant remains so that they accumulate as peat and eventually insulate the growing vegetation of the surface from the underlying mineral substratum. Other kinds of permanently wet habitat occur in topographic situations causing laterally seeping drainage water to collect at the ground surface. Where this kind of waterlogging extends along broad depressions and on terraces, or as soakways within blanket bogs, there arises a different type of bog, best designated 'flush bog', usually with a rather shallow peat, a variety of bog-mosses including *Sphagnum recurvum*, *S. auriculatum*, *S. palustre* and *S. squarrosum*, and a selection of sedges, notably common sedge (*Carex nigra*), star sedge (*C. echinata*), white sedge (*C. curta*) and bottle sedge (*C. rostrata*). Other characteristic vascular plants include bog violet (*Viola palustris*), marsh willow-herb (*Epilobium palustre*), bog asphodel, tormentil, grasses and the cotton-grass *Eriophorum angustifolium*. Probably the largest area of this type of vegetation was a stand of *Carex rostrata-Sphagnum recurvum* bog containing the very rare *Sphagnum riparium* in its only known Teesdale locality, forming a marshy tract alongside the broad and almost stagnant section of the Tees not far above Cauldron Snout (pp. 190–2). This tract, once known as the Weel, was totally inundated by the new reservoir and the rare northern water sedge (*Carex aquatilis*), which grew along the river-edge, was also lost. It has more recently been discovered in a new site near Middleton (p. 194). In many places, occupying ground more severely disturbed by man and his grazing animals, there are flush bogs dominated by common rush (*Juncus effusus*) and often containing much hair-moss (*Polytrichum commune*) as well as *Sphagnum recurvum*. Similar sites receiving a slightly more nutrient-rich drainage water often show dominance of sharp-flowered rush (*J. acutiflorus*) and a larger variety of herbs and mosses.

Where emerging drainage water is more highly localized, there are springs with rills draining from them. These may feed more diffuse flushes occupying larger areas of several square metres but less extensive than the typical flush bogs. Flushes occur in a wide variety of situations and some are of an intermittent kind, irrigated by running water only periodically, during wet weather. Where the drainage water is nutrient-poor the springs and flushes are mostly dominated by the bog-mosses typical of the flush bogs, forming bright green or reddish-brown spongy carpets which the fell-walker soon learns to avoid. Where the water has a slightly higher mineral content, the bog-mosses give way to a variety of other mosses and liverworts such as *Philonotis fontana, Dicranella squarrosa, Drepanocladus exannulatus, Acrocladium sarmentosum, Scapania undulata* and *Solenostoma cordifolium*. These also form similarly variegated spongy cushions, but there is a greater variety of vascular plants. Familiar lowland species such as blinks (*Montia fontana* agg.), bog stitchwort (*Stellaria alsine*), golden saxifrage (*Chrysosplenium oppositifolium*), dwarfed forms of marsh marigold and various grasses and sedges. These flushes, springs and rills are also the habitat of various montane plants, especially at higher elevations. Starry saxifrage (*Saxifraga stellaris*) is the most frequent, but chickweed willowherb (*Epilobium alsinifolium*) occurs quite widely, and in places there is the very local forget-me-not *Myosotis stolonifera*, confined to a few areas of northern England and southern Scotland. Above 610m, the alpine willowherb (*Epilobium anagallidifolium*) grows in these habitats, and there are several localities on the Cross Fell range for the interesting alpine foxtail grass (*Alopecurus alpinus*), a high montane plant occurring widely through the Arctic regions, though not in Scandinavia. A few high springs have a form of thyme-leaved speedwell (*Veronica serpyllifolia*) approaching the distinctive large-flowered subspecies *humifusa* of the Scottish mountains. A few northern bryophytes such as *Pohlia wahlenbergii* var. *albicans, Bryum weigelii, Splachnum vasculosum* and *Scapania uliginosa* occur in these high springs, which are of the type commonly associated with the cold melt-water from late snow patches in the Scottish Highlands.

Screes and cliffs

The exposures of acidic gritstone, shale and Whin Sill in the form of litters of rock-debris of varying size and steep faces, have a rather limited flora. There is a wealth of bryophytes and lichens, and distinctive communities are recognizable to the specialist in these groups. The vascular plants include many species typical of the acidic heaths and grassland, such as ling and bell heather, bilberry and cowberry, giving patchy development of fairly widespread communities, though sometimes in places where they have been lost from the adjacent, unprotected ground through burning and grazing. For block screes, and still more the inaccessible ledges of cliffs, give protection from these effects, and there are some plants, such as great woodrush (*Luzula sylvatica*), rose-bay willowherb (*Epilobium angustifolium*) and golden-rod (*Solidago virgaurea*), that grow mainly or only in these more secure habitats. Block screes are good habitats for ferns, and there is local abundance of the parsley fern (*Cryptogramma crispa*), whilst broad buckler fern, hard fern and various forms of male fern (*Dryopteris filix-mas*, *D. borreri* and *D. abbreviata*) are widespread species sometimes reaching considerable elevations. Stable, high-level block screes often have much woolly fringe-moss and lanky growths of fir clubmoss. The serrated wintergreen (*Orthilia secunda*) is one of the rare plants of acidic cliffs (Whin Sill), but a few hawkweeds (*Hieracium* spp.) also grow in these habitats.

THE LIMESTONE UPLANDS

The vegetation giving Upper Teesdale its unique botanical character amongst the British uplands is that associated with the sugar-limestone, most particularly in the rather small areas at 370–550m altitude on Widdybank and Cronkley Fells where it is the principal parent material of the soil. The sugar-limestone has evidently made a substantial contribution to the general spread of glacial drift below and downstream from its main outcrops, but the resulting mixed calcareous soils are derived from various rocks and their most significant feature is the large area they cover. Areas of unaltered limestone adjoin the metamorphosed rock in places, and many others appear at all elevations between the valley bottoms (*c.* 250m) and the tops of certain fells (*c.* 750m). While many plant species are centred on the sugar-limestone, very few are actually confined to the soils derived from it, and the unaltered limestone similarly has only a few species of its own. There is nevertheless a difference in botanical composition between the principal sugar-limestone communities and the widespread types found on ordinary Carboniferous limestone here and in many other parts of the Pennines. The transition between the two is gradual, but there are extreme types which differ quite markedly.

Dry grassland

On the gentle western slope of Widdybank Fell, and near the summit of Cronkley Fell, the dark and sombre expanses of heather moor and blanket bog are abruptly broken by bands and broad patches of bright green, where the sugar-limestone appears at the surface and bears a contrasting type of vegetation (Plate III). The most characteristic community of dry sugar-limestone areas, with their thin sandy rendzina soils (pp. 134–5), is a close-cropped grassland in which sheep's fescue, blue sesleria (*Sesleria albicans*), quaking grass (*Briza media*), crested hair-grass (*Koeleria cristata*), carnation grass (*Carex panicea*), harebell (*Campanula rotundifolia*), eyebright (*Euphrasia officinalis* agg.), purging flax (*Linum catharticum*), wild thyme (*Thymus praecox* ssp. *arcticus*), and common dog-violet (*Viola riviniana*) are the plants most constantly present. Other familiar species which are abundant are mouse-ear hawkweed (*Hieracium pilosella*), ribwort plantain (*Plantago lanceolata*), devil's-bit scabious (*Succisa pratensis*), Sterner's bedstraw (*Galium sterneri*), felwort (*Gentianella amarella*), rock-rose (*Helianthemum nummularium*), glaucous sedge (*Carex flacca*), spring sedge (*C. caryophyllea*), meadow oat-grass (*Helictotrichon pratense*) and heath-grass (*Sieglingia decumbens*). The more constant mosses include *Rhacomitrium lanuginosum*, *Hypnum cupressiforme*, *Ctenidium molluscum* and *Ditrichum flexicaule*.

These species together form a grassland community widespread in the Pennines and, if *Sesleria* be omitted, on calcareous soils in many northern districts. On the sugar-limestone soil the turf is diversified by the addition of many other small herbs of more or less local distribution. Some are widespread northern plants with many other Pennine localities, such as alpine bistort (*Polygonum viviparum*), cat's-foot or mountain everlasting (*Antennaria dioica*), alpine cinquefoil (*Potentilla crantzii*), hoary whitlow-grass (*Draba incana*) and lesser clubmoss (*Selaginella selaginoides*). Among the true montane plants, hair sedge (*Carex capillaris*) is found mainly in the Highlands, where kobresia (*Kobresia simpliciuscula*) also has a few localities. Bird's-eye primrose (*Primula farinosa*) and spring sandwort (*Minuartia verna*) are found mainly in northern England; Teesdale violet (*Viola rupestris*) and bitter milkwort (*Polygala amara*) are extreme rarities of this region, while spring gentian (*Gentiana verna*) is confined to Upper Teesdale in Great Britain though it is also in Co. Clare in western Ireland. There are also two distinctive southerners in the rare spring sedge (*Carex ericetorum*, Plate 12) and horse-shoe vetch (*Hippocrepis comosa*, Plate 9) though the latter is now very rare on the sugar-limestone. A few other species of varied ecological and geographical affinities grow in the dry turf, such as sea plantain (*Plantago maritima*), kidney vetch (*Anthyllis vulneraria*) and dark-red helleborine (*Epipactis atrorubens*). Among the more notable mosses *Tortella tortuosa* var. *curta* is constant but *Rhytidium rugosum* (Plate 15) is very local.

A careful search would have to be made to see all these plants, for many are inconspicuous and no one piece of grassland contains every one, while a few are extremely rare in the area. They nevertheless form a group of outstanding interest, especially in the range of geographical and ecological distributions they represent, all within a single type of habitat and a relatively small area. Botanists familiar with the chalk downland of southern England will at once see certain similarities in the list of species, but the characteristically southern species of the chalk are mostly replaced by northerners. On the other hand the ground is often somewhat reminiscent of the sandy calcareous grass-heaths of the Breckland of East Anglia or many coastal sand-dunes. This is because the friable sugar-limestone soil is easily eroded, giving rise to numerous bare patches of coarse-grained 'sand' and stones. This is especially true of the plateau of Cronkley Fell, where the tunnelling and scratching of a large rabbit colony, assisted by burrowing moles, has produced numerous blow-outs and areas of redeposition and colonization. Here and there are little scarps of bedrock, not unlike the bare crumbly banks on some of the steeper chalk downs. The whole terrain seems somehow out of character on these high moorlands, surrounded by great expanses of heather and bog, as though it really belonged somewhere else altogether (Plate III). It is an unusual habitat and quite fittingly one for unusual plants. The only other comparable habitats in the British Isles are on certain low hills round Blair Atholl and Pitlochry in Perthshire, where metamorphosed Dalradian limestone has the same friable and coarsely granular texture and is exposed in similar situations on the crests and slopes of rather low hills. The flora of these Perthshire sugar-limestone outcrops is more limited in variety but includes an abundance of bearberry, restricted in Teesdale to acidic rocks and soils.

On an upper terrace of Cronkley Fell, at White Well, there is an interesting variation from the prevailing sugar-limestone turf, dwarf shrubs partly replacing the grasses over an area of many square metres. There are dense prostrate patches of mountain avens (*Dryas octopetala*, Plate 9) and an abundance of hoary rock-rose (*Helianthemum canum*, Plate, VIII) as well as common rock-rose and wild thyme. Crowberry is plentiful, although it is ordinarily a plant of acidic soils. Heaths dominated by mountain avens are a characteristic feature of many Arctic 'fell-field' habitats and occur widely, though mostly as fragments on cliff faces and ledges, in the Scottish mountains. An example resembling that on Cronkley in situation occurs at 885m on the Cairnwell in Perthshire, though it has rock sedge (*Carex rupestris*), and the crowberry is *E. hermaphroditum*.

The dry sugar-limestone sward of Upper Teesdale is thus in some respects intermediate between southern lowland and northern montane types of calcareous grassland. The affinities are more distinctly northern, though some of the most notable species are rare or absent in Scotland (blue sesleria, spring sandwort, kobresia, bird's-eye primrose, spring gentian, Teesdale violet and bitter milkwort), so this is in no sense an outlying southern occurrence of a widespread Highland vegetation type. And while communities with mountain avens, spring gentian and blue sesleria occur on limestone in western Ireland, there is a rather limited resemblance between them and the Teesdale swards. Indeed, no calcareous grasslands elsewhere in Britain have the combination of species found on Widdybank and Cronkley Fells, and there are no precise counterparts in the mountains of continental Europe either though close parallels occur in the Alps and Jura.

On Widdybank Fell some of the swards on unaltered limestone do not differ appreciably in floristic composition from closely adjoining sugar-limestone turf, but with increasing distance between the two rock types there is a gradual loss of the more distinctive species. Kobresia and rare spring sedge are the first of the abundant sugar-limestone species to disappear; hair sedge is slightly more widespread, and spring gentian has numerous localities within the Upper Teesdale catchment besides just spilling over into those of the Lune and South Tyne. Of the rare species, Teesdale violet has a locality on a grassy limestone edge overlooking the Eden Valley, whilst old records of three other localities for mountain avens within the district suggest that this species was once more widespread and has lost ground though grazing in swards on unaltered limestone. New species are added locally as others disappear. Dovedale moss (*Saxifraga hypnoides*) is plentiful and characteristic in ordinary limestone swards, especially at higher levels, but rare or absent on sugar-limestone.

Where bands of limestone girdle the upper slopes of the highest fells at 700–750m, they carry close-grazed grassland of a characteristic type. The best examples are on Mickle and Little Fells where, in places, there is a profusion of the beautiful alpine forget-me-not (*Myosotis alpestris*), more dwarfed than that growing in its few other British localities in the central Highlands. On Little Fell, in a good season, the abundance of its flowers colours the turf blue in places. Spring gentian is here, though more sparingly, and there is abundance of spring sandwort and Dovedale moss. Small forms of alpine scurvy-grass (*Cochlearia pyrenaica*) are frequent and cat's-foot, hoary whitlow-grass, alpine bistort, northern bedstraw (*Galium boreale*) and mountain pansy (*Viola lutea*) occur more sparsely. In some years the little moonwort (*Botrychium lunaria*) is plentiful.

At these high levels nutritious limestone grasslands are heavily cropped by sheep. Whilst some species, notably the alpine forget-me-not, have adapted well to this treatment, others are clearly at some disadvantage and persist as small non-flowering forms. Limestone grasslands are in general derived from more original vegetation types of unknown composition, though it may reasonably be supposed that those on unaltered limestone were taller-growing than the grazed communities of the present day and probably had some woody species such as willows. Those on sugar-limestone, however, may have changed much less, partly because of the instability of the granular soil but also because of its poverty in plant-nutrients (pp. 136–7), both factors tending to prevent the shading out of some of the original low-growing and light-demanding species by potentially more vigorous species for which conditions were unfavourable. It is in this sense that the vegetation of the sugar-limestone may be termed 'relict', implying the survival of many of its component species from much earlier times (pp. 22–3, 89).

Limestone heath

Where the raw sugar-limestone soils grade into types with considerable amounts of glacial drift derived from gritstone or shale there is a change to the more acidic moorland vegetation, though in places transitional types occur. On Widdybank Fell especially there is an interesting kind of heath community in which heather has a lower cover than on really acidic soils and is mixed with grasses and other plants characteristic of the limestone turf, such as sheep's fescue, blue sesleria, harebell, common dog-violet, eyebright, wild thyme, yarrow and even alpines such as spring gentian, alpine bistort and alpine meadow-rue (*Thalictrum alpinum*). Crowberry is abundant and even replaces heather in places. Mountain pansy is present but is still more typical of short fescue-bent grassland on soils intermediate between calcareous brown earths and acidic podsols (pp. 137–8). It is abundant on some of the pastures towards High Force, but seems to be most profuse and luxuriant in ungrazed places associated with old lead mines and their spoil.

The herb-rich heather and crowberry community might be regarded as a northern equivalent of chalk heath, the very local type of downland vegetation in which ling and bell-heather are intimately mixed or form a mosaic with lime-loving herbs. A type comparable with that in Upper Teesdale occurs on calcareous drift soils, derived partly from Carboniferous limestone, on Tarn Moor near Orton in Westmorland. Other examples have been seen in a few places on Dalradian limestone in the Highlands, but this is a rare kind of vegetation.

Marshes and flushes

Where sugar-limestone soils are wetter there is a change to marsh communities which contrast markedly with the bogs of the acidic moorlands. The first signs are the increase in kobresia, bird's-eye primrose and lesser clubmoss and the appearance of moisture-loving species absent from the dry grasslands. These intermediate communities grade into marshes dominated by a low growth of sedges and with a copious ground-layer of mosses and liverworts. In places kobresia is the most abundant sedge and this rare plant probably grows here in greater quantity than in any of its few Scottish localities. The other plentiful species, which replace kobresia locally, are tawny sedge (*Carex hostiana*), flea sedge (*C. pulicaris*), upright yellow sedge (*C. lepidocarpa*) and common sedge (*C. nigra*). Sheep's fescue remains abundant, but grasses are not prominent. Characteristic herbs include tormentil, self-heal (*Prunella vulgaris*), purging flax, eyebright, bird's-eye primrose, alpine meadow-rue and autumnal hawkbit (*Leontodon autumnalis*). There is a patchy carpet of the moss *Ctenidium molluscum* and other typical mosses include *Cratoneuron commutatum*, *Campylium stellatum*, *Drepanocladus revolvens*, *Fissidens adianthoides*, *Bryum pseudotriquetrum*, *Rhacomitrium lanuginosum* and the rarer *Cinclidium stygium*. On still wetter ground common sedge largely replaces the other sedges and there is often a more continuous carpet of mosses, with *Philonotis fontana* typically present. The marsh horsetail (*Equisetum palustre*) tends to replace lesser clubmoss and lady's smock (*Cardamine pratensis*) becomes constant.

The last of these communities is a widespread type, both in the Pennines and elsewhere in the British uplands, but the mixed sedge marsh is more local. The *Kobresia* facies occurs nowhere else in England or Wales and is very rare even in the Highlands, whilst bird's-eye primrose is almost confined to northern England. In the Highlands, however, there is a greater variety of calcareous montane marsh vegetation, including a high-level type with russet sedge (*Carex saxatilis*) which is unknown farther south.

Perhaps the most distinctive community associated with wet ground on sugar-limestone is that where ground-water emerges at the surface in open gravelly and stony flushes with only a patchy vegetation cover. The ground usually appears wet, except after drought, and in some places water courses quite strongly over the soil surface. These flushes may occur with a zone of sedge marsh separating them from drier vegetation, or they may appear as quite sharply defined patches, channels or networks among the latter. They are sometimes fed from springs dominated by domed and golden patches of the lime-loving moss *Cratoneuron commutatum*. The typical flushes, however, have smaller, dark, knobbly cushions of the mosses *Gymnostomum recurvirostrum* (Plate 24) and *Catoscopium nigritum*. Most of the mosses found in the sedge marshes occur in the open flushes but usually with rather low cover, and there are other characteristic species such as *Meesia uliginosa* and *Amblyodon dealbatus*. The cushion-formers become encrusted below with calcium carbonate precipated from the calcareous water, and this builds up over the years as a solid though rather porous deposit of *tufa*. In time the uneven cushions, living moss above and friable 'lime' below, begin to erode, and their various cycles of decay and then redevelopment have been described by Pigott (1956). These tight moss cushions and the exposed tufa are the typical habitat of the most noteworthy of all the Teesdale rarities, bog sandwort (*Minuartia stricta*, Plate VI) which has no known British locality other than Widdybank Fell. Here it grows sparingly and very locally in the open flushes, often accompanied by its more conspicuous relative, spring sandwort (*M. verna*). It is a delicate, slender little plant which not surprisingly seems to have a need for habitats where competition from other species is minimal.

Other noteworthy montane or northern species grow in these gravelly and mossy flushes. Many of those found in the marshes or even the dry grasslands are frequent or abundant, examples being kobresia, hair sedge, bird's-eye primrose and alpine meadow-rue. Others such as yellow mountain saxifrage (*Saxifraga aizoides*), alpine rush (*Juncus alpinoarticulatus*), three-flowered rush (*J. triglumis*), Scottish asphodel (*Tofieldia pusilla,* Plate 13) and variegated horsetail (*Equisetum variegatum*) belong especially to the wet open habitats. There are also more widespread marsh or flush plants of fairly constant occurrence, such as dioecious sedge (*Carex dioica*), upright yellow sedge, carnation sedge, few-flowered spike-rush (*Eleocharis quinqueflora*), jointed rush (*J. articulatus*), butterwort (*Pinguicula vulgaris*) and knotted pearlwort (*Sagina nodosa*). Thrift (*Armeria maritima*) grew in one flush system on Widdybank Fell, and sea plantain (*Plantago maritima*) is more widespread in such habitats. These vascular plants mostly form a sparse open growth within the flushes or around their edges. Many of them grow in the closed vegetation of the marshes, into which the flushes grade in places. Yellow mountain saxifrage becomes more abundant where the drainage water is concentrated into rills or seeps continually down steep banks or rocks.

The foregoing range of marsh and flush communities is found especially on the higher ground of Widdybank and Cronkley Fells. On the lower slopes, where glacial drift makes a larger contribution to the calcareous soils, there are communities of moist ground combining features of the dry grassland, the marshes and the flushes. These occur particularly on Widdybank Pastures and lie in part within the enclosed field systems of the upper farms. They are thus grazed by cattle and ponies as well as sheep, and the trampling of the larger animals on the wet clayey soils contributes towards their distinctive character. These 'turfy marshes' are variably fed by springs which spread out into broad soakways with bare calcareous muddy gravel in which plant cover ranges from a sparse open growth to a patchwork of vegetated hummocks. These last owe their form at least partly to the puddling effect of cattle in the soft muddy soil, and many are steep-sided and unstable. The hummock tops are sufficiently dry to support plants typical of the well-drained sugar-limestone grassland, such as blue sesleria, spring gentian, self-heal, hair sedge and glaucous sedge (*Carex flacca*), and this is especially the habitat of the rare alpine bartsia (*Bartsia alpina,* Plate 11). Yet the ground is moist enough to carry an abundance of several of the marsh sedges and rushes, together with purple moor-grass, bird's-eye primrose, grass of Parnassus (*Parnassia palustris*), marsh valerian (*Valeriana dioica*), broad-leaved cotton-grass (*Eriophorum latifolium*), *Blysmus compressus*, marsh arrow-grass (*Triglochin palustris*), yellow mountain saxifrage, kobresia, Scottish asphodel, alpine rush and marsh horsetail. Bird's-eye primrose is in sufficient profusion to flush the pastures with pink during May and early June. C. D. Pigott noted that these habitats and their flora were replaced in certain ungrazed situations by damp *Molinia* grassland with globe-flower and wood cranesbill on an unbroken soil surface, suggesting strongly that the 'poaching' caused by cattle is important in producing the open hummocky structure and hence in maintaining the competition-free conditions needed by many of the smaller species. Communities with obvious similarity to the turfy marshes occur on the moist unstable clayey banks of some moraines, and on the alluvium deposited by some of the smaller streams, but they grade into the drier type of grassland. A drift bank above Langdon Beck has one of these intermediate grasslands with a particularly fine colony of spring gentian.

Calcareous marshes and flushes are frequent and locally quite extensive at higher levels on the fells where water drains from unaltered limestone. The open muddy type of flush is, however, rare away from the sugar-limestone and the most usual kind has a closed vegetation with a high cover of mosses and liverworts and an abundance of vascular plants. Common sedge, yellow sedge (*Carex demissa*), flea sedge, dioecious sedge, marsh horsetail and jointed rush are plentiful and there is usually an abundance of herbs such as meadow buttercup (*Ranunculus acris*), lesser spearwort (*R. flammula*) and autumnal hawkbit. These little marshes and flushes lack some of the noteworthy species of Cronkley and Widdybank Fells but they are the characteristic habitat of a rare northern plant not found on the sugar-limestone, the yellow marsh saxifrage (*Saxifraga hirculus*). This has its British headquarters within the Tees catchment but is absent from many suitable habitats. It sends up incon-spicuous tufts of narrow leaves through the moss carpets, and its delicate flowering stems are often cropped down by sheep. The hairy stone-crop (*Sedum villosum*) is fre-quent in these flushes at higher altitudes, and the three-flowered rush occurs in a few places.

The varied moss and liverwort flora includes *Cratoneuron commutatum* and its var. *falcatum*, *C. filicinum*, *Campylium stellatum*, *Drepanocladus revolvens* and its var. *intermedius*, *Scorpidium scorpioides*, *Fissidens adianthoides*, *Philonotis calcarea* and *P. fontana*, *Mnium punctatum*, *M. pseudopunctatum*, *M. seligeri*, *Ctenidium molluscum*, *Bryum pseudotriquetrum*, *Brachythecium rivulare*, *Cinclidium stygium*, *Aulacomnium palustre*, *Climacium dendroides*, *Pellia fabbroniana*, *Riccardia pinguis* and *R. multifida*, *Plagiochila asplenioides*, *Chiloscyphus polyanthos* and *Trichocolea tomentella*.

There is one distinctive high-altitude moss in *Oncophorus virens*, found typically where the seepage of water is slight or intermittent, at the flush edges. The northern species *Camptothecium nitens* also occurs in a few places, but is rare. There are transitions to the high-level spring and flush communities fed by less nutrient-rich waters, as described on p. 72, and some bog-mosses such as *Sphagnum contortum*, *S. teres* and *S. warnstorfianum* grow in intermediate types. A local type of marsh occurring in a few low-level localities on the Cross Fell range is dominated by dense growths of the sharp-flowered rush but has a fairly large number of the herbs and bryophytes found in the widespread calcareous marshes.

The enclosed meadows and river banks

The enclosed grasslands of the Upper Teesdale farms are managed either as per-manent pasturage for animals, especially cattle, or for the production of hay. The hay-meadows are usually grazed in the later part of the year, after the crop has been taken off, but until recently their botanical composition had much in common with the field-layer communities of the remaining upland woodlands on basic soils, suggesting that the one was derived from the other largely by removal of the trees and with little other deliberate modification. Partial grazing would favour an increase in grasses at the expense of the other herbs, but over a long period the hay-meadows had reached an equilibrium in which dicotyledonous herbs maintained a fairly high cover in relation to grasses and sedges. These traditional upland hay-meadows were one of the most spectacular botanical displays to be seen in this country, with an impressive richness and variety of colour. They reached their finest development in the limestone dales of northern England and were nowhere better represented than in Upper Teesdale. Modern farming practice has, however, regarded these ancient mixed herbaceous communities as inefficient converters of energy and nutrients into fodder. Return of nutrients in manure is judged insufficient and, to boost productivity, large amounts of artificial nitrogenous and phosphatic fertilizers have been added. The enhancement of nutrient levels has also often been accompanied by complete replacement of the original vegetation by commercial grass seeds mixtures with rye-grass and timothy, involving herbicide treatment, ploughing and reseeding. Some former hay-meadows are now used as permanent pasture.

The result of this agricultural intensification has been to cause a rapid loss of the old-fashioned botanically rich hay-meadows, to the point where only a few good examples now remain. Similar deterioration through use of fertilizers is affecting some of the unenclosed botanically rich limestone grasslands. The problem is so acute that even within its Upper Teesdale National Nature Reserve the Nature Conservancy Council is having to pay substantial compensation to tenant farmers for reducing the amount of fertilizer, and thus the crop yield, on certain meadows and pastures.

Earlier descriptions of the Teesdale hay-meadows by Pigott (1956) and by Bradshaw & Clark (1965) thus relate to a vanishing type of vegetation which is in special need of urgent conservation measures. The problem is, indeed, widespread and concerns traditional hay-meadows all over Britain.

The most characteristic kind of upland hay-meadow has a mixture of meadow grasses associated with a great variety of mainly tall-growing herbs, the presence or absence and relative abundance of the individual species being largely controlled by variations in soil-moisture. More locally, where the surface soil has become leached, the total number of species may be substantially reduced and indicators of acid conditions may appear. The grasses normally include sweet vernal grass, red fescue, Yorkshire fog, creeping bent, cock's-foot, crested dog's-tail and tall oat-grass, with some wavy hair-grass where the surface has become acid. Amongst the most conspicuous herbs are globe-flower, wood cranesbill and melancholy thistle, with meadow-sweet, valerian, angelica, hogweed, sorrel, ox-eye daisy, earthnut, meadow buttercup, water avens, great burnet, hedge woundwort, bush and tufted vetch and meadow vetchling. Two plants suspected of being introduced to this country, sweet cicely (*Myrrhis odorata*) and bistort (*Polygonum bistorta*), occur widely. The three common and widespread lady's-mantles (p. 20) are normally present and, more locally, the northern-montane *Alchemilla glomerulans* and the three species, *A. acutiloba*, *A. monticola* and *A. subcrenata*, whose only known British localities are in Teesdale and neighbouring Weardale. Orchids are also a feature of these hay-meadows, amongst them common spotted orchid (*Dactylorhiza fuchsii*), early purple orchid (*Orchis mascula*), fragrant orchid (*Gymnadenia conopsea*), frog orchid (*Coeloglossum viride*) and twayblade (*Listera ovata*).

In some meadows the tallest of these herbs are replaced by shorter-growing species which often include yellow rattle (*Rhinanthus minor*), red and zigzag clover (*Trifolium pratense* and *T. medium*), betony (*Betonica officinalis*), rough hawkbit (*Leontodon hispidus*), self-heal (*Prunella vulgaris*), mountain pansy (*Viola lutea*), mountain eyebright (*Euphrasia montana*), harebell (*Campanula rotundifolia*), lady's

PLATE 3. *Above*, Falcon Clints, cliffs of Whin Sill above the Tees. *Below*, bends of the Tees about 2 miles above Cow Green, showing grassland on alluvium contrasting with heather-dominated vegetation further from the river.

PLATE 4. *Above*, Cronkley Fell and Langdon Beck Hotel. *Below*, Widdybank Farm, with hay-meadow in foreground and Widdybank Fell behind.

bedstraw (*Galium verum*), crosswort (*G. cruciata*) and field gentian (*Gentianella campestris*). There is a suggestion here of somewhat drier conditions with a lower level of plant nutrients and slight surface leaching, consequences of less regular flushing with nutrient-rich water and perhaps of some differences in management practice as compared with the central type of hay-meadow. The striking luxuriance of the typical hay-meadow must be largely maintained by active flushing. Good examples especially of the drier hay-meadow communities may be seen on roadside verges.

Where flushes or runnels traverse the meadows, markedly moisture-loving plants like marsh hawk's-beard (*Crepis paludosa*), ragged robin (*Lychnis flos-cuculi*), marsh cinquefoil (*Potentilla palustris*), marsh valerian (*Valeriana dioica*), and marsh lousewort (*Pedicularis palustris*) may become prominent, often with early marsh orchid (*Dactylorhiza incarnata*) and northern fen orchid (*D. purpurella*). These wetter communities, when extensive, are usually grazed, not managed for hay. The meadow grasses are well represented in them, but there is usually an abundance of rushes and sedges including soft rush, sharp-flowered rush and jointed rush, carnation and common sedges and the cotton-grass *Eriophorum angustifolium*. This damp meadow community grades into the turfy marshes (p. 78) and sedge-moss marshes (p. 79).

The alluvial river banks of the Tees, within the walled and fenced farmland, are ungrazed and in places carry the herb-rich communities of the hay-meadows. The characteristic trio of globe-flower, wood cranesbill and melancholy thistle is well represented and alpine bistort and northern bedstraw grow tall and flower freely. On open shingly and sandy margins coltsfoot (*Tussilago farfara*), bird's-foot trefoil, lady's bedstraw, red clover, wild thyme, sea plantain and cat's-foot (*Antennaria dioica*) are typically present. This type merges into open communities on steep unstable clayey banks which are subject to downslope movement. The famous Cetry Bank, a morainic mound below Widdybank Farm, is the best example, with many of the characteristic plants of the turfy marshes and muddy flushes, including alpine bartsia, spring gentian, broad-leaved cotton-grass, kobresia and hair sedge. The most notable plant of the river banks is, however, the shrubby cinquefoil (*Potentilla fruticosa*), which locally forms quite dense patches or even thickets (Plate V) on dry alluvium. Although there is a large patch of this medium-sized shrub in a hollow of Cronkley Fell, well back from the Tees, most of it lies within the flood-zone of the river so that its soils collect fresh sediment periodically. Shrubby cinquefoil virtually forms a community of its own where it is dominant and it has no special group of associates. Many of the herbs of the river bank may be found with it in places and it may become mixed with juniper. Scattered bushes, clumps or fringes of willows, amongst them tea-leaved willow (*Salix phylicifolia*), occur along the sides of some streams as vestiges of a once widespread type of scrub.

Rock habitats

The solid exposures of limestone are largely of non-metamorphosed beds, and where sugar-limestone is exposed as crag its flora is not sufficiently distinctive to merit separate description. Where water from limestone seeps downwards over crags of acidic rock, the faces and ledges of the latter become calcareous, as for example where limestone overlies the Whin Sill at High Cup Scars. In a few places there are outcrops of calcareous shale, also with a somewhat calcicolous flora.

Unaltered limestone offers four main bare rock habitats: screes, cliffs, tabular pavements and pot-holes. Limestone pavements with well-developed clint and grike structure are rather poorly represented in the Upper Teesdale area, though there are examples on Hillbeck Fell and Long Fell on the Eden Valley side and fragments occur on the summit plateau of Little Fell. Pot-holes are frequent in places and occur up to 763m on Knock Fell, but they are often shallow and accessible to sheep. Limestone screes and cliffs are more frequent and extensive, but more especially on the Eden Valley scarp-slope. Bands of sugar-limestone occur in the crags of both Falcon Clints and Cronkley Scars, giving rise to flushed patches on these otherwise mainly acidic cliffs of Whin Sill.

Rock habitats are important in providing freedom from competition and grazing. They also give a range of microclimate from extreme dryness and insolation to high humidity and deep shade, depending on the steepness and aspect of the slopes and the depth of crevices. The deep crevices between large blocks in a stable scree, the vertical grikes of pavements, the shafts of pot-holes and the clefts and niches of steep cliffs share many plants in common, with ferns especially prominent. Wall-rue and maidenhair spleenworts (*Asplenium ruta-muraria* and *A. trichomanes*) grow on both sun-exposed and shaded rocks, but brittle bladder-fern (*Cystopteris fragilis*), green spleenwort (*Asplenium viride*) and hart's-tongue (*Phyllitis scolopendrium*) favour a measure of shade, the last being especially characteristic of grikes in pavement. Male fern grows on many limestone outcrops but is by no means confined to rock habitats. Some ferns are eagerly eaten by sheep and restricted to rocky situations on that account. This is true of hard shield-fern (*Polystichum aculeatum*) and its much rarer montane relative holly fern (*P. lonchitis*), which still survives in very small quantity. The two most characteristic ferns of limestone, rigid buckler-fern (*Dryopteris villarii*) and limestone polypody (*Gymnocarpium robertianum*) are rare in the Teesdale area, though both have good colonies on the screes of Scordale on the Eden Valley side.

The flowering plants characteristic of the drier limestone rocks at lower levels include many of the typical grassland species such as common rock-rose, small scabious (*Scabiosa columbaria*), blue sesleria (usually luxuriant and free-flowering), salad burnet (*Poterium sanguisorba*), glaucous sedge (*Carex flacca*), early purple orchid, Sterner's bedstraw, quaking grass, purging flax, burnet saxifrage (*Pimpinella saxifraga*), cowslip (*Primula veris*) and occasionally horse-shoe vetch, together with others usually found in more open habitats such as hairy rock-cress (*Arabis hirsuta*), rue-leaved saxifrage (*Saxifraga tridactylites*), biting stonecrop or wall pepper (*Sedum acre*), shining cranesbill and wood melick grass. The rare bird's-foot sedge (*Carex ornithopoda*) grows on Hillbeck Scars. Common mosses of the dry rocks include *Grimmia apocarpa*, *G. pulvinata*, *Tortula muralis*, *T. ruralis* and *T. subulata*, *Orthotrichum anomalum* var. *saxatile*, *Tortella tortuosa*, *Dicranum scoparium*, *Camptothecium lutescens*, *Entodon orthocarpus*, *Hypnum cupressiforme* and *Encalypta streptocarpa*. Species which, although they can grow in dry places, prefer shadier conditions are *Fissidens cristatus*, *Ditrichum flexicaule*, *Mnium marginatum*, *Neckera crispa*, *Ctenidium molluscum*, the liverworts *Scapania aspera*, *Plagiochila asplenioides* and *Frullania tamarisci* and the lichen *Solorina saccata*. The shadier limestone rocks have a flora recognizable as belonging more typically to the field-layer of woods on basic soils or to meadows and roadside verges. Certain individual species flourish in deep crevices, but the larger cliff-ledges with a deep soil layer may carry several components of woodland and meadow communities. The contrast between their luxuriant growth of medium to tall herbs and the close-cropped sward at the cliff-foot illustrates quite vividly the effect of protection from large grazing animals. Scattered trees or bushes of ash, hazel, birch, rowan and bird-cherry are frequent on many of the steep scars. The most usual plants are hogweed (*Heracleum sphondylium*), hedge parsley (*Anthriscus sylvestris*), valerian, angelica, red campion, wood cranesbill, golden-rod, rosebay willow-herb (*Epilobium angustifolium*), broad-leaved willow-herb (*E. montanum*), stone bramble, raspberry (*Rubus idaeus*), wild strawberry, barren strawberry, herb Robert, wall lettuce (*Mycelis muralis*), dog's mercury, wild garlic, lady's-mantles and especially *Alchemilla glabra*, water avens, marsh hawk's-beard, germander speedwell, false-brome (*Brachypodium sylvaticum*) and male fern. Jacob's ladder (*Polemonium caeruleum*) was once a member of this group but seems to have been eradicated by sheep from its single known locality in the district. Sheep sit and shelter in some of the accessible rocky spots and their influence in enriching the soil is typically marked by the presence of beds of stinging nettle.

The more elevated scars of limestone or flushed whinstone lack some of the above plants, though some of them reach 750m or more. Conversely, whilst certain alpines are restricted to the higher-lying rocks, others descend to quite low levels. Contributing to these natural rock-gardens are several plants of limestone grassland growing much larger and flowering more freely than in grazed turf, such as hoary whitlow-grass, northern bedstraw, alpine scurvy-grass, alpine cinquefoil, alpine bistort, Dovedale moss and mountain fescue. A few of the more strictly montane species are confined to steep rocks, among them rose-root (*Sedum rosea*), *Alchemilla wichurae*, alpine saxifrage (*Saxifraga nivalis*), alpine penny-cress (*Thlaspi alpestre*), alpine meadow-grass (*Poa alpina*), Balfour's meadow-grass (*P. balfourii*), alpine timothy (*Phleum alpinum*) and oblong woodsia (*Woodsia ilvensis*). The last is believed to be extinct (p. 19) but evidently grew on Whin Sill where this was influenced by the contiguous limestone. Whilst these plants all grow on rather steep bare rocks, they hardly form a recognizable community, since some are rare and no single locality contains all of them. A variety of hawkweeds grow on the more basic crags, *Hieracium anglicum* being the most consistently present. The characteristic mosses of the higher limestone outcrops include many common at lower levels together with *Distichium capillaceum*, *Plagiobryum zierii*, *Encalypta ciliata*, *Grimmia funalis*, *G. torquata*, *Mnium orthorrhynchum*, *Plagiopus oederi*, *Orthothecium intricatum* and *Pseudoleskea catenulata*.

The alpine rock-ledge flora of Upper Teesdale is not particularly well developed, mainly because the limestone exposures, especially of crag, are rather small, dry and of limited extent, especially at high altitudes. It does not compare with that of the great cliffs of the calcareous Scottish mountains nor even with the adjoining Lake District mountains. Several locally plentiful Lakeland plants of cliff-face and cliff-ledge are unknown in the Upper Teesdale area, such as purple saxifrage (*Saxifraga oppositifolia*), moss campion (*Silene acaulis*), mountain sorrel (*Oxyria digyna*) and alpine saw-wort (*Saussurea alpina*). The complete absence from Upper Teesdale of alpine lady's-mantle (*Alchemilla alpina*) is still more unexpected, as this is so abundant a plant in dry hill-grasslands, as well as in a range of rock habitats, in many parts of Lakeland.

Lead-mine spoil

Where waste from long-abandoned lead-mines contains much calcareous material it provides a specialized habitat having affinities with limestone grassland. Colonizing species on the open debris of the dumps include many common plants of swards on unaltered limestone, especially sheep's fescue, crested hair-grass, thyme, harebell, white clover, common dog-violet, ribwort plantain, purging flax, bird's-foot trefoil, felwort and mosses such as *Tortella tortuosa*. But there is typically an abundance of three northern plants: spring sandwort, alpine penny-cress and alpine scurvy-grass. Where a continuous sward has developed mountain pansy is often abundant, and a few localities near Alston have quantities of thrift (*Armeria maritima*).

Comparison with Continental European Vegetation-types

It is of interest and importance to see how closely or otherwise the plant communities recognized in Upper Teesdale fit into any existing scheme of vegetation-types for the European mainland. The formal system of the Zurich-Montpellier school, based on the work of the founding father of plant sociology, J. Braun-Blanquet, has been used by Durham botanists for such a comparison.

For readers wishing to know more about the aims and methods of plant sociology the book by D. W. Shimwell (1971) provides a useful summary of the various approaches. The common purpose is a taxonomic one, the attempt to provide a *specification* and *classification* of types of vegetation, with a suitable terminology, which can act as a language enabling botanists to communicate easily about the floristic composition of vegetation and the inferences that may be drawn from it. Agreed names of widely recognized vegetation-types can then be used for rapid description of an area and can be translated readily into cartographic units for vegetational mapping.

As in the taxonomy of individual plants it is thought appropriate that a vegetational classification should be hierarchical in structure, reflecting a series of different levels of similarity. The taxonomic sequence of species, genus, family, order and class represents the successive groupings of taxa (classificatory units) of lower rank to form higher ones, and plant sociologists have devised a comparable hierarchy of units. The lowest units are the *associations*, which have something of the same relationship to actual stands of vegetation as species have to individual plants which reach an appropriate level of similarity and meet certain other tests of specific identity. Both *species* and *associations* are abstractions in the sense that neither of them consists merely of a finite set of members existing at one time. They are defined so as to cover all past and present and also all potential future members. The association is an abs-

PLATE 5. View of Harwood Valley taken from over the high ground immediately west of High Force and looking NNW. The Tees enters the picture from the west, is joined by the Harwood Beck and then turns south-eastwards under Cronkley Bridge. The high ground at the back is Langdon Common, and between it and the centre of the picture the Langdon Beck Hotel can be identified by its sheltering trees. It stands by the main road (B 6277) from Middleton to Alston, which runs up the Harwood valley. Gill Town (Plate 19) is one of the groups of houses in the top left-hand corner, and is just west of the Harwood Beck. Note the white-washed farm-houses and the distinction between the settled enclosed 'inby' land round the farm-houses and the rough unenclosed 'outby' land on higher ground.

PLATE 6. *Above*, Slapestone Sike on Widdybank Fell, now largely submerged, showing outcrops of sugar-limestone over Whin Sill. The experimental enclosures on the left protect grassland with much kobresia from sheep. *Below*, Red Sike, Widdybank Fell.

traction in another sense as well, there being no concrete and delimitable assemblage of plants of two or more species that can be recognized as one of the individual communities making up a given association in the way that individual plants really are component units of a plant species. There are sometimes clear-cut boundaries between one species-assemblage and another, but very often the assemblages inter-grade to a smaller or larger extent and boundary-lines can only be artificial and arbitrary. The best that can be said is 'This marked area here should be regarded as representing such-and-such an association'.

To be regarded as representatives of the same association areas of vegetation must share a set of diagnostic species (p. 65). Then associations are grouped, on the basis of a lower degree of correspondence in their diagnostic species, into *alliances*, alliances into *orders* and, finally, orders into *classes*, just as species are grouped into genera, families and so on. The units of different level are given names with distinctive endings: *-etum* for associations, *-ion* for alliances, *-etalia* for orders and *-etea* for classes. These terminations may at first appear unduly elaborate and daunting to the layman, but in practice the standardization of form is a simple and useful device. The units of various rank are named after the most consistently shared of the diagnostic species of the unit in question. This naming procedure has two drawbacks that have not always been avoided: that an order or class may include a variety of vegetation-types too wide to be covered adequately by a name based on the customary one or two diagnostic species; and that species chosen for naming particular units may turn out to be absent from some of the countries where those units are later recognized as being represented. The attempt to apply a modified Braun-Blanquet system to British vegetation is often confronted with this unsatisfactory situation.

The following summarized comparison is based on that given by M. E. Bradshaw & A. V. Jones, of Durham University, in their Guide to the vegetation-maps of Widdybank Fell (1976).

Teesdale Association	Alliance	Order	Class
1. Unnamed lichen, bryophyte and fern communities of open, acidic Whin Sill rocks	*Androsacion vandellii*	*Androsacetalia vandellii*	*Asplenietea rupestris*
2. *Seslerio-Caricetum pulicaris.* Short lime-stone grasslands from dry to slightly moist	*Mesobromion erecti*	*Brometalia erecti*	*Festuco-Brometea*
3. *Minuartio-Thlaspeetum* Open herbaceous communities of old lead-mine spoil	*Thlaspeion-calaminariae*	*Violetalia calaminarae*	*Violetea calaminariae*

4. *Cratoneuretum commutati* Springs with slightly to strongly calcareous water — *Cratoneurion* — *Montio-Cardaminetalia* — *Montio-Cardaminetea*

5. *Festuco-Nardetum* Acidic to basic grasslands — *Ranunculo-Anthoxanthion* — *Arrhenatheretalia elatioris* — *Molinio-Arrhenatheretea*

6. *Violo-Epilobietum palustris.* Sedge and rush marsh on slightly basic soils — *Caricion curto-nigrae* — *Caricetalia nigrae* — *Caricetea nigrae*

7. *Pinguiculo-Caricetum dioicae* Flush and short marsh communities on limestone — *Caricion davallianae* — *Tofieldietalia*

8. *Narthecio-Ericetum* Wet heaths and flush bogs on acidic soils — *Ericion tetralicis* — *Ericetalia tetralicis* — *Oxycocco-Sphagnetea*

9. *Erico-Sphagnetum magellanici* and *Vaccinio-Ericetum tetralicis.* Blanket bogs — *Sphagnion fusci* — *Sphagnetalia magellanici* — *Oxycocco-Sphagnetea*

10. *Nardo-Juncetum squarrosi* Acidic grasslands on damp soils — *Violion caninae* — *Nardetalia* — *Nardo-Callunetea*

11. *Calluna vulgaris, Vaccinium myrtillus* and *Deschampsia flexuosa* communities on acidic soils — *Empetrion nigri (boreale)* — *Calluno-Ulicetalia*

D. J. Bellamy regards the fragmentary birchwoods and the juniper scrub as belonging to the class *Quercetea robori-petraeae* of European phytosociologists, and the more mixed woods on basic soils as falling within the more nutrient-rich *Querco-Fagetea*. The tall-herb communities of the sub-alpine birchwoods and hay-meadows would appear to belong to the alliance *Lactucion alpinae* of the order *Adenostyletalia*. The range of montane heaths and grasslands on acidic soils can probably be assigned to the alliance *Loiseleurieto-Arctostaphylion* of the order *Caricetalia curvulae*.

The associations recognized by Bradshaw & Jones vary greatly in the area they occupy on Widdybank Fell. Thus the *Minuartio-Thlaspeetum* (Association 3 in the above table) occurs as fragments covering a minute area in total, while the *Seslerio-Caricetum pulicaris* (Association 2) includes a wide range of limestone grassland extending over a fairly large area. Many of these associations have in fact been divided into smaller groupings or variants which are still important enough to be used as mapping-units for the maps at a scale of 1:2500. In the map at 1:10,000, on the other hand, the mapping units are alliances, that is, groups of associations.

This commendable and successful attempt to integrate the Teesdale plant communities into the European phytosociological system enables the differences between these and their European counterparts to be identified and studied. Bradshaw & Jones conclude that the following units are confined to Widdybank Fell:

The *Calluna-Empetrum, Carex ericetorum* and *Kobresia* variants of the association *Seslerio-Caricetum pulicaris*.

The *Carex dioica* and typical subvariants of the association *Cratoneuretum commutati*.

The association *Festuco-Nardetum*.

The *Potamogeton* variant and the *Carex lepidocarpa* and *Polygala serpyllifolia* subvariants of the association *Viola-Epilobietum*.

The subassociation *Equisetosum variegati* and *Juncus acutiflorus* facies of the association *Pinguiculo-Caricetum dioicae*

The *Festuca ovina* variant of the *Vaccinium myrtillus-Calluna vulgaris* complex.

The Upper Teesdale district as a whole has a number of plant communities not yet classified within the continental system. The types of vegetation showing least affinity with those of the mainland tend to be strongly oceanic and man-made communities. The greatest interest, however, attaches to the few communities which have no exact counterparts either in mainland Europe or elsewhere in Britain, the outstanding example being those within the association *Seslerio-Caricetum*.

From their vegetation-maps Bradshaw & Jones conclude that the Cow Green Reservoir has submerged between 5% and 10% of the *Festuco-Brometea* and of the *Caricion davallianae* communities, and 10% of the *Ranunculo-Anthoxanthion* communities. Within these groups the most serious loss has been of the dry sugar-limestone turf with Teesdale violet and the kobresia-dominated sedge-marsh, both of which are confined to Widdybank Fell.

CHAPTER 4

The History of the Vegetation and Flora

Introduction

UPPER Teesdale has long been visited by botanists and other plant lovers, who are attracted by its interesting flora. As early as 1868, J. G. Baker listed 32 rare species from an area of something like four square miles. More recently, in describing the vegetation of Upper Teesdale, Professor Pigott compiled a list of 75 rare flowering plants for the upper dale. Some of these plants, particularly the spring gentian (*Gentiana verna*, Plate VI) and bird's-eye primrose (*Primula farinosa*, Plate VI), attract the attention even of the casual visitor with their gay colours. For the botanist, however, they are interesting because of their varied and somewhat unexpected geographical distributions. One of the most beautiful, the hoary rock-rose (*Helianthemum canum*, Plate VIII), which carpets patches of the sugar-limestone in June, is a plant of southern Europe. Why, one wonders, is it growing in one of the coolest and wettest places in England? The spring gentian is abundant near the permanent snow-line in the Alps. So is the mountain avens (*Dryas octopetala*, Plate 9). Why are they growing on the gently rolling Pennine hills so far from the bright light and rocky outcrops of their main centres of distribution? The lady's-mantle *Alchemilla wichurae* occurs in the arctic and sub-arctic and there are 24 species, including the mountain avens and alpine bartsia (*Bartsia alpina*, Plate 11), which grow in both the Alps and the Arctic. The sea thrift (*Armeria maritima*), which, as its name suggests, is more commonly found around our coasts, is a plant of oceanic northern Europe, whereas the melancholy thistle (*Cirsium heterophyllum*) is a continental northern species. Why should plants with such widely different geographical ranges occur together within so small an area as Upper Teesdale?

It is now generally agreed that what these rare plants have in common is that they are a relict flora from the end of the ice-age, surviving in Teesdale surrounded by tracts of bog and heather moor. Knowledge of Britain's flora at the end of the last glaciation, the so-called late-glacial period, comes from the pollen grains, leaves, seeds and twigs that have been found in geological deposits dating from the period. From these fossils we have a good idea of what the vegetation was like at that time, from 15,000 to 10,000 years ago. There were no trees, though there were a few low growing shrubs like the dwarf willows (*Salix herbacea* and *S. reticulata*), dwarf birch (*Betula nana*) and a prostrate form of the juniper (*Juniperus communis*), plants which are common in arctic regions today. In and around the numerous pools, which were formed each summer by the melting ice and snow, were aquatic and marsh plants, including aquatic grasses and sedges. On the stony, better drained places between and along the courses of the streams were more grasses and sedges and a wide variety of small herbs. These herbs included a number of species which, like mugwort (*Artemisia*) and the docks (*Rumex* species), are common weeds today, growing in places like ploughed fields and quarries where the soil has been disturbed, or along the sides of paths where the vegetation is regularly trampled, or in pastures where, because of grazing, no tall growing trees or shrubs can establish themselves. There were also a number of species like the saxifrages, mountain avens and alpine meadow-rue (*Thalictrum alpinum*) which are rare today and tend to be restricted to a few specialized habitats in the mountains where there is less competition from more vigorous-growing vegetation. Even this group of now rare plants was widespread then. Sub-fossil fruits of the dwarf birch, for example, have been found in Cornwall, Devon and Hampshire, although today Teesdale is the most southerly locality for the living plant and, similarly, sub-fossil leaves and fruits of mountain avens have been found in Essex, again many miles south of where it grows today. Many other such examples could be given. There can be no doubt that the now rare plants were widespread all over Britain 15,000 to 10,000 years ago, in the lowlands of the south as well as in the uplands of the north and west, as part of the varied late-glacial vegetation.

This late-glacial flora existed for 5000 years and was particularly rich between about 12,000 and 10,800 years ago when, following an amelioration in the climate, birch trees established themselves for a short while in southern and lowland parts of the country. But about 10,300 years ago this late-glacial flora died out rather rapidly over most of the country as trees – birch, aspen and pine – began to spread in response to the warmer climate that followed the last really cold spell of the ice age. It is only in Upper Teesdale and a relatively small number of other places like Snowdonia, the Burren area of western Ireland and some of the Scottish mountains like Ben Lawers, that any sizeable fragment of this flora can still be found today, apparently having survived for some 10,000 years in these places, despite, in the case of Upper Teesdale, the development of extensive areas of both forest and peat around them. Elsewhere in Britain the late-glacial flora died out, being replaced by the developing woodlands.

The idea that the Teesdale flora is a relict one from late-glacial times was first put forward in 1949 by Sir Harry Godwin and since then it has never seriously been questioned by scientists, although interestingly enough, there has been very little positive evidence from Upper Teesdale itself to support the idea until quite recently. In fact in 1956 when C. D. Pigott discussed the ecological factors which may have contributed to its survival he pointed out the need to complete the evidence by finding traces of the rare plants from local peat deposits dating from the whole of the last 10,000 years. A few were subsequently found but it was only when it became clear that some of the best peat deposits, the ones most likely to contain such fossil remains, were to be flooded by the proposed reservoir, that concerted efforts were made by a number of scientists to look for the necessary evidence before it was too late.

The challenge was an exciting one. Somewhere entombed in the peats about to be flooded should be the well preserved remains of the rare plants, their leaves, their seeds, their pollen. What might one expect to find?

The Methods Employed

The leaves and seeds of plants growing on bogs can become buried in the accumulating peat almost unchanged and with a little practice such fossils can readily be identified, sometimes at the species level. The fossil leaves of the dwarf birch (*Betula nana*) that were found by T. C. Hutchinson in 1965 (Plate 14) had become preserved in this way. The chances of finding the leaves and seeds of plants which do not grow on bogs, however, are much more remote and comparatively few of the relict Teesdale species do grow on peat. Many grow on the sugar-limestone or in and around the small streams, known locally as sikes, and their leaves and seeds are unlikely to be preserved in any quantity. Fortunately, however, the same is not true of their pollen. These microscopic structures can travel in the wind for considerable distances from the parent plant before settling to the ground. And those grains falling on the surface of a bog will be preserved every bit as well and sometimes even better than larger parts of plants. This is because the outer wall or exine of the otherwise delicate pollen grain is made of a substance called sporopollenin which is extremely resistant to the normal processes of fungal and bacterial decomposition. This exine reveals under the microscope a highly structured pattern, which is not only strikingly beautiful but also quite distinctive, sometimes even of the actual species that produced it. And so, provided a species produces pollen with its own unique structure or stamp upon it, its presence is recorded for all time when its pollen falls upon a bog surface and becomes preserved in the accumulating peat. And this is a real possibility for species of grassland, stream sides and woodland as well as bogs, especially for those plants which produce a lot of pollen. On the whole, plants which are wind-pollinated produce much more pollen than those that are insect- or self-pollinated and their pollen is also more freely dispersed, as sufferers from hay fever are all too aware, and therefore more likely to become preserved.

Peat deposits have often accumulated slowly over thousands of years, with a few centimetres of partially decayed plant litter being added to the top of the bog each century. This means that the pollen grains preserved in successive levels of the bog from the base upwards reflect the vegetation of the region century by century during the whole of the time the peat was accumulating.

So much pollen is produced and preserved each year that even very small samples of peat yield hundreds or even thousands of grains when, after treatment, they are studied under a microscope and identified. This provides the basis for one of the best methods of studying past vegetation, namely pollen analysis. This is a method that involves the systematic extraction and identification of large numbers of pollen grains from samples of peat taken at different depths in a bog and comparison of the amounts of the various types of pollen in successive samples. Results can be presented graphically as, for example, in Fig. 13, and such a graph, or pollen diagram, shows visually how the plants producing the pollen have changed in frequency relative to each other over long periods of time.

Where peat deposits have been drained and exploited commercially there are often accessible vertical faces from which samples for pollen analysis can be taken at regular intervals. Also in places where extensive peat erosion has occurred and isolated mounds of peat have been left, as for example on Mickle Fell, the sides of the hollows or of the haggs can be cleaned with a spade and a series of pollen samples collected from the peat face. This was possible at a few of the bogs in Upper Teesdale but most of these have an unbroken surface and the samples had to be collected with a peat borer. Most peat borers take samples 50cm long and 3–5cm in diameter. A closed sampling chamber is pushed by means of a series of extension rods to the required depth, opened, filled and closed from the surface by twisting a handle attached to the extension rods, and then pulled to the surface again. The pollen is extracted from the peat samples in a laboratory by sieving off the larger plant fragments and dissolving the smaller ones in various chemicals which do not affect the pollen. The grains can then be mounted in glycerine jelly on glass slides and identified under a microscope.

Many pollen analyses have been carried out since the 1930s. By the late 1940s they had provided a clear understanding of how the vegetation of England and Wales had changed since the glaciation, enabling Godwin to suggest that the Teesdale flora was a relict one. But within Upper Teesdale itself, even by 1967, there were only two diagrams available. The first, which was from Mickle Fell, had been published by Kathleen Blackburn as early as 1931, but showed only tree pollen. The second, published by Johnson and Dunham in 1963, came from Valley Bog on the Moor House National Nature Reserve. Both these sites are just over three miles from Cow Green and the localities of many of the rare plants. So pollen analyses from Cow Green, Widdybank and Cronkley Fells were obviously required. Accordingly, as well as looking for remains of the rare plants, scientists also carried out systematic analyses on all the major peat deposits to be flooded, and on the deposits on Widdybank and Cronkley Fells, in order to obtain all possible information on what the vegetation had been like in these places during the last 10,000 years. Some of the peats examined in this way were also dated by the radiocarbon method and so it was possible to date with reasonable accuracy past vegetational changes of the region.

The results of these analyses proved very interesting, for they gave both a general picture of what the vegetation had been like in the Cow Green basin and on Widdybank and Cronkley Fells and also a number of new records of the rare species. The following account describes the main conclusions yielded by our Teesdale research by these methods.

The History of the Vegetation and the Rare Species

THE VEGETATIONAL HISTORY

Dating plant-remains in peat

Green plants take carbon dioxide from the air and use light-energy to make from it the carbon-containing substances of which they are largely composed. Atmospheric carbon dioxide contains carbon atoms that are not quite all of the same kind. Most are of ordinary radio-inactive carbon, but about one in a million million are radio-active. These lose half their radio-activity every 5500 years or so, a quarter being left after 11,000 years, only one-sixteenth after 22,000 years, and so on. Meanwhile the small proportion of radio-active carbon atoms is kept up through cosmic radiation. If then we can suppose that this proportion has remained constant for a sufficiently long period and that, once dead, plants incorporate no more carbon atoms from the air into their structure, it should be possible to estimate the age of plant-remains in peat by measuring how much radio-activity has persisted in them. The method has been used extensively, but it has become clear that the first of these assumptions is not wholly justified. The age of a sample of wood from the trunk of a very old tree, known by counting annual rings from the outside to the point of sampling, does not agree precisely with estimates on that same sample by radio-carbon dating, and this must be largely because the proportion of radio-carbon in the air has not in fact remained quite constant. It is possible to correct for this in material of no greater age than the oldest living trees, but no easy and certain way has yet been found to correct radio-carbon dates for much older material. Archaeologists have accordingly adopted a convention which is followed in this chapter. This is to write 'b.c.' instead of 'BC' for estimates of dates before the Christian era based on radio-carbon measurements, the small letters being a warning that the dates may be some decades or even a few centuries in error.

The end of the Ice-Age

In Teesdale the earliest vegetational information dates from 10,000 years ago. In many parts of the country there is evidence from much earlier times because there are deposits with plant-remains dating from the last three or four thousand years of the ice-age. But no such late-glacial deposits have yet been found within Upper Teesdale, and it is unlikely that there are any in the immediate area of the reservoir. The nearest is at Romaldkirk, just below Middleton-in-Teesdale, but there is some evidence about the vegetation at the very end of the ice-age from within Upper Teesdale itself. It comes from two bogs, one, Red Sike Moss on Widdybank Fell between Red Sike and the Tees, and the other, Weelhead Moss, which lay at the head of the Weel within the reservoir basin (see map on p. 143). At the base of the first was 10cm of peat, and at the base of the second 50cm, that had formed during a short period radio-carbon dated to about 8000 b.c. A single date of 7950 ± 190 b.c. was obtained from the first and two dates, 8120 ± 190 and 8070 ± 210 b.c., from the bottom and top respectively of peat at the second site.

The peat contains many pollen grains of grasses and sedges, grains of marsh plants like meadow sweet (*Filipendula ulmaria*), of weeds like mugwort (*Artemisia*) and plantain (*Plantago* species) and also pollen of plants which are less common today like Dovedale moss (*Saxifraga hypnoides*) and starry saxifrage (*S. stellaris*) and spores of the little fern, moonwort (*Botrychium lunaria*). There is also pollen of willows and juniper. The full list of pollen types closely resembles lists from deposits of this age from elsewhere in Britain, confirming that Teesdale's vegetation at the end of the late-glacial period was little different from that of the rest of the country. This is the earliest evidence there is of the vegetation, since older organic deposits have not been found within the area.

PLATE 7. *Above*, stone stripes on gently sloping ground at the summit of Cross Fell, Great Dun Fell on the sky-line. *Below*, eroding sugar-limestone on Cronkley Fell.

PLATE 8. *Above*, Currack Wood, a high-level birchwood, from Force Garth Pastures. *Below*, juniper scrub below High Force, showing variation in form.

The spread of forest

The two bogs with the late-glacial peat stopped growing between 8000 b.c. and 6800 b.c. so the next available evidence is from just over 1000 years later when not only did peat start forming again on Red Sike Moss and Weelhead Moss but also on the ground on the opposite side of the river from Weelhead Moss, near both Dead Crook and Foolmire Sikes. And so from 6800 b.c. there is a more or less continuous pollen record from at least four, and later from several more, sites within the immediate area of the reservoir.

By 6800 b.c. there were far fewer grasses and sedges than at the end of the ice-age and fewer herbs of any sort. Juniper had virtually disappeared and the amount of willow was decreasing. But trees had appeared. Birch, pine and hazel were growing in the area for the first time and also a little alder, oak and elm. Hazel appears to have been the most abundant tree, particularly on the limestone soils.

From then onwards the trees continued to increase. Eight hundred years later, at about 6000 b.c., most of the willow had gone and the other trees had firmly established themselves. The fells were wooded and were to remain so for many thousands of years. Had one been able to fly over the area in an aeroplane, one would have been surprised by the amount of woodland. It covered Widdybank and Cronkley Fells, West Common and Meldon Hill. Even on the few places where peat was already forming, there were scattered birches and willows. Trees were also growing on the slopes of the higher fells, Mickle, Dufton and Cross Fell, up to 760m (2500ft) above sea-level. Remains of this woodland can still be seen today. Branches, roots and twigs mainly of birch and willow, but also juniper and aspen, like those shown in Plate 17, can be found buried beneath the peat that subsequently formed over much of the fells. In many of the high-level cols, where the streams have cut back into the peat and eroded steep-sided gullies, there are distinct layers of wood in the lower levels and at the bottom of the peat.

There was quite a lot of local variation in these woods particularly with regard to the tree species. The commonest tree in the Cow Green area was pine, with the pine pollen in the peat comprising as much as 80% of the tree pollen at some sites. This pine-dominated area was not, however, all that large. Higher up the fells, on the Moor House National Nature Reserve for example, it was not nearly so abundant and lower down the Tees valley it occurred only sporadically. Within the Cow Green area itself, there was more pine on the better-drained soils than elsewhere. Two things indicate this. On the positive side, the highest pollen frequencies for pine were recorded from the bogs nearest the well-drained soils and, negatively, virtually no remains of pine wood have been found on the poorly drained soils which later became covered with peat. This negative evidence is significant because in the Derwent valley only 15 miles as the crow flies to the north-east, another area, which like Cow Green carried a pine forest at that time, there are abundant remains of pine stumps in peats overlying poorly drained soils. And if the pine preserved so well there it is highly probable it would have done so at Cow Green, had it in fact been growing there on comparable soils. Interestingly enough one of the rare Teesdale sedges, *Carex ericetorum* (Plate 12), which grows on the sugar-limestone, is a characteristic species of pine woods and, although it may seem out of place there today, it would not have been so 6000–8000 years ago.

The pollen record shows that these trees were not growing as densely as they would have been in the lowlands. They were well-spaced with sufficient room between them for a rich variety of herbs to grow including grasses, sedges and ferns. With increasing altitude, the woodland became more scrubby and certainly by 760m (2500 ft) the trees had thinned to nothing. No wood has been recorded in peats from above that height and only smallish twigs and branches just below it.

Besides the pine, hazel was still quite abundant and there were very small amounts of elm, oak and alder. Birch was quite common, especially on the higher fells where willow also continued to grow. Both birch and willow grew on the peaty areas that are now the reservoir basin.

The woods did not, however, remain static during the next few thousand years. The less common species, especially oak and alder grew more and more profusely as time went on, first in the relatively sheltered places like the reservoir basin and then on the more exposed slopes of the fells until by 3000 b.c. there were virtually no pines left and the woods were fully deciduous.

In Teesdale at that time not only was the forested landscape different from today's but so too was the climate. It is thought that average temperatures were about 2°C higher then than now and as this is similar to the difference in mean annual temperature between a good and a bad year today, our Mesolithic predecessors who left their artefacts on the high fells must have been hunting deer in more pleasant conditions – one imagines sheltered sun-speckled glades – than today's hikers enjoy as they tramp across the wind- and rain-swept moorland.

But one must not exaggerate. More pleasant it may have been for a couple of millennia, but there is plenty of evidence pointing to the fact that after about 5000 b.c., although it remained warm, it became much wetter. It was so wet that a lot of the peat which was forming on the bogs in the reservoir basin was washed away as it was growing, so that very little accumulated.

This wetter climate not only slowed down peat formation on the bogs of the reservoir basin, but it also had a more long-term and serious effect on the soils. In climates with a heavy rainfall and a low evaporation rate, some of the soil minerals together with compounds derived from the humus move downwards through the soil and concentrate at lower levels, sometimes forming a distinct layer known as a pan, which is often rich in iron. This process is known as podsolization. Such iron pans formed in many of the soils on the fells after 5000 b.c., impeding the drainage and so making them particularly suitable for alder, a tree which can withstand having its roots wet. This is one reason why it was able to spread at the expense of other trees at that time.

Where the waterlogging was most severe the woodland gradually gave way to peat. Old trees died, young seedlings were unable to establish themselves and eventually only plants like reeds, sedges, cotton grass and bog moss, which are specially adapted to withstand growing in such wet conditions, were able to flourish. As they died and only partially decayed they formed peat and, as the years went past, this became deeper and deeper. Most of the deep blanket peats on the higher fell plateaux began to form at this time and so too did the peat which now occupies some of the slight hollows on the lower fells: places like the upper reaches of Slapestone Sike on Widdybank Fell. Most of the area around Cow Green, however, remained wooded for another four and a half thousand years and the vegetation did not change again significantly until about three to two and a half thousand years ago.

Only two things are of note during the period. Firstly, peat began to accumulate more rapidly on the bogs in Cow Green after 3000 b.c., implying that after that date the climate was not quite as wet as it had been. This new peat does not contain as many fragments of sedges or the reed (*Phragmites australis*) as the earlier peat and is composed almost entirely of bog rather than fen species. And secondly, there is now for the first time unambiguous evidence in the vegetational record that there were people in the region. The evidence which deals specifically with man in the dale is fully discussed elsewhere (Chapter 7); here it is enough to say that Neolithic man's presence in the region does not appear to have had any more effect on the vegetation than that of his Mesolithic predecessor. So for some 6000 years, from 7000 to 1000 b.c., Upper Teesdale was clothed with woodland: a woodland that had developed slowly and which changed in species composition in response to maturing and deteriorating soils and the long term trends in climate, and which at all times undoubtedly varied locally in structure, over very short distances with regard to both the density and the types of trees.

Only on the high plateaux and in a few hollows at lower altitudes was there peat and it could only have been on the comparatively few areas of exposed limestone above 760m (2500 ft) that there was any local freedom from both peat and woodland. Together with the cliffs at High Cup Nick, Falcon Clints and Cronkley Scar, and the river banks, especially where the Tees was cutting through moraines or meandering in the now buried channels above the Weel, such places may have acted as *refugia*, or centres where a wider variety of species, including the rarities, could have survived.

The spread of blanket bog and grassland

It was only after 1000 b.c. that this long period with woodland vegetation drew to a close. The woodland was replaced by grassland and blanket bog; grassland on the better-drained limestone soils and blanket bog on the worse-drained boulder clays. The spread of the grassland has been radiocarbon-dated on two of the pollen diagrams, to 1200 ± 100 b.c. at Weelhead Moss and to 620 ± 80 b.c. at Red Sike Moss (Fig. 24, p. 143), and it seems likely that it was at least partly due, either directly or indirectly, to man's activities in the upper dale. Browsing by herds of domesticated cattle and, later, sheep-grazing would have interfered with the growth and establishment of young tree seedlings within the woodland to a much greater extent than the native populations of deer and wild cattle had done previously, and this may well have reduced the natural regeneration of trees to a level below that necessary to maintain woodland. The felling of trees for timber may also have been a factor. The climate was deteriorating at the time and the shortened and cooler growing season would certainly not have favoured tree growth in exposed situations.

The blanket peat, that replaced the woodland on the boulder clay soils, now varies in depth up to about a metre. There is no evidence that trees ever grew on it again: heather, cotton-grass and bog moss have been the major peat-forming communities

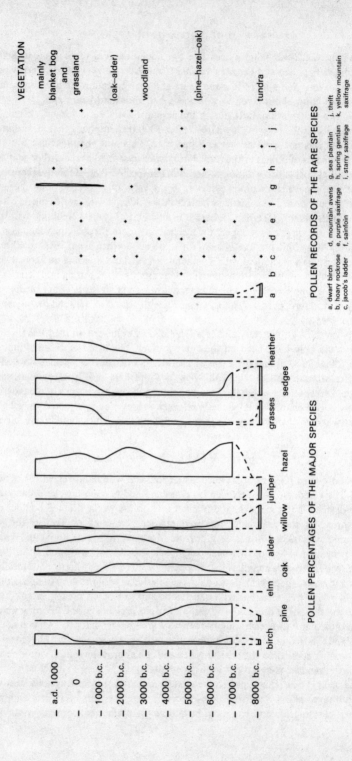

FIG. 13. Pollen diagram of peat from the site of the reservoir.

VEGETATION

mainly
blanket bog
and
grassland

(oak–alder)

woodland

(pine–hazel–oak)

tundra

POLLEN RECORDS OF THE RARE SPECIES

a, dwarf birch   d, mountain avens   g, sea plantain   j, thrift
b, hoary rockrose   e, purple saxifrage h, spring gentian   k, yellow mountain
c, jacob's ladder   f, sainfoin   i, starry saxifrage   saxifrage

a   b   c   d   e   f   g   h   i   j   k

heather   sedges   grasses   hazel   juniper   willow   alder   oak   elm   pine   birch

POLLEN PERCENTAGES OF THE MAJOR SPECIES

a.d. 1000

0

1000 b.c.

2000 b.c.

3000 b.c.

4000 b.c.

5000 b.c.

6000 b.c.

7000 b.c.

8000 b.c.

throughout the last 3000 years. This blanket peat, like the grassland, may well have originated by a combination of increased grazing pressure and a worsening climate over the years, leading to further podsolization and eventually waterlogging of the soils, thus allowing history to repeat itself on these lower fells, with the trees dying and peat-forming plants taking over much as they had done some 4000 years earlier at higher altitudes. By the end of the first millennium before Christ, therefore, the present vegetation of the upper dale had been established and during the last 2000 years, despite man's increasing ability to modify and control his environment, only relatively minor changes have occurred.

THE HISTORY OF THE RARE SPECIES

All these changes in the vegetation are summarized in Fig. 13 which shows the pollen content and dates of a typical peat deposit from the reservoir area. With this information in mind, we can now consider the relict flora which has had to survive for long periods of time surrounded by peat and for long periods of time, earlier in the post-glacial, in a wooded environment with a considerably warmer climate. For several of the rarities the evidence that they did so is beyond dispute.

One of the most impressive examples is the dwarf birch (*Betula nana*, Plate 14), which until recently was known to survive in Britain only in the Highlands of Scotland, its nearest reputable colony being in Perthshire, 130 miles away. It was mentioned in Gibson's 1722 revision of Camden's *Britannia* as growing on a bog near Birkdale in Teesdale, but was not recorded in the nineteenth century. It was rediscovered in 1965 by T. C. Hutchinson and has since been found in Northumberland. The present Teesdale colony consists of a small group of plants, the largest of which is only 15cm high. They are growing amongst heather and cotton grass on the surface of a bog. Hutchinson also found some sub-fossil leaves in a fen peat not very far from the living plants, buried between 90 and 105cm from the surface (Plate 14). Many of these leaves were in an excellent state of preservation and have been dated from the types of pollen associated with them to the period between 4000 and 3000 b.c., in other words part of the period when the area was wooded and the climate somewhat warmer than it is today.

As well as these sub-fossil leaves, pollen grains have also been found by Valerie Hewetson in the peat from near the living plants. These grains occurred in 15 of the 27 different levels of the peat that she looked at. Many of these levels date to the early period when woodland was developing in Teesdale, many to the last few thousand years when grassland and blanket peat were spreading and some, like those containing the leaves, are from the time when the area was covered with forest. Hewetson also found dwarf birch pollen at another site, Widdybank Moss (Fig. 24, p. 143), on the top of Widdybank Fell, where it occurs in 9 of the 19 levels she looked at, levels which date from the forested period through to near the present day. So it seems likely that in the past dwarf birch was also growing on the very top of Widdybank Fell, even though it does not do so today.

Dwarf birch usually grows in tundra or in sub-alpine plant associations. In Teesdale, growing on peat, it is not in its most characteristic surroundings. It does, however, occur in upland fen and wooded bog vegetation in southern Sweden. In view of this there can be no difficulty in understanding the evidence that it has been growing at the same place for more than 10,000 years, originally as a widespread member of the late-glacial tundra vegetation and later, when this vegetation was replaced by woodland, in a more restricted number of places on the fens and bogs which have always been present in the area. Its long-term continued survival, even leaving aside the hazards of increased human pressures in the region, can at best be regarded as precarious, for 10,000 years have seen it reduced from being as abundant as perhaps heather is today, to one small colony of a few plants.

Sub-fossil remains of several of the plants which now grow on the sugar-limestone have also been found in the post-glacial peats. One of these is the mountain avens (*Dryas octopetala*, Plate 9) which used to be a very important member of the late-glacial flora all over Britain. Today it is restricted to a few places in the Highlands of Scotland, western Ireland, Snowdonia and northern England (p. 43). Within Upper Teesdale there is a small colony on Cronkley Fell. F. A. Hibbert has discovered its pollen grains in eight different levels in the peat of two bogs now beneath the reservoir, at Weelfoot Moss and at Foolmire Sike (Fig. 24, p. 143). These levels are all scattered within the period 6000 b.c. to 1000 b.c., which means that mountain avens was definitely growing in Upper Teesdale during the whole of the time that the region was well wooded. Throughout its range in Britain mountain avens is a calcicole growing on open soils and in Teesdale a suitable habitat is provided for it by the continually eroding sugar-limestone. As made clear in an earlier chapter (p. 76) the sugar-limestone rock has been eroding throughout the post-glacial period and so has provided a succession of open base-rich soils ever since the late-glacial, although during the forest maximum the shelter provided by the trees may well have reduced the amount of erosion that could occur, so that there were actually fewer available habitats than there are today. Once restricted during the post-glacial, mountain avens has remained so ever since. Exclosure experiments (p. 208) have shown that its growth and fruiting are adversely affected by the excessive grazing of rabbits and sheep and this probably accounts for the fact that it has not become more widespread with the recently increased erosion. Like that of the dwarf birch its survival can only be regarded as precarious, irrespective of human pressure in the area.

Another plant which, like mountain avens, grows only on the sugar-limestone of Cronkley Fell, although over a greater area, and which has an even more restricted British distribution, is the hoary rock-rose (*Helianthemum canum*, Plate VIII). Teesdale is its most northerly locality; it also occurs just south of the Lake District, in a few places in western Ireland and in north and south Wales. Unfortunately its pollen is often difficult to distinguish from that of the much more common rock-rose (*Helianthemum nummularium*) which is also widespread in Teesdale today. So the large numbers of sub-fossil pollen grains that have been found in every peat bog that has been examined could be the pollen of either species. However, one grain that is definitely the now rarer *H. canum* has been recognized by Miss Robin Andrew from a level in the peat corresponding to the forest period. It comes from one of the bogs now beneath the reservoir, some distance from the present site of the plant, thus indicating that it grew in Upper Teesdale in the past. Like the mountain avens this plant grows only on the relatively flat areas of porous, free-draining sugar-limestone and it too must have survived the whole of the forest period on the restricted number of such habitats, probably including that where it occurs today. Also like mountain avens, the hoary rock-rose has become less and less frequent with time and its chances for the future seem equally slender.

Another Teesdale rarity which grows on the sugar-limestone, but in the more or less closed grassland, is the spring gentian (*Gentiana verna*, Plate VI). It also grows in calcareous marshy areas and, not being restricted to recently eroded areas, it is much more widespread within Upper Teesdale as a whole than either the hoary rock-rose or the mountain avens (p. 50). Elsewhere in Britain, it occurs only in western Ireland. Its pollen has been found in the peats of four different bogs on Widdybank Fell from levels which date to the full forest period and later. During the forest period there were no large stretches of limestone grassland such as there are today and so the gentian may have been growing mainly in the calcareous flush areas associated with the sikes. It does occur in similar situations in the Pyrenees and Dolomites. Later when trees were no longer growing on the thin limestone soils the gentian was able to extend its range and may well have been much more abundant during the last 2000 years than it has been at any other time since the late-glacial. In this respect it differs from the rare plants already discussed and, were it not for the fact that it has become even more vulnerable than it was because of the increased number of visitors each year, it would seem to have an excellent chance of continuing survival.

Two species, thrift (*Armeria maritima*) and the sea plantain (*Plantago maritima*), are of interest because they are plants normally associated with the coasts, where they are common in Britain, but are infrequent inland. The highly patterned and quite distinctive pollen grain of thrift has been found in peat of the forest period in one of the bogs now under the reservoir. It must have been growing, as it does today, mainly in the gravel flushes on the fells. Several grains of sea plantain pollen have also been found from the upper levels of six different bogs. Unlike the thrift grain, they come from a later period, after the beginning of the spread of blanket peat and grassland. In some ways the sea plantain resembles the gentian for it grows not only on the limestone grassland but also along stream edges and in sedge marshes in Teesdale today. Although there is as yet no positive proof of its presence in the forest period, the large number of records associated with the spread of bog and grassland can only lead one to suppose that it was similarly restricted to stream edges and marshy areas during most of the post-glacial and only became more abundant when it was able to expand in the newly formed grassland.

Pollen grains of several of the other rare species have been found, including several of the saxifrages, all of which have a northern distribution in Britain today. The grains include a number of the *Saxifraga stellaris* pollen type. As well as pollen of the starry saxifrage (*S. stellaris*) this type also includes the pollen of *S. nivalis*, *tenuis* and *hieraciifolia*. Although the fossil grains cannot be attributed on morphological grounds to any one of these species it seems on ecological grounds more likely that they are from the starry saxifrage than from the other three species. Neither *S. hieraciifolia* or *S. tenuis* occurs in the British Isles today. *S. nivalis*, a plant of wet rocks, was seen growing in the basalt ravines at High Cup Nick by James Backhouse Jr in 1843 and by Miss M. Heelis of Appleby in the 1890s, but has only been seen occasionally since. *Saxifraga stellaris* however, grows in the damp flushes on the higher parts of Mickle, Knock and Dun Fells ascending to 780m (2560ft) on Little

Dun Fell. There are today and would have been thoughout the last 10,000 years plenty of suitable habitats for it along the streams and lines of water seepage on these higher fells. So the fossil grains would appear to be those of the starry saxifrage and indicate that probably it (or if not, then *S. nivalis*) was growing in Teesdale in the forest period.

Another saxifrage which likewise has been recorded from the forest period and afterwards is the yellow mountain saxifrage (*S. aizoides*). Its pollen was recognized by H. J. B. Birks. It too grows in and beside streams but unlike the starry saxifrage it still grows on Widdybank Fell today. The pollen of a third saxifrage, the purple saxifrage (*S. oppositifolia*), which differs only slightly from the pollen of the yellow mountain saxifrage, has also been found from the forest period and afterwards and this is particularly interesting because this saxifrage is not currently a member of the Teesdale flora. It does grow further south in the Pennines on Pen-y-Ghent and Ingleborough and also in a number of sites in Scotland, the Lake District and north Wales. It must formerly have grown in Teesdale, occurring as it does elsewhere today, on rock ledges and steep slopes such as exist along Cronkley Scar and Falcon Clints. Exactly when it died out we do not know, but certainly it was not until well after the spread of blanket bog and grassland some two and a half to three thousand years ago.

Another plant, no longer a member of the Teesdale flora, the pollen of which has been found at several sites is Jacob's ladder (*Polemonium caeruleum*, Plate 9). Its pollen occurs at five different levels in the peat at Foolmire Sike, spanning most of the last 10,000 years, and also at three other sites during the forest period. Jacob's ladder is found today on calcareous scree slopes and cliffs, where the soil has a high moisture content, growing in tall herbaceous communities often in open woodland. It also grows in lowland fens on the continent. There would have been plenty of such habitats available for it during both the late-glacial and the forest period but once blanket peat and grassland had replaced the woods, and bogs succeeded the fens, the number must have been severely reduced until today Jacob's ladder can no longer be found. It was last seen in Teesdale on Dun Fell early last century.

The pollen of sainfoin (*Onobrychis viciifolia*), another plant no longer growing in Teesdale, has also been found in the peats of both Widdybank and Cronkley Fells, some in levels dating to the forest period. R. Squires has found quite large amounts of it at Cronkley Pastures at a level corresponding to when the blanket peat was spreading. Today sainfoin is a plant of south-eastern Britain where it is thought to be native in the chalk and limestone grassland. On the continent it is also a member of calcareous grassland communities including many of the alpine meadows. It is therefore of considerable interest to know that it once grew in Teesdale and it must be counted as one of the rarities which, like the purple saxifrage, did not survive.

It is unfortunate that not all the Teesdale rarities have pollen which is diagnostic. The pollen of shrubby cinquefoil (*Potentilla fruticosa*), for example, looks exactly the same as the pollen of the common tormentil (*P. erecta*) or the pollen of silverweed (*P. anserina*). The pollen of the melancholy thistle (*Cirsium heterophyllum*) is identical with that of several other thistles and the pollen of the northern bedstraw (*Galium boreale*) with that of other bedstraws. Bedstraw, thistle and cinquefoil pollen grains have all been found in the peat but there is no means of telling whether the particular grains are from the rare or a common species of the various groups.

PLATE 9. Rare Teesdale plants with contrasting distribution-patterns. *Above left*, mountain avens (*Dryas octopetala*): chiefly on mountains in North Wales, Northern England and the Scottish Highlands but reaching sea-level in West Scotland and West Ireland. *Right*, horse-shoe vetch (*Hippocrepis comosa*) at its northern limit in Teesdale. *Left*, Jacob's ladder (*Polemonium caeruleum*): in a few scattered localities in Northern England, but now no longer known in Upper Teesdale.

PLATE 10. Some lady's-mantles (*Alchemilla vulgaris* agg.) found in Upper Teesdale. *Above left*, *A. acutiloba*, known in this country only in Teesdale and Weardale. *Above right*, *A. monticola*, restricted like *A. acutiloba* to Teesdale and Weardale. *Right*, *A. glomerulans*, in England only in Teesdale and at Malham, otherwise confined to mountains in Scotland.

It is also unfortunate that several of the rare species that do produce diagnostic pollen are insect-pollinated and therefore do not disseminate their grains as freely as do wind-pollinated plants. Two species of this kind are the birds-eye primrose (*Primula farinosa*) and the Scottish asphodel (*Tofieldia pusilla*) and it is not really surprising that their pollen has not been recorded. In fact, when one considers the infinitesimal proportion of the total peat that has been examined, one realizes that the chances of finding the pollen of all the possible rare species were quite remote. What has been achieved is that of the 16 species with diagnostic pollen, eleven have been recorded.

The sub-fossil remains that have been found during the last ten years or so, form the final piece of evidence that the flora is indeed a relict late-glacial one. They prove beyond any shadow of doubt that many of the critical species have been in Upper Teesdale during the subsequent 10,000 years. The data that have been collected on the general vegetational history of the area are also of value for they enable us to appreciate more fully the different environments in which the individual species have survived and thus make it possible to assess more realistically the chances of the continued survival of the flora.

At least three species that once belonged to the relict flora have died out within comparatively recent times, sainfoin and the purple saxifrage since the spread of grassland and blanket bog, and Jacob's ladder within the last 150 years. And there are other species, still extant, which now seem likely to suffer the same fate in the near future. Dwarf birch has already been mentioned. If these 'at risk' species are to continue to grow in Teesdale extreme care is required to avoid damage to their habitats.

Several of the Teesdale species, however, have survived conditions in the past which would appear to have been more unfavourable for them than those of today. Alpine plants, like the spring gentian, have grown for many centuries in a warmer climate than our present one; non-woodland species have existed for millennia when much of the area was covered with trees. There is no reason why the present rich and interesting flora of Upper Teesdale should not survive, with relatively few changes, for many centuries to come, if that is what society wants. It will obviously require the goodwill and cooperation of everyone concerned, of industrialists and farmers who may want to use the areas for other purposes, and even of nature lovers who may inadvertently damage vulnerable areas or wantonly collect specimens. As one of the people who value the flora for both its scientific interest and its intrinsic beauty, I would like to think that others may have the possibility of doing so for a long time to come.

CHAPTER 5

Climate and Vegetation

Introduction

ORGANISMS respond to their environment as a whole and, moreover, their very presence modifies their surroundings. No clearer evidence for the intimacy of this relation exists than in the moorlands which surround the head-waters of the Tees. Heather, cotton-grass and moss flourish on wet peaty soils in which high rainfall, low evaporation and low temperatures combine to slow down decomposition. The plants require only small quantities of minerals for their growth and their tissues are poor in mineral content. The microbes and animals which feed upon them or cause their decay accept this meagre diet and only small quantities of minerals are released to support the new growth of the vegetation. This chapter will be primarily concerned with the influence of climate on the vegetation of Teesdale and the chapter which follows with the soils, but this is partly an artificial separation to allow the complexity of the environment to be simplified.

The climate within the layer where most plants and animals live is very largely determined by the amount of solar radiation the surface receives, the movement of air and the availability of water. When an organism or the soil is exposed to radiation, part is reflected and part is absorbed so that when the surface is dry its temperature will rise causing in turn an increased radiation back from the surface and a warming of the adjacent air. If the surface is wet, the rise of temperature will be offset by the evaporation of water. Both warm air and water vapour will disperse only slowly in still air, but on a windy day both will be carried away rapidly. The balance of these processes determines the actual conditions organisms experience, and in rooted plants different parts of the same organism may be exposed to quite different conditions simultaneously. Moreover, these will differ considerably from those recorded in a standard meteorological station. It is meaningless therefore to think in terms of there being a characteristic climate of Teesdale, rather there is a variation of climates both in space and time which nevertheless has its normal range and limits related to the climate of the whole region.

The climate of a region is determined by its latitude, its proximity to the sea and its relief. Teesdale is in latitude 54° 40′ N, and the upper dale lies almost in the middle of the narrowest part of Britain, so that it is only 70–80km from the Irish Sea and 60–70km from the North Sea. The Tees at High Force is about 300m above sea-level and surrounding the head of the dale there extends a large area of land at an altitude over 500m rising to almost 900m at Cross Fell, which is the highest point along the great escarpment of the Pennines. A marked effect of the Atlantic Ocean on the climate of Britain as a whole is that, for its latitude, the winters are surprisingly mild but the summers are cool. The altitude of upper Teesdale is sufficient to offset the oceanic influence on temperatures in winter but exaggerate it in summer.

Altitude also has a marked influence on cloudiness and rainfall. The flow of air over the British Isles is generally from the south-west so that moist air moving north-east from the Irish Sea has to cross the Lake District before encountering the high escarpment of the Pennines. Compared with the extraordinarily high rainfall on mountains of similar altitude in the central Lake District, the rainfall of Teesdale seems quite moderate but the tendency for cloud to form along the escarpment and extend north-eastwards over Teesdale is a marked feature of the climate, causing a reduction in the amount of solar radiation reaching the ground.

For such a remote and largely uninhabited area, the head of Teesdale is exceptional in having had three meteorological stations maintained for varying numbers of years. Records were started at Moor House (557m) and at Dun Fell (848m) by Manley (1936, 1942 and 1943) and since 1952 and 1963 respectively both sites have supplied records to the Meteorological Office. In 1968 a station was set up on nearly level ground at the top of the west slope of Widdybank at 510m and close to the main outcrops of sugar-limestone. Records from this station are available from 1968 to 1975 and provide a basis for comparing this site with the much longer period of observations from Moor House.

Solar radiation is measured at very few stations in Britain and most values are based on periods of less than ten years. Measurements were started at Moor House in 1967 and average daily values are set out in Table 4 where they are compared with

TABLE 4. Average daily means of solar radiation received on a horizontal surface (Mj m^{-2} per day) at Moor House (1972–1974), and at Kew (1956–1960), for three-month periods.

	November to January	February to April	May to July	August to October
Moor House	1.6	7.8	14.3	8.3
Kew	2.2	7.6	16.2	8.7

data from Kew (latitude 51.5°N). The difference of latitude affects the direct radiation from the sun, because of the difference of solar elevation, but not the radiation received indirectly from the sky. The difference between Moor House and Kew is mainly a consequence of the more persistent cloud-cover over the hills. This is also clearly shown by the difference in hours of bright sunshine recorded at Newton Rigg near Penrith at 171m (1340 hours), Moor House (1190 hours) and the summit of Dun Fell (870 hours). As would be expected there is a very significant correlation between hours of bright sunshine and direct radiation and a less significant correlation with total radiation.

About a seventh to a quarter of the incoming radiation is reflected by short grass and there is a net loss of long-wave radiation from the vegetation back to the sky. The difference between gain and loss, called net radiation, is positive during the day but negative at night and, overall, net radiation is about 0.6 of total radiation. Net radia-

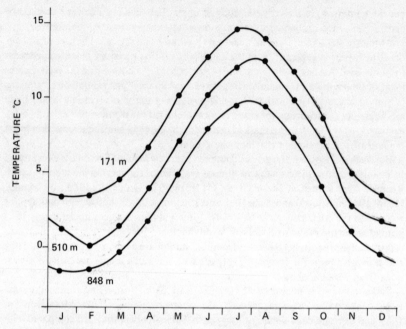

FIG. 14. Average air temperatures for each month on the summit of Dun Fell at 848m (estimates for 1911–49 based on measurements from 1937–40); on Widdybank at 510m (1968–74) and at Newton Rigg at 171m (1906–35).

tion is of fundamental importance because it represents the energy available for evaporation or to heat the soil, vegetation and air above.

Measurements of temperatures are available for all three upland stations and include measurements of temperature of the air made in standard conditions at 1.3m above the ground in a well ventilated screen, at 30cm depth in the soil and the minimum temperature recorded at night by a thermometer lying exposed on the surface. Air temperatures for Widdybank are summarized in Fig.14. When compared with Moor House for the same period (1968–1975), mean temperatures are higher at Widdybank by about 0.5°C from October to April and by almost a degree from May to September. A difference of this order is to be expected as Widdybank is 48m lower in altitude. A fall in air temperature with altitude is one of the most familiar features of the climate of mountains because it is so conspicuously demonstrated by the persistence of snow. The physical explanation is the decrease in atmospheric pressure with increasing altitude, so that air moving upwards expands and in so doing cools. This cooling may be calculated and is termed the adiabatic lapse rate which for dry air is about 1°C for 100m and is lower but more variable (0.67–0.80°C/100m) for air saturated with water vapour. Moor House is almost 50m higher than Widdybank so that the actual difference in temperature is more or less as expected in winter but larger in summer. The fall in temperature over a greater range of altitude is shown by comparing Widdybank and Moor House with Newton Rigg (171m) and Great Dun Fell (848m). During the summer Widdybank is about 3°C colder than the surrounding lowlands and there is a similar depression of both the mean daily maxima and minima. At Widdybank the highest daily maxima occur during August and September but these only just exceed 16°C and the highest temperature recorded in the period 1968–1975 was 25.8°C.

The upland sites have a very high frequency of frosts. Moor House is in a broad valley though not at the bottom of it, and subject to accumulation of cold air, while on Widdybank, the site was on the crest of a slope from which cold air would drain down to the Tees. Nevertheless air frosts were recorded in every month except July and August, with minima as low as −17.8°C in January. Ground frosts may occur in every month although only on one or two days in August. At a depth of 30cm in the soil the mean temperature in the coldest months of February and March is above freezing (1.7°C) but does not exceed 12°C in August, the warmest month of the year.

The general pattern of distribution of rainfall over the north Pennines is described by Glasspoole (1932). The highest rainfall is along the western escarpment with an estimated average on Dun Fell of about 2290mm, and a general decrease with distance eastwards. For the period 1968–1975 the average annual rainfall at Moor House was 1773mm and on Widdybank, 7.5km to the south-east, 1523mm. The wettest months are November to January and the driest May and June, but still with over 100mm of rain in both months. There is no significant difference in the number of rain days at Moor House and Widdybank with 240 days in the year and no month with less than half the days with rain. The general wetness of the upland climate is in very marked contrast to the neighbouring lowlands with Wigton to the west and Darlington to the east having annual rainfalls of 865mm and 656mm respectively.

On over 50 days in the year snow is present on the ground in the morning, though May to September are almost free of snow. In winter depths of snow may be considerable but the general windiness results in a very uneven cover with exposed areas blown free and deep drifts in hollows. Evaporation from the vegetated ground surface has not been measured, but for vegetation well supplied with water it is normally almost equal to net radiation in terms of the energy needed for evaporation (2.5 Mj/kg). It is also possible to calculate evaporation from a wet surface from standard meteorological data using the method described by Penman (1956). This is described as potential evaporation because actual evaporation will be less whenever the surfaces are dry. By plotting the potential evaporation and the rainfall for each month (Fig.15) the water balance is readily demonstrated, and for Widdybank there is no month in which average evaporation exceeds rainfall so that there will be net movement of water down through the soil throughout the year. This means that vegetation will usually not be seriously short of water and, even where the rooting-depth is shallow so that storage is limited, the high frequency of rain-days even in the driest months will result in frequent recharging of the surface layers of the soil. In a whole year the excess of rainfall over evaporation is 1186mm which means that at least 1186kg or litres of water percolate through a square metre of the ground.

The other outstanding characteristic of upland climates in Britain is their windiness. Completely still days are very rare while gales are frequent. Average windspeeds at Widdybank are highest in winter and lowest in summer, ranging from

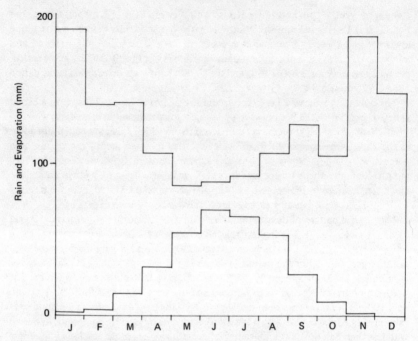

FIG. 15. Average monthly rainfall (upper histogram) and estimated potential evaporation (lower) for Widdybank. The difference between the two histograms is the minimum quantity of water draining through the soil.

7.2m/s in December to 4.3m/s in August with the average for the year 5.5m/s (19.8km/hour or 10.7 knots). Estimated values for the summit of Great Dun Fell give an average for the year of about 10m/s (36km/hour).

The Length of Growing Season

Anyone who visits Teesdale, or indeed any part of the Pennines during the winter, will be familiar with the overall brownness of the winter landscape varying from the rusty brown of heather and bracken through the pale browns of grasslands to almost white where mat-grass is dominant. In contrast the pastures close to sea-level remain green throughout all but the severest winters, and in mild winters grasses continue to grow so that lawns become ragged and cattle remain in the fields through the coldest months. This change starts in October when the upland pastures begin to turn brown and they remain in this condition until April or even May at the highest altitudes. There is thus a reduction in the length of the growing season of several months, although the difference of altitude between much of the upland area and the lowlands is only of the order of 500m.

At the latitude of Britain, most plants show a marked change in their rate of growth during the year. In winter many species are dormant and growth begins in spring,

TABLE 5. Meteorological information from Widdybank Fell (altitude 510m) for the period 1968 to 1975 inclusive

		Jan	Feb	Mar	Apr	May	Jun	Jul	Aug	Sep	Oct	Nov	Dec	Year
Mean daily maximum temperature	°C	3.7	2.5	4.2	7.6	11.2	14.4	15.7	16.1	12.9	10.1	5.1	4.2	9.0
Mean daily minimum temperature	°C	−1.2	−2.8	−1.7	0.1	2.9	5.8	8.4	8.6	6.5	4.3	0.1	−0.7	2.5
Mean daily temperature	°C	1.2	−0.2	1.3	3.8	7.0	10.1	12.0	12.4	9.7	7.2	2.6	1.8	5.7
Highest maximum temperature	°C	12.8	10.0	14.4	16.7	19.4	23.3	24.4	25.8	21.1	18.5	12.0	14.4	16.7
Lowest minimum temperature	°C	−17.8	−14.4	−10.0	−8.3	−2.7	−3.3	2.2	0.6	0.0	−4.8	−8.9	−7.8	−17.8
Lowest grass minimum temperature	°C	−16.8	−17.8	−14.4	−13.3	−8.9	−7.1	−3.1	−2.8	−6.1	−8.6	−12.2	−12.8	−17.8
Average earth temperature at 1 ft. 0900 G.M.T.	°C	2.2	1.7	1.7	3.5	6.2	9.2	11.2	11.8	10.3	7.9	4.9	3.1	6.1
Rainfall	°C	190	140	141	108	86	89	93	108	127	107	186	148	1523
Rain days		24.9	19.8	20.5	20.3	18.9	15.9	17.9	17.9	18.0	18.5	23.6	22.4	19.9
Days with snow or sleet falling		6.1	7.5	7.4	3.4	0.4	0.1	0	0	0	0.1	4.0	5.3	35.3
Days with snow lying 0900 G.M.T.		8.9	13.7	12.4	3.9	0.4	0.1	0	0	0	0.1	6.1	8.3	53.9
Days with air frost		19.1	22.6	22.4	14.6	5.7	0.6	0	0	0	3.8	15.3	17.6	121.7
Days with ground frost		23.1	24.3	27.5	21.2	13.8	6.9	2.7	1.4	4.1	10.4	19.7	23.0	178.1
Total sunshine hours		20.5	49.0	84.0	116.7	158.7	182.7	149.7	142.0	90.3	77.5	47.1	35.3	1151
Mean number of hours of bright sunshine per day		0.7	1.8	2.7	3.9	5.1	6.1	4.8	4.6	3.0	2.5	1.6	1.1	3.2
Total snow fallen	cm	16.9	46.2	33.1	15.2	0.9	0.4	0	0	0	0.1	26.0	18.4	157.2
Average wind speed	m/s	6.5	5.6	5.5	4.9	4.8	4.6	4.7	4.3	5.1	5.9	6.8	7.2	5.5
Penman evaporation	mm	1.5	3.5	14.6	32.3	55.2	70.1	65.9	54.1	28.1	10.1	1.9	0	337

reaches a maximum in early summer, declines in late summer and ceases in autumn. Variation in rate of growth is approximately sinusoidal and is correlated with the sinusoidal variation of day-length, irradiance and temperature. At latitude 54°, the period of daylight varies from about 7 hours at midwinter to 17 hours at midsummer, but there is, of course, no difference between upland and lowland sites at the same latitude. The annual variation of both irradiance and temperature has already been described (Table 5) and there is a significant effect of altitude on temperature. This is influenced by the local effect on irradiance related to cloudiness.

Although the dormancy of some species cannot be broken easily in the middle of winter, it may be shown experimentally that by early spring most grasses will start into growth if their temperature is raised. For the common grasses of lowland pastures the beginning of growth of the shoots coincides with the date at which mean air temperatures first exceed 5.5°C. That such a relation should exist is at first sight surprising and it is based on the work of Blackman (1936) who showed, over a period of six years, that onset of growth of lowland pasture coincided with the temperature reaching 5.5°C at a depth of 10cm below the surface of the soil. At this depth the marked diurnal fluctuations of temperature at the surface are greatly reduced and it so happens that the temperature is almost exactly the same as the mean temperature of the air in a screen at 1.3m above the ground. The cessation of growth of grasses in the autumn is probably related to temperature both directly and indirectly through the induction of dormancy. After midsummer, many plants show changes in the pattern of their growth and often substances begin to accumulate in underground storage organs. In grasses obtained from parts of Europe where the winter is cold, dormancy can be induced by exposing them to temperatures of 5°C and this is marked by deposition of a starch-like substance, fructosan, in the swollen bases of the shoots (Cooper, 1964). With the assumption of dormancy, although the shoots may die back, the living parts of the plant become hardened and resistant to damage by frost. A feature of great interest is that the ability to become dormant varies genetically within single species, so that, for example, cocksfoot from Norway and eastern Europe becomes dormant and ceases to grow at 5°C, while plants from south-west Europe and even western Britain remain active at this temperature but are frost-sensitive. Cocksfoot from 400m in the Pennines, when grown at nearly sea-level, is intermediate in this respect between Norwegian and Welsh races.

In simple terms, therefore, the growing season for pastures is that period when mean temperatures, as measured in standard conditions, are above 5.5°C. Variation in the length of this period in Britain, both in relation to the influence of the Atlantic and of altitude, has been discussed very fully by Manley (1952). He draws attention to a very important feature of the annual variation of temperature in Britain which to a large extent explains the very great influence of altitude. Compared with central Europe, for example, the difference between the warmest and coldest months, that is the amplitude of the annual cycle, is small. Because the rise and fall of temperature during the year is gradual, the decrease in temperature with altitude causes a rapid decrease in the length of the growing season. For 100m increase of altitude there is a fall in mean temperature of 0.67°C but a shortening of the growing season by over two weeks. In Teesdale, the growing season at 450m is from April 18 to October 23, while at 670m it is May 4 to October 16 (Manley, 1958). It will be noticed that as a result of

PLATE 11. Alpine bartsia (*Bartsia alpina*), confined to Northern England and mountains in Scotland.

PLATE 12. Two interesting small sedges found in Upper Teesdale: *above*, *Kobresia simpliciuscula*, elsewhere only in the central Highlands; *below*, rare spring sedge (*Carex ericetorum*), with a few scattered localities, almost all in eastern England.

the asymmetry of the curve of mean temperature about midsummer, the delay in the start of growth is much greater than the advance in the date on which growth ceases.

The late start of the growing season has important consequences for the whole growth-cycle of plants. Not only is the start of vegetative growth delayed, so reducing the amount of leafy material produced before midsummer, but for many species the development of flowers is later and therefore the period available for ripening seed is shortened. In the days when farms in the remote uplands were to a much greater

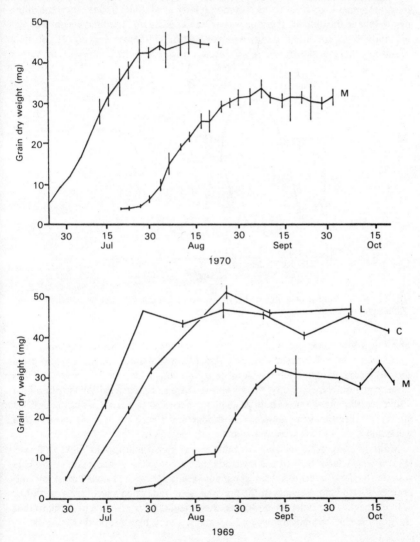

FIG. 16. Average dry weight of individual grains of barley grown at Lancaster (46m), at Malham in the Pennines (460m) and at Cambridge.

extent self-sufficient, cereals were grown almost to the altitudinal limit at which a crop of ripe grain might be expected in most years. However, the grain could not normally be harvested until September or October and the yield of oats or barley at altitudes above 300m was usually below half of that obtained in the lowlands.

The effect of altitude on the growth of barley has been investigated by Prince (1976). Plants were grown on small plots of similar soil at 46m above sea-level at Lancaster and at 460m at Malham in the Craven Pennines. In 1970 the ears emerged from the uppermost sheath almost a month later at Malham and the increase in the dry weight of the individual grains was slower at Malham. The final weight was significantly lower and attained over a month later in mid-September (Fig. 16). In spite of this late filling of the grains, they eventually dried out to the same extent in the two

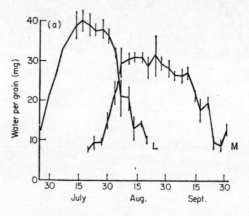

FIG. 17. Water content of grains of barley grown at Lancaster (46m) and Malham in the Pennines (460m).

sites but a low value was not reached at Malham until late September, about five weeks later than at Lancaster (Fig. 17). Measurement of the temperatures of the grain showed a consistent difference with those at Malham on average 3°C cooler, which is close to the difference of daytime air temperature to be expected for the altitudinal difference of about 400m. In both years plants were also grown at Cambridge and it is interesting that the delay between Cambridge and Lancaster was not more than a week and final weights were not significantly different.

Many of the grasses which grow naturally at higher altitudes in Teesdale flower several weeks later than in the lowlands, but a conspicuous exception is the blue sesleria (*Sesleria albicans*). This, like many alpine species and unlike most lowland grasses, forms inflorescences in the previous year and, when vegetative growth has scarcely begun, the violet-tinged spikes extend and the flowers open in April, so that the grain is ripe by midsummer and normally a very high proportion is fertile.

THE UPPER ALTITUDINAL LIMIT OF TREES

Many of the rare species of plants for which Teesdale is noted seem now to be restricted to vegetation which is characteristic of unshaded sites, so that the presence of these species in Teesdale has been attributed to the probability that sites have remained naturally treeless throughout the post-glacial forest period. To what extent the upland climate is responsible for poor tree-growth is therefore a matter of particular interest.

There is, in fact, a broad correlation between the upper altitudinal limit of woodland and the length of the growing season, and woodland is not usually found above an altitude where the mean temperature fails to exceed 10°C for at least two months in the summer (Manley, 1952). The present limit of woodland in Teesdale, in the absence of man and his flocks of sheep, would therefore be about 600m, which is considerably above the tops of Widdybank and Cronkley Fell but below the western escarpment and the ridges which extend eastward to form the watershed between the Tees and Wear to the north and Lune to the south.

What little evidence remains at the present day supports this conclusion. The trees of birch and rowan which survive on inaccessible ledges on Falcon Clints and up to 500m on Cronkley Scar are well-grown and healthy. A few trees grow at 460m near Birkdale, which is itself a name of interest as it is probably Scandinavian in origin, though not recorded at this site until 1742. Quite large trees of sycamore, a species introduced to Britain from the mountains of central Europe, grow by farms in the Harwood valley and there is one at about 570m. However, the most convincing evidence comes from a number of plantations which were planted just before or at the beginning of this century on the northern slopes of Cross Fell. They are mentioned by Manley (1952) and described in more detail by Millar (1964). They were intended to provide shelter or, in some instances, timber for lead-mines and they are composed of Scots pine (*Pinus sylvestris*), spruce (*Picea abies*) and larch (*Larix decidua*). A plantation of pine at an altitude of 460m produced usable timber from trees about 13m tall, but in a higher plantation at 640m the trees of both pine and larch, though probably of the same age as those in the lower plantation, are only about 5m tall. In a plantation of larch at 580m the trees in the open have all died but stunted trees still survive in the head of a gully and growth improves down the gully. The largest plantation is at Ashgill and its upper edge is at 600m. At this altitude, trees of spruce, although over 70 years old, form low compact bushes but only survive in the shelter of the boundary wall and have died in more exposed situations. At a slightly lower altitude, trees of larch have assumed an entirely prostrate growth.

On the basis of this type of evidence Manley (1952) has suggested that the tree-line is probably determined by both temperature and wind-speed, so that the tree-line is depressed in the more Atlantic parts of Europe. The actual effect of wind could, of course, be partly through a reduction in temperature of the young shoots. Certainly wind-shear of tree-crowns is very characteristic, not only of coastal situations, but also of trees at high altitudes, so that trees tend to be stunted on slopes exposed to the west, when compared with those protected by growing in gullies or against cliffs.

In this respect, it is significant that the outcrops of sugar-limestone on Widdybank are fully exposed to the south-west and those on Cronkley form raised knolls. Moreover, the ground immediately below the outcrops is in many places very wet from the springs which emerge at the junction of the limestone and the underlying dolerite. The wetness of the soil would restrict the root development of most trees, and alder, the species most tolerant of such conditions, has a very low altitudinal limit. It seems unlikely that trees could survive the combination of poor conditions for rooting and severe exposure. Evidence that trees, and probably woodland, were formerly much more widespread on the hills surrounding the head of Teesdale is provided by their remains in the base of the hill-peat. Unfortunately the distribution of these remains has not been studied in detail but they are widespread and occur commonly at altitudes well above the few surviving native trees. For example, remains of trees were reported by Lewis (1904) at 720m on Meldon Hill, and above Moor House remains are widespread up to 760m but the trunks are of small diameter and the trees were clearly stunted (Johnson & Dunham, 1963). The remains show that the woodland was composed predominantly of birch with willow, juniper and more rarely aspen. The age of the remains is discussed by Turner in Chapter 4. In general they date from the period 7500–5000 years ago, when it has been estimated from the more northerly occurrence of various species in Europe that mean temperatures were about 1.8°C warmer than at present, so that as now the actual tree-line was then just below the upper limit of 800m predicted from climatic data. At that period, conditions would have been correspondingly more favourable for tree-growth at the altitude of the sugar-limestone, though evidence from further south in the Pennines indicates that even then alder would not have occurred above about 420m.

The Influence of Altitude on the Structure of Vegetation and Production of New Growth

With increasing altitude not only does woodland become sparser and the trees more stunted, but there is a general decrease in the vigour of vegetation. Grasslands tend to become shorter and heather becomes more compact in its growth. At about 600m the whole aspect of the vegetation is stunted, with grasses tending to be replaced by small sedges and moss. An increasing area of bare rock is exposed and this is partly a result of rocks moving to the surface in soils that are frequently frozen and thawed. On Cross Fell there are well developed stone-stripes in which there are alternate parallel bands of large stones and fine compact sandy soil (Plate 7). Although such features may not now be active, there is clear evidence that patterned arrangements of stones can form at this altitude at the present day (Hollingworth, 1934).

The stunting of vegetation with increasing altitude can be described quantitatively by measuring the dry weight of the living material, both of the shoots above ground and the roots below, on plots of known area. This quantity is referred to as *biomass*. It is, of course, the above-ground biomass which is related to the appearance of the vegetation but, of more importance, it will give some measure of the extent to which there will be shading of one species by another. This may be regarded as competition for light or more strictly that part of solar radiation in the waveband which activates photosynthesis. A better measure would be the total leaf-area on a plot, but this is more difficult to measure. In a region where there is adequate water in the soil and low

PLATE V. *Above*, shrubby cinquefoil (*Potentilla fruticosa*) with some juniper (*Juniperus communis*) below Cronkley Scars. *Below*, shrubby cinquefoil, Co. Clare, West Ireland.

PLATE VI. *Above*, spring gentian (*Gentiana verna*), Widdybank Fell. *Below left*, bog sandwort (*Minuartia stricta*), Widdybank Fell. *Right*, bird's-eye primrose (*Primula farinosa*).

rates of evaporation, competition underground will be only for nutrients. In fact, many measurements of biomass refer only to the parts of plants above ground as these are quite easily made by clipping plots to ground level. Measurements are available from various types of vegetation in Teesdale and when compared with similar lowland vegetation the values are very low. For example, the above-ground biomass of heather at Moor House ranges from 0.45–0.60kg/m^2 (Allen 1965) and values up to 2.0kg/m^2 have been obtained at lower altitudes in Teesdale (Bellamy & Holland, 1966), and for mixtures of heather and cotton-grass. Comparable values from lowland sites are about 3.0kg/m^2. Grasslands on the dry parts of the sugar-limestone have a very low shoot-biomass, especially in the early summer because of the late start of growth and heavy grazing by sheep. Values of the order of 0.1kg/m^2 are frequent and only when grazing is prevented are values of 0.44–0.6kg/m^2 achieved. Even these values are much less than those for lowland pastures. In grassland the biomass of the roots is often larger than that of the shoots.

In vegetation composed of perennials, part of the biomass persists through the winter and this contains substances which are utilized for growth at the beginning of the summer. The initial increase of shoot-biomass is therefore not entirely from current photosynthesis. The actual production of new materials is not simply measured as the increase in biomass, because it also includes the shoots eaten by sheep and the material consumed by all other herbivorous animals. Also, even while new material is being produced, other material is decaying. True production can only be estimated by measuring the change in biomass and adding to this the quantities lost to these other processes.

A much simpler measurement is to prevent sheep from grazing the grassland and then clip the vegetation at frequent intervals to a height which is approximately that to which sheep bite. Measurements from several sites at different altitudes where, so far as possible, other differences have been eliminated, show that the amount of regrowth which can be harvested decreases with altitude (Morris & Thomas 1972). At five sites in the Forest of Bowland ranging in altitude from 49m to 303m, five species of grass were sown on plots to which lime, combined nitrogen, phosphorus and potassium had been applied. The sward was cut to 3cm above the surface of the soil at each harvest. Each plot was cut at intervals of about six weeks but in a staggered sequence, so that harvests for each species were taken every two weeks. Some of the results are illustrated in Fig. 18. The start of the growing season, defined as the period when growth exceeds 1g/m^2 per day, becomes later with altitude, and in 1969 growth at the highest site began 33 days after the lowest. In contrast, there was no significant difference in the date in early October when growth again fell below this value.

During 1969 the total quantities of dry grass harvested from the plots decreased from a mean of 0.84kg/m^2 at 49m above sea-level to 0.38kg/m^2 at 303m. In 1970, the differences were smaller because of the very dry spring which reduced growth at low altitudes. The decrease in production is caused not only by the shorter growing season but also by a marked decrease in the rate of growth during the early summer. For perennial rye-grass (*Lolium perenne*), a species characteristic of lowland pastures, the maximum rate decreased from 10.9g/m^2 per day at 49m to 0.9g/m^2 per day at 303m, for sheep's fescue (*Festuca ovina*) from 5.9 to 1.2g/m^2 per day and for creeping bent (*Agrostis stolonifera*) from 8.0 to 2.3g/m^2 per day. Overall this is a decrease of about

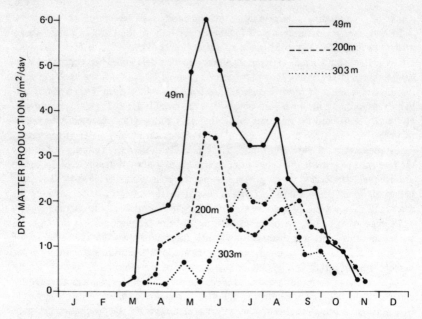

FIG. 18. Production of dry matter by perennial rye-grass *(Lolium perenne)* during 1969 at altitudes of 49m, 200m and 303m above sea-level in the Bowland fells.

1.6g/m² per day for each 100m increase in altitude.

It seems probable that this decrease in production is a direct response to temperature. The leaves of grasses grow from near their base, which in a pasture is almost at the surface of the soil. Measurements on Widdybank show that, although the temperature at the soil surface is more variable than in the air above, its true mean is almost the same as the mean temperature of the air calculated conventionally as half the sum of the maximum and minimum measured in a standard screen. Consequently the temperature experienced by grasses may be expected to decrease by about 0.7°C for each increase in altitude of 100m (p. 104). The close dependence of the growth of grasses on temperature has been demonstrated experimentally. For example, the mean rate of leaf-elongation, and therefore of increase in leaf-area of a grass, has been shown for sheep's fescue to be directly proportional to mean temperature between 8°C and 25°C (Arnold & Monteith, 1974).

The Influence of Climate on the Growth of Individual Species

An interesting feature of the results reported by Morris & Thomas (1972) is that perennial rye-grass, which is the most productive species at low altitudes, suffers a much greater reduction with altitude than, for example, sheep's fescue or creeping bent. Rye-grass is a lowland species, rarely occurring above 350m although extending to about 460m in favourable sites. In contrast, sheep's fescue is widespread, often reaching 900m in the Lake District and Scotland.

The decrease in production with altitude results then, not only from a decline in growth-rate of the same species, but also the disappearance of more productive lowland species, and sometimes their replacement by others which are more or less confined to high altitudes. In this respect the rare species of plant which are concentrated in upper Teesdale may be classified into three groups. There are a few quite large and vigorous herbaceous species, such as soft hawk's-beard (*Crepis mollis*), which are characteristic of wet woodland and hay-meadows, and these, although rare in Britain, mostly occur in similar vegetation elsewhere in northern England and Scotland. However, the majority of the rare species are plants of low stature and very slow growth. These may be divided into a group which occur in lowland situations further south, such as the sedge *Carex ericetorum* (Plate 12) or bitter milkwort (*Polygala amara*), and those like mountain avens (*Dryas octopetala*, Plate 9) or Scottish asphodel (*Tofieldia pusilla*, Plate 13), which are essentially species of high mountains but occur at low altitudes in the Arctic and even on the coast of Scotland. Some of these plants grow extraordinarily slowly: for example, mature plants of Scottish asphodel, even when grown at low altitudes without competition, take as long as two years to double their dry weight, while the rhizome extends no more than 3–5mm a year. It seems unlikely that the presence in upper Teesdale of those species which elsewhere occur in warmer and drier regions can be related directly to the cool and moist characteristics of the climate. Yet it is possible that indirectly they benefit because of the absence, or much reduced growth, of more vigorous and productive species. Unfortunately no experimental evidence is available but it seems probable that some of these species, for which Teesdale is almost their northern limit, would in the absence of competition be favoured by a warmer and drier climate. The sedge *Carex ericetorum* (Plate 12), for example, grows on freely drained sandy soils in Breckland where the summer rainfall averages only 280mm and the soils frequently become very dry, evaporation almost ceases and the surface temperature in the early afternoon may rise to 30–35°C. As on the sugar-limestone, the soil is deficient in some mineral nutrients and the vegetation is sparse and stunted.

In contrast, those species which constitute the other group are elsewhere found on high mountains and a number occur well within the Arctic circle. Their occurrence in Teesdale is remarkable because of the low altitude at which some of them are encountered. For example, spring gentian (*Gentiana verna*) grows near Langdon Beck at an altitude of about 400m, while on the west coast of Ireland it grows at sea-level. In central Europe, although it occurs in the limestone hills north of the Alps, it is most plentiful in the Alps from 1000 to 2500m. This feature of upper Teesdale is part of a general tendency for the lower altitudinal limit of species which are confined to high altitudes in Southern Europe to decrease with latitude northwards.

The cause of the restriction of plants to high altitudes has been the subject of a great deal of speculation for well over a century, but there have been relatively few experimental studies. Although there are many differences between the climate in upland regions and the adjacent lowlands, the only variable which changes consistently with altitude, apart from barometric pressure, is temperature. Consequently, if plants are restricted in their distribution by altitude, they will inevitably show significant correlations with temperature. This has been clearly demonstrated by Dahl (1951) for Scandinavia and by Conolly & Dahl (1970) for the British Isles. From measurements

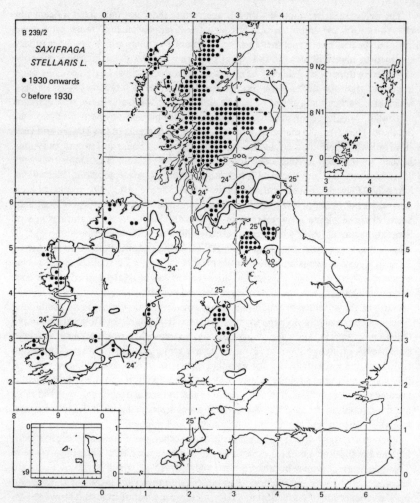

FIG. 19. The distribution of starry saxifrage *(Saxifraga stellaris)* in relation to the isotherms for maximum summer temperatures of the summits of mountains.

of mean maximum temperatures at mostly lowland meteorological stations, the equivalent temperatures for neighbouring mountains can be calculated using the theoretical lapse rate. Isotherms may then be drawn to include all summits at which the mean maximum temperature in the warmest month of the year will not exceed particular values. The geographical distributions of many of the more widespread mountain species are found to be within particular isotherms. Thus, for example, the distribution of starry saxifrage *(Saxifraga stellaris)* in Britain lies entirely within an area where the maximum summer temperature at the highest altitudes does not exceed 25°C but within this area in Scotland its distribution is even more precisely defined by the 24°C isotherm (Fig. 19).

On the basis of these correlations it has been argued that the distribution of the species must be limited by summer warmth. The explanation for such limitation put forward by Dahl (1951) is that the species with a well-defined lower altitudinal limit suffer direct injury when exposed to the high temperatures of lower altitudes, and to support this he quotes instances of damage occurring in warm summers in, for example, the Botanic Gardens in Oslo. However, he points out that the actual temperatures of the plants in their natural habitats will be higher than the limiting isotherm and so also are the temperatures which cause injury. In this case, it is difficult to understand why the correlations are so exact, because it is unlikely that maximum temperatures of plants will be simply related to mean air maxima, more especially because the rate of evaporation from the leaves has a significant effect on their temperature.

In fact, many plants which occur naturally at high altitudes will grow quite healthily in the lowlands and often flower freely and regenerate from seed. The essential requirement seems to be that they should not be overgrown by weeds, and although some species benefit from light shade, others grow well in full sun but may require extra water in dry periods during the summer. Thus, for example, mountain avens (*Dryas octopetala*) thrives on many lowland rock-gardens but it is generally found that purple saxifrage (*Saxifraga oppositifolia*) requires a north-slope and needs water during droughts. Even more surprisingly, some species such as yellow saxifrage (*Saxifraga aizoides*) and stiff sedge (*Carex bigelowii*) grow well and flower in a heated glasshouse. Experience of growing mountain species in the lowlands shows that some easily rot during mild winters, when at higher altitudes they would normally be frozen. Unfortunately, this has not been investigated in detail.

The direct method of investigating the response of plants to altitude is by transplant experiments in which growth and development are analysed. Simultaneously the conditions they experience may be measured and then, by using controlled environments, experiments can be devised to discover if the responses in the transplants can be caused by, for example, realistic differences of temperature.

Two species which occur in upper Teesdale have been studied in this way: rose-root (*Sedum rosea*) which grows on ledges at about 570m on the Maize Beck and in abundance on the dolerite cliffs of High Cup Nick, and alpine timothy (*Phleum alpinum*) which is restricted to altitudes of 900m on Cross Fell. Both species were compared with lowland species belonging to the same genera.

The response of rose-root to altitude was compared with that of the lowland species orpine (*Sedum telephium*) by growing plants from seed on a uniform soil in boxes placed at a range of altitudes on Glaramara in the Lake District (Woodward & Pigott, 1976). The height of the shoots and the area covered by the leaves of individual plants at the end of the first season, when grown in competition, are plotted in Fig. 20. Rose-root scarcely responds to altitude, while orpine, which is a very much larger plant when grown at 50m, decreases in size with altitude until at 500m there is no significant difference between the two species. This is, just above the known altitudinal upper limit of orpine in northern England and is the lower altitudinal limit of rose-root.

A more detailed analysis (Woodward, 1976) shows that the greater growth-rate of orpine at low altitudes is entirely explained by the greater expansion of the leaves, so that for a given dry weight there is a larger photosynthetic area.

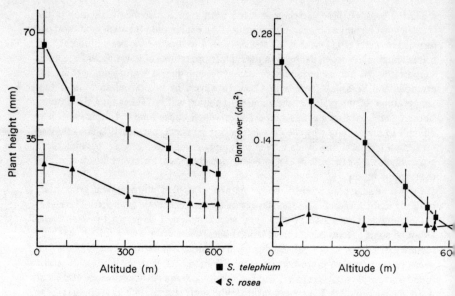

FIG. 20. The height of shoots and the area covered by leaves of plants grown from seedlings of rose-root *(Sedum rosea)* and orpine *(S. telephium)* at different altitudes on Glaramara.

The actual temperatures experienced by the plants at each altitude were measured and then a series of experiments were designed to compare the growth of the two species in artificial environments in which temperature could be controlled. In general, the results show that the growth-rate of rose-root is very little affected by temperature within the range it is likely to experience in natural habitats, whereas

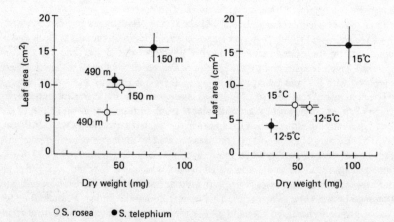

○ S. rosea   ● S. telephium

FIG. 21. The height of shoots and the area covered by leaves of plants grown from seedlings of rose-root and orpine at two different altitudes and in controlled environments at mean temperatures of 12·5° and 15°C.

orpine grows much more rapidly at high temperatures and its growth-rate decreases at lower temperatures (Fig. 21). Again the response to temperature is almost entirely accounted for by the influence on leaf-expansion and not on photosynthetic rate. Almost exactly the same results were obtained from experiments with alpine timothy, which is relatively insensitive to temperature, while the lowland species *Phleum bertolonii* shows a large response.

In one experiment, the two species of *Sedum* were grown in competition and the day and night temperatures were adjusted to be the mean daily maxima and minima recorded in the field at two altitudes 230m apart. The difference of the daily mean was only 1.67°C. The responses of the plants were almost exactly similar to those in the field. At the higher temperatures, orpine grew taller and expanded its leaves so that it soon over-shaded the much shorter plants of rose-root, while at the lower temperatures both species remained dwarf, so that rose-root remained unshaded. Thus a difference of less than 2°C can change the outcome of competition.

It would be unwise to assume that results obtained for so few species are of general validity, but it seems clear that the important feature of rose-root is that its growth-rate is scarcely affected by altitude or by a difference in temperature corresponding to its altitudinal range. There is no evidence that it is injured by temperature in the lowlands and it flowers freely, sets fertile seed and sows itself. In contrast, orpine like other lowland species (for example, perennial rye-grass) achieves its full vigour only at low altitudes and with increasing altitude, or decreasing temperature, its growth-rate is significantly reduced, until at about 500m it is no different from that of rose-root.

Convincing evidence of the reality of this difference may be seen in the Lake District, where the two species grow together at about 450m. The plants of rose-root consist of large tufts of leafy shoots up to 25cm tall, while the plants of orpine are dwarfed and do not exceed 5cm in height. By growing the two species in competition with each other, their ability to compete with other species may be estimated. The tall growth of orpine in the lowlands allows it to survive on hedgebanks and even at the edges of woodland where it is in competition with lowland grasses. Rose-root is likely to be shaded out in such situations. Above 450m, however, rose-root can still grow to its full size and is as tall as most of the species with which it is associated on cliff-ledges.

Conclusion

Finally, it may be asked whether the climate of Upper Teesdale is in some ways exceptional and therefore offers at least part of the explanation of the survival there of several unusual types of vegetation in which so many rare plants are present.

It must by recognized at once that there is unlikely to be any simple relationship. Although many of the rare species have their main distribution in the mountains of central and southern Europe or in the Scandinavian mountains and Arctic, the most remarkable feature of the assemblage as a whole is its geographical heterogeneity. In fact, some of the species have a predominantly southern or central European pattern of distribution and reach their northern or north-western limit in upper Teesdale. The problem is not simply to seek to explain the occurrence of mountain avens (*Dryas octopetala*) or the rare spring sedge (*Carex ericetorum*) in these localities, but to understand what allows them to grow together. It seems improbable that the same exceptional climatic conditions could be favourable for both.

In fact, the occurrence of so many arctic-alpine species at such low altitudes is in keeping with the general tendency for the lower altitudinal limits of species to decrease with latitude. Several of the species, such as mountain avens, spring gentian and rose-root, grow at sea-level in Scotland or the west of Ireland. This is correlated with the decrease in summer temperatures at sea-level, not only in more northerly latitudes, but also as a result of the influence of the Atlantic. The isotherms for the warmest months run more or less latitudinally across Siberia and eastern Europe, but then swing south as they approach the Atlantic coasts.

The few experimental studies of some of the arctic-alpine species show that they can grow quite healthily in the lowlands, at least in the north of England, and temperatures a few degrees higher than those they normally experience cause neither injury nor impair their reproduction. On the other hand, the species studied are surprisingly insensitive to temperature and do not respond to higher temperatures by an increased growth-rate. In this they differ very clearly from most lowland species, so that the low temperatures and shorter growing-season of upper Teesdale is perhaps more important in keeping vigorous lowland species out, or at least preventing them from achieving their full potential. The vegetation has for this reason a low production of dry matter and usually a low biomass, so that there is a lower intensity of competition and the slower growing arctic-alpine species are not disadvantaged.

Simply in terms of the measurements available from Dun Fell, Moor House and Widdybank it seems that the climate of upper Teesdale is not significantly different from that of either other parts of the Pennines or the Lake District at comparable altitudes. Because the Pennines reach their highest altitudes along the escarpment above the headwaters of the Tees it is here also that the lowest temperatures and generally most extreme conditions occur, but many of the rare species, and such extraordinary features as vegetation dominated by kobresia, occur at altitudes of only 500m where the climate is probably much the same as over many square miles elsewhere in the Pennines. There is, in fact, convincing evidence that climatic conditions are suitable for arctic-alpines elsewhere in the uplands of northern England because almost all the species of this group present in Teesdale do occur elsewhere. For example, the vegetation on the limestone cliffs of Ingleborough and Pen-y-ghent in the Craven Pennines contains several of these species as well as the purple saxifrage (*Saxifraga oppositifolia*) which is surprisingly absent from Teesdale. Elsewhere the species tend to grow isolated or in smaller groups, while in upper Teesdale there is a considerable concentration of them, although even then the species differ in the details of their distributions. Thus mountain avens occurs only on Cronkley and is absent from what seem to be very similar habitats on Widdybank. This suggests what can never be proved, that there has been an element of chance in the survival of the various species in habitats of such limited extent. It is perhaps significant that two of the species, kobresia and bog sandwort (*Minuartia stricta*, Plate VI) which do not occur elsewhere in northern England are restricted to 'sugar-limestone', while alpine forget-me-not (*Myosotis alpestris*) occurs at an altitude of about 750m on some of the highest outcrops of limestone in northern England.

Among the southern species at their northern limit in upper Teesdale are the Teesdale violet (*Viola rupestris*), hoary rock-rose (*Helianthemum canum*, Plate VIII), the rare spring sedge (*Carex ericetorum*, Plate 12) and horse-shoe vetch (*Hippocrepis comosa*, Plate 9). These four species seem to have rather similar requirements in north-west England where they all occur, sometimes together, on very shallow soils over limestone, usually on south-facing aspects and often at much lower altitudes. Unfortunately almost nothing is known about the conditions which limit their extension northwards. In all their localities they grow in very sparse and stunted vegetation. In Teesdale they are restricted to vegetation of this character on 'sugar-limestone', where there is evidence which is discussed in the following chapter that severe deficiencies of mineral nutrients are largely responsible for the very low biomass and sparseness of the vegetation. Nevertheless, the severe climate may play a part in maintaining these conditions so that paradoxically these southern plants may benefit indirectly from climatic conditions which directly are unfavourable.

CHAPTER 6

Geology, Soils and Vegetation

SOME knowledge of the geological structure of a region is fundamental to any real understanding of the nature of its landscape. This is particularly true in the north Pennines where so many features of the landscape are related to variations in thickness and hardness of the succession of limestones, shales and sandstones. It is these which have also influenced drainage, the extent of erosion and the distribution of glacial drift and peat. The country surrounding the headwaters of the Tees is really no different from the rest of the Pennines, except that its scale is rather larger and the hills are a little higher. Above the limits of enclosure, moorlands predominate, broken here and there by outcrops of pale grey limestone and low cliffs or 'scars' of darker sandstones. But the upper part of Teesdale is different and has a character all of its own, which is also derived from a geological feature, the Great Whin Sill. This hard dark grey rock is extensively exposed on both sides of the Tees to form high cliffs, and where the Tees crosses the sill are the two great waterfalls of High Force and Cauldron Snout (Plate 2). The extent of the influence of the Whin Sill is the unique feature of Teesdale.

Geology

The bedrock or solid formations that underlie upper Teesdale consist of a folded Lower Palaeozoic basement overlain by the complete stratigraphical succession of the Carboniferous rocks of the northern Pennines. Slates and ash of the Lower Palaeozoic basement are only exposed in a small inlier below Cronkley Scar which is called the Teesdale Inlier. The basal Carboniferous rocks, conglomerates with shales, sandstone and limestone bands, overlie the Lower Palaeozoic slates and form the Carboniferous Basement Group. The Lower Limestone Group follows the Basement Group and is mainly composed of thick light-coloured limestone called the Melmerby Scar Limestone. Towards the top of the Lower Limestone Group sandstone and shale bands divide the limestone sequence and the repeated cyclic succession of limestone, shale and sandstone characterizes the overlying Middle Limestone Group. The top of the Middle Limestone Group coincides with the top of the Lower Carboniferous and lies at the base of the Great Limestone, a particularly good marker horizon throughout northern England. The Upper Carboniferous, Namurian, sequence begins with the Great Limestone, but above this band limestones become thin and the bulk of the succession is composed of sandstone and shale. These beds are restricted to the tops of the fells in Upper Teesdale. The Great Whin Sill igneous intrusion is present within the Carboniferous succession and forms spectacular waterfalls in the

TABLE 6. Geological succession in Upper Teesdale

SUPERFICIAL FORMATIONS (DRIFT)

Recent and Post-glacial:
Blanket and basin peat.
Periglacial solifluxion deposits; sandy and stony clays.
Boulder clay.

SOLID FORMATIONS (BEDROCK)

Upper Carboniferous (Namurian):
Upper Limestone Group (Pendelian and Arnsbergian); sandstones, grits and shales with coal seams and limestone bands about 180m thick.
Lower Carboniferous (Dinantian):
Middle Limestone Group (Brigantian); a rhythmic sequence of limestones, shales, sandstones and coal seams about 250m thick.
Lower Limestone Group (Asbian); massive limestones overlain by thin bands of shale, sandstone and limestone about 53m thick.
Basement Group (Holkerian); conglomerate with sandstone, shale and thin limestone bands about 20m thick.

Great Unconformity

Ordovician:
Skiddaw Slate Group; slates and ash bands.

Tees. Mineralization of the Carboniferous rocks is widespread and lead, zinc, fluorspar and barytes have been mined in Teesdale. The full succession of drift and bedrock formations in Upper Teesdale is summarized in Table 6.

The geology of Upper Teesdale has been described by several writers and regional geological surveys have been conducted and revised on several occasions. The geological succession was first determined by Westgarth Forster (1809) and his account forms the earliest published work on the stratigraphy of the Pennines. His book went into three editions (1809, 1821 and 1883) the last of which was published 50 years after his death. Further work on Teesdale was published by John Phillips (1836) and Wallace (1861). The primary survey of the region by the Geological Survey was conducted mainly during the third quarter of the last century when detailed 6-inch scale maps were produced, but unfortunately no descriptive memoirs were published. An account of the stratigraphy, mineralization and mines of the region was produced by Dunham (1948) and a detailed memoir of the geology of the upper part of the Tees Valley, above the Cow Green Reservoir, was published by Johnson & Dunham, (1963). Detailed studies on the stratigraphy, the Great Whin Sill intrusion, mineralization and glacial deposits in Teesdale are given in Johnson & Hickling (1970).

STRUCTURE AND MINERALIZATION

Upper Teesdale lies on the crest of the Teesdale dome, a broad uplift which affects the high ground between Stainmore and the Tyne Valley; this region is called the Alston

Block. The uplift imparts a gentle easterly dip to the strata, such that the oldest rocks outcrop in the west and as one goes progressively eastwards younger rocks are exposed. Thus the Lower Carboniferous dominates the upper part of the Tees Valley, but downstream the Upper Carboniferous has wider and wider outcrops as it stretches down the valley sides. The structural unit of the Alston Block is caused by an underlying granite batholith, the Weardale Granite, that is not seen at the surface. It was originally found during a gravity survey of the northern Pennines (Bott & Masson-Smith, 1953) and later proved in drilling the Rookhope Boring (Dunham et al., 1965). The low density granite is buoyant and tends to rise relative to the surrounding regions. It has tended to produce an uplifted area since the time of emplacement of the granite in the Devonian about 392 million years ago. With this movement a series of faulted hinge belts has developed along the margins of the granite that are today used to delimit the margins of the Alston Block. The Weardale Granite is part of a much larger batholith that underlies the Lake District (Bott, 1975).

A major north–south structural feature which crosses Upper Teesdale between Langdon Beck and Noon Hill is the Burtreeford Disturbance. It is a faulted east-facing monocline with downthrow east of up to 152m. On the west side of the structure the Carboniferous Basement Group is uplifted to outcrop on the sides of the Tees Valley and the underlying Lower Palaeozoic strata appear low down in the valley forming the Teesdale Inlier.

The general eastward dip of the strata in Teesdale is disrupted by faults whose direction can be divided into well-defined groups. The faults are often persistent over wide areas, but may vary greatly in displacement laterally. Many of the fault-lines were channels for movement of late and post-Carboniferous mineralizing fluids. Ore minerals such as galena (lead sulphide), sphalerite (zinc sulphide), fluorspar (calcium fluoride), barytes (barium sulphate) and quartz were laid down in the fractures to form mineral veins. These ore minerals have been worked in Teesdale since mediaeval times.

TEESDALE INLIER

The Lower Palaeozoic Ordovician strata only outcrop in the floor of the Tees Valley below Cronkley Scar on the west side of the Burtreeford Disturbance. This region of the valley is deeply covered with glacial drift and the Ordovician rocks can only be seen well in the banks of the Tees at Pencil Mill. Here the soft, greenish highly cleaved slates were worked in a small quarry and formed the raw material for slate pencils. Five mica-lamprophyre dykes cut the slates and can be seen on both sides of the river. Volcanic rocks are also known in the inlier, but their relationship to the slates is uncertain. Rhyolitic tuffs outcrop in a few places on the south side of the Tees opposite Widdybank Farm, but the extent of the volcanic rock outcrop below the drift is unknown. Borehole evidence has established that the slates are present below drift at Widdybank Farm and they were proved again at Wrentnall Shaft of Cow Green mine to the north. Further boreholes on the north side of the inlier have shown that it is more restricted in area than was originally anticipated.

The age of the slates has been proved by the presence of graptolites including *Didymograptus* and *Glyptograptus dentatus* (Brongn.) as Ordovician Skiddaw Slates

(Llanvirn) and this has been confirmed by the study of microfossils (acritarchs). A full account of the geology of the Teesdale inlier is given in Johnson & Hickling (1970).

CARBONIFEROUS SEDIMENTS

The surface topography of Upper Teesdale is sculptured from the Carboniferous sequence with its contained Great Whin Sill intrusion. The Carboniferous rocks are mainly masked by drift deposits on the lower slopes and in the valley bottoms, but above the deep drift the land-form is largely dictated by hard and soft bands in the sedimentary sequence. Thus the sandstone and limestone bands are relatively hard and resistant to erosion and form scarps and benches on the valley sides, whereas the shale bands are soft and erode more rapidly to form gentle concave slopes. A step-like topography of hard and soft bands is conspicuous on many of the hill sides. Where subsurface drainage is strong, such as on limestone outcrops, swallowholes form above open joints in the limestone. They can develop through superficial drift cover of peat and boulder-clay. The position of outcrop of a limestone band below drift can often be traced by the line of swallowholes. Subsurface drainage is one of the ways in which exposed limestone surfaces are produced in Teesdale. Drainage through the limestone carries away peat and clay eventually clearing the drift, except for large stones and boulders, from the limestone surface. On these surfaces residual drift clay and insoluble matter from the limestone combine to form a fertile red-brown loam. Every stage of this process of exposing limestone surfaces is present in Teesdale, from swallowholes to verdant islands of limestone grassland surrounded by thick drift deposits. It will be clear that over most of Upper Teesdale the bedrock has only minor influence on the mineral soils, peat and vegetation owing to the intervening seal of impervious drift clay.

The succession of Carboniferous rocks is given in Fig. 22 and the broad distribution of the divisions of strata is shown on the geological map (inside back cover). The oldest part of the sequence, the Basement Group, is found on the west side of the Burtreeford Disturbance ringing the Teesdale inlier. The strata are not well exposed, but the lower beds of quartz pebble conglomerate can be seen below Cronkley Scar. Here the unconformity with the underlying Skiddaw Slates has been exposed in excavations near Pencil Mill. The upper part of the sequence is composed of sandstone, shale and fossiliferous limestone bands that are well seen at Falcon Clints.

The Lower Limestone Group is similarly restricted to the western flank of the Burtreeford Disturbance, but extends up the Tees Valley to the western end of the Cow Green Reservoir. This division is dominated by the light-coloured Melmerby Scar Limestone about 40m thick. The limestone is particularly free from carbonaceous and muddy impurities as compared with most other limestones in the Carboniferous succession. The lack of carbon allows it to change by metamorphism to a coarsely crystalline marble adjacent to the Great Whin Sill intrusion (Robinson, 1971). These marbles occur only on Widdybank and Cronkley fells and have important bearing on the occurrence and survival of the Teesdale arctic-alpine flora. The overlying Robinson Limestone is light coloured, but the Peghorn is darker and contains rather greater amounts of impurities. These latter limestones are separated by bands of shale and sandstone and initiate a cyclic repetition of limestone,

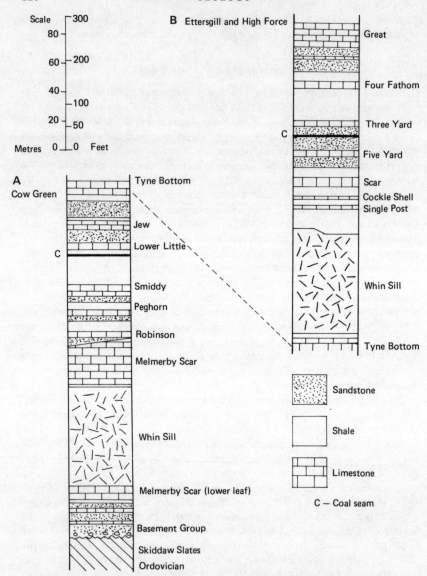

FIG. 22. Comparative vertical sections of Carboniferous, Middle and Lower Limestone Group strata to west (A) and east (B) of the Burtreeford Disturbance, Upper Teesdale.

shale and sandstone that persists to the top of the Lower Carboniferous.

The Middle Limestone Group has a wide outcrop throughout the region. It is composed of ten sedimentary cycles of limestone, shale and sandstone (Fig. 22). Each limestone represents a transgression of the Carboniferous Sea north and east over the region and the shale and sandstones were formed by broad, shallow delta flats that spread south and west from the shoreline in the north. Sedimentation tended to be faster than sinking of the region and only shallow seas were formed. The delta flats often became exposed near to water-level allowing terrestrial vegetation to become established which is now represented in the sequence by thin coal seams. Most of the limestone bands are of the darker, impure variety, but two of them, the Jew and Single Post, are lighter coloured and change to crystalline marble when in near proximity to the Great Whin Sill. Jew Limestone marble can be seen in small outcrops near Force Burn and the Single Post limestone forms a coarsely crystalline marble just above the sill near Scoberry Bridge, Newbiggin.

The Upper Carboniferous, Namurian, starts with the Great Limestone, a persistent band of fossiliferous limestones about 18m thick. It is well exposed high on the fell sides at many places in Upper Teesdale and it is particularly well seen at High Hurth Edge, Langdon Beck. Evidence from index fossils has shown that the base of the Great Limestone is near the junction between the Upper and Lower Carboniferous. Above the Great Limestone the Namurian strata are dominated by shale and sandstone bands, limestone bands being thin and relatively rare. The sandstones are hard and more resistant to erosion, so that they form strong scarps on the fell sides. Cross Fell and the Dun Fells are capped by conspicuous Namurian sandstone bands. The outcrop of the Namurian is restricted to the tops of the fells in Upper Teesdale and in the west it forms an outlier on the Pennine watershed ridge. Eastwards the regional dip brings in more continuous exposures and the Namurian sequence extends upwards into coarse-grained sandstones and grits that herald the proximity of the overlying Coal Measures. A detailed account of the Carboniferous rocks and their fossils is given in Johnson & Dunham (1963).

GREAT WHIN SILL

An important feature of the geology of Upper Teesdale is the Great Whin Sill quartz-dolerite intrusion. This series of horizontal sheets of dark-coloured, finely crystalline igneous rock was emplaced as hot magma into the Carboniferous sediments in late Carboniferous times; the event is dated at 295 million years (Stephanian). The rock is hard and resistant to erosion so that it forms spectacular cliffs such as Cronkley Scar and Falcon Clints and fine waterfalls as High Force and Cauldron Snout. The sill does not keep to one stratigraphical horizon. It is lowest in the sequence in the vicinity of the west side of the Burtreeford Disturbance where it lies within the Melmerby Scar Limestone. North and west of this in Teesdale the sill rises in steps to the horizon of the Tyne Bottom Limestone. On the east side of the Burtreeford Disturbance the sill lies shortly above the Tyne Bottom Limestone and it is exposed at this horizon in the High Force waterfall (Fig. 22). Owing to the displacement of the Burtreeford Disturbance the sill appears to cut almost horizontally from the Tyne Bottom horizon on the east to the Melmerby Scar Limestone on the west. This indicates that the sill post-dates the disturbance. There is evidence that the fractured ground of the disturbance was actually utilized as a feeder through which the molten magma rose to form the horizontal sills.

The hot Whin Sill magma baked the Carboniferous sediments above and below the sills causing contact metamorphism. Sandstones adjacent to the Whin Sill are converted into white quartzite. Shales are altered to porcellaneous rocks, often called whetstones, near the contact but, further away, spotting is developed in the shales owing to the development of new minerals up to 30m from the contact. Limestones are the most reactive rocks to metamorphism at the Whin contact, particularly impure, sandy or muddy limestones. Metamorphic minerals found in these rocks include garnet, epidote, feldspar, irocraise, diopside and chlorite. Pure limestones undergo recrystallization. The degree of recrystallization is dependent on the organic content of the limestone. The light-coloured limestones, containing little free carbon, recrystallize to a coarse-grained marble. Darker limestones contain free carbon that inhibits the growth of crystals during metamorphism and only fine and limited recrystallization takes place. The only extensive development of coarsely recrystallized limestone is found where the Whin Sill is intruded into the pure Melmerby Scar Limestone on the west side of the Burtreeford Disturbance. The sill is at its lowest known horizon here and the wide outcrops of granular marble on Cronkley and Widdybank fells are exceptional. Further details of the Whin Sill and its associated metamorphism are given in Johnson & Hickling (1970) and Robinson (1971).

GLACIAL DEPOSITS

The last period of earth history is the Quaternary which extends up to the present day. It is characterized by a major episode of continental glaciation of the northern hemisphere that in Britain has been called the Ice-Age. It is suggested that the beginning of regional climatic cooling was about 1.8 million years ago though this figure is uncertain and the Quaternary may eventually go back as far as 2–3 million years. Three glaciations separated by two warmer inter-glacial periods have been recognized in Britain. The sequence of deposits formed during this period is only complete at the margin of the continental glaciers in southern England. Elsewhere the strong eroding power of the ice-sheets removed previous glacial deposits and only the deposits laid down by the last glaciation have survived to today. Thus in Upper Teesdale, where the erosive activity of glaciers was strong, all the glacial deposits belong to the last Weichselian (Devensian) glaciation. They were formed mainly between 25,000 and 13,000 years ago. The last glacial event was a minor corrie glaciation which formed small glaciers in the Pennines and ended some 10,000 years ago. Since then the dominant geological processes in Teesdale have been erosional with the removal of vast quantities of glacial drift and the formation of the present drainage system. These processes continue at the present day.

Evidence of glacial plucking on the Cross Fell watershed ridge suggests that even the highest ground in the region was over-ridden by ice at the maximum advance of the Quaternary ice-sheets. At this time boulder-clay was laid down thickly below the ice masking the bedrock and filling the valley bottoms. The surface of the boulder-clay was rounded and sculptured by moving ice into drumlins that can be identified below Cronkley Scar. One drumlin is cut by the Tees at the confluence with Harwood Beck and shows grey boulder-clay derived from local sources with no far-travelled erratic boulders. The peaks of the Cross Fell range appear to have been the centre of

PLATE VII. *Above*, wood cranesbill (*Geranium sylvaticum*) at Bowlees. *Left*, globe-flower (*Trollius europaeus*) near Cronkley Farm.

PLATE VIII. *Right*, hoary rock-rose (*Helianthemum canum*) on Cronkley Fell. *Below*, Teesdale violet (*Viola rupestris*) on Widdybank Fell.

ice dispersal for the Upper Teesdale glacier. Below Middleton-in-Teesdale the Stainmore ice entered the Tees Valley and abundant erratic boulders from the Lake District become conspicuous in the boulder-clay.

The final glacial stage was a period of shrinking of the glaciers and start of rapid erosion of the superficial deposits. The elongate mass of drift below Cronkley Scar may well have been a lateral moraine formed beside the reduced Teesdale glacier at this time. Moraines of gravelly and stony drift that occur in the Upper Tees valley about Lady Vein and Hearth Hill may also date from this time. Erosion was rapid before a mantle of vegetation developed over the region giving protection to the drift deposits. Almost all the drift was swept from the upper slopes of the fells. Boulder-clay is not found above 610m (2000ft) on the fell sides. In the valley bottoms erosion removed much glacial drift and laid down wide spreads of alluvium in some places, but much of the valley floors are still masked by drift. Ancient river channels have not been re-excavated and still lie deeply infilled with drift deposits. The drift-filled valley of the Tees is visible on the west side of Cauldron Snout. The new course of the river over the waterfall is on the precipitous east side of the old river channel. Similarly the old river valley is to the east of the present river in front of Cronkley Scar and to the west of it at Dine Holm. The diversion of the Tees over bedrock at High Force is also presumably of glacial origin.

Solifluxion was also a major feature of the post-glacial period. Periglacial conditions may have lasted for a lengthy period on the Pennine uplands and the record of cryoturbation is clear throughout the region. Solifluxion deposits occur widely on top of boulder clay and soil structures such as stone polygons are widely developed. These features have been well preserved to the present day below blanket peat deposits. Detailed accounts of the glacial and periglacial features of the region will be found in Johnson & Dunham (1963) and Francis in Johnson & Hickling (1970).

Soil Development in Relation to Parent Materials

In Upper Teesdale, as in all of northern Britain, the Weichselian glaciation was of great importance in determining the nature and distribution of soils at the present day. From the distribution of features of glacial erosion, such as striated and plucked rocks, and of deposits of glacial drift containing rocks which are not of immediately local origin, it is clear that ice-sheets extended up to an altitude of at least 600m and probably higher. In fact, calculations based on studies of the profiles of existing ice-fronts suggest that, at the maximum extent of the Weichselian ice, the whole western escarpment including Cross Fell was over-ridden.

When the ice melted away, the surfaces which were then exposed were either glacially eroded or formed of freshly deposited glacial drift, so that all traces of former soils, though not necessarily of deep weathering, had been destroyed.

Soils form from their parent materials partly by physical disintegration but also partly by chemical weathering, a process occurring very slowly in cool upland situations at the latitude of Teesdale. Consequently soils which have formed since the end of the Weichselian glaciation are relatively young and those which are composed predominantly of mineral materials are usually shallow and greatly influenced by the nature of their parent material. On the other hand, cool wet climates allow remains of plants to become water-logged and to decay slowly so that considerable thicknesses of peat accumulate whose nature is quite unlike the underlying mineral material. There is, therefore, a very striking contrast between the mineral soils which are usually no more than 20–40cm deep and adjacent deposits of peat which may be ten times these depths.

The sandstones, shales and limestones of Carboniferous age and the intrusive dolerite of the Great Whin Sill are the parent materials of almost all the soils in upper Teesdale but frequently it is not the solid rock but glacial drift composed of one or more of these rocks from which the soil has formed. The distribution of soil-types is therefore very closely related to topography because this to a large extent determines whether surfaces have been eroded or subject to deposition. Erosion exposes the hard underlying rocks to form steep convex slopes, outcrops and cliffs, but where there is deposition the solid rocks are buried under varying thicknesses of boulder-clay or alluvium. The distribution of soils is only partly related to solid- geology so that, for example, large areas of limestone are buried by non-calcareous drift, while drift containing limestone may overlie sandstones, shales or dolerite.

The presence of so much glacial drift is important in another respect. Although it has a very variable composition in terms of the quantity, size and nature of the boulders it contains, the matrix is characterized by a very high proportion of fine sand. Usually well over half this material proves to be fine sand (0.02–0.2mm in diameter) and there are surprisingly small proportions of coarse sand (0.2–2.0mm) and clay (less than 0.002mm). In undisturbed boulder-clay, the fine sand is very closely packed and the cavities between the particles are usually less than 0.03mm across. The drainage of water through cavities less than this diameter is extremely slow, so that in a region with frequent rain and low rates of evaporation, the surface layers remain almost permanently water-logged. This illustrates very clearly the influence of climate on soil development because, in a region with a dry summer, such material would dry out by evaporation, so that roots could penetrate deeper to leave cavities which would improve the drainage.

The tendency for drainage to be impeded is a dominant feature in the processes of soil development throughout not only Teesdale but most of the Pennines. The most widespread soils are those described as hydromorphic, in which water-logging is caused either by the impervious nature of the substrate itself or by the topographical position of the site in relation to the true water-table. These soils cover vast tracts of the uplands and probably constitute more than nine-tenths of the land above the limit of agricultural enclosure in the north Pennines as a whole. At first sight, it may seem that a knowledge of conditions in soils which are so widespread can have little relevance to the problems presented by the assemblage of rare species which characterize upper Teesdale. In fact, quite the reverse is true, and if the conditions in these widespread soils which are unfavourable to the rare species can be identified, then it partly explains why the plants and the types of vegetation in which they grow are so rare.

Hydromorphic soils are not only characterized by their wetness, but also by their poor aeration. The amount of oxygen which will dissolve in water is quite small, and diffusion of oxygen (or carbon dioxide) is ten thousand times slower in solution than in the gaseous state. Consequently the rate at which oxygen enters a water-logged soil is very slow and it is immediately removed by the respiration of roots and micro-organisms, so that the soil remains anaerobic. When anaerobic the fine-textured matrix of boulder clay is usually greyish-blue but becomes orange-brown on prolonged exposure to the air. This change is the result of the oxidation of iron from the relatively soluble ferrous state to the less soluble ferric state. The greyish-blue colour is a marked feature of hydromorphic mineral soils but in peat is masked by the dark colours of the humus. A more characteristic feature of anaerobic conditions in peat is the unpleasant smell of hydrogen sulphide, a substance which is formed only when free oxygen is quite absent, and which is poisonous to most living organisms. In describing hydromorphic soils, considerable importance is attached to whether water-logging is caused by topography or the impervious nature of the soil material. This is essentially a hydrological distinction and, because of the high rainfall and widespread distribution of glacial drift, the simple fact is that most soils in Teesdale remain almost saturated with water throughout much of the year. So long as the water near the surface is supplied directly by rain, only small quantities of salts present in the rain are added and there is little influence on the vegetation. However, if the ground water rises close to the surface and contains a significant concentration of calcium salts in solution, then there is a very marked change in the vegetation. The vegetation and soils associated with calcareous springs are described in a later section.

The widespread hydromorphic soils are acid with a pH commonly in the range of 3.5 to 4.5. They vary from mineral soils to deep accumulations of peat. The mineral soils support a vegetation often dominated by mat-grass with some heather, heath-rush and sometimes common rush. The soils are typically peaty gleys in which a layer of partly decayed leaves, matted together by rhizomes and roots, passes gradually into a relatively shallow layer of almost black, strongly humified organic matter. This overlies an almost structureless pale grey or greyish-blue mineral horizon, often with rust-coloured markings, especially down the channels formed by roots. This passes gradually below the level of the roots into undisturbed boulder-clay. The term gley refers particularly to the mottled horizon where the anaerobic parts are greyish-blue and depleted of iron, and the brown markings indicate penetration of air and an accumulation of hydrated iron oxides.

There is no clear distinction between peaty gleys and the deeper organic soils carrying blanket-bog, although the depth of peat at which the living roots no longer penetrate to the mineral layer is a difference of biological significance.

In general, peaty gleys occur on sloping ground where the water can drain away laterally, but they grade into organic soils as the angle of slope decreases and becomes horizontal. Whereas in a well-aerated soil, plant-residues are almost entirely decomposed and oxidized away to leave only traces of the amorphous brown substances known as humus, in anaerobic situations, and especially those which are strongly acid, the rate of decomposition is reduced and gradual oxidation leads to humification. Fungi, which are normally active in acid conditions, are inhibited by the lack of oxygen, while bacteria, which include many anaerobes, cannot tolerate strong acidity. Essentially the conditions are those used in pickling vegetables in vinegar and as a result even the cellulose structures of plants are preserved though often stained brown by humus. As the depth of peat increases, so the underlying mineral material becomes deprived of any oxygen and the features of gleying are eventually lost.

Because of their excellent state of preservation, the plants which formed the peat can be identified and even a superficial study in the field will usually reveal the fibrous sheaths and dark roots of cotton-grass, twigs of heather and seams of bog-moss (*Sphagnum* spp.) and sometimes fringe-moss (*Rhacomitrium lanuginosum*). These same plants now grow on the surface of the peat but their proportions often appear to have changed: there is less bog-moss and more cotton-grass and heather. A careful search will often show fragments of charcoal in the surface layers of the peat and, as was shown by Pearsall (1941) on Stainmore to the south of Teesdale, it is burning of heather and grazing by sheep which have probably largely caused this change. It is a very important change because burning first destroys the raised hummocks of bog-moss and then causes a more general change: as bog-moss disappears, the surface loses its spongy cover and becomes less wet and retentive of water. Growth of the peat decreases and stops, while heavy rain, instead of being held in the spongy carpet, flows across the less absorbent surface of compact peat and begins to erode it. As channels form they gather more water and, with no bog-moss to block them, erosion accelerates so that gullies form on slopes and gradually eat back into the deep peat on horizontal surfaces. The heavy rainfall which originally caused peat to form now simply hastens its erosion, and water, instead of being retained in a great natural reservoir, is discharged rapidly causing violent fluctuations in river-levels. Erosion of peat in Upper Teesdale is now so extensive that it is not unreasonable to suggest that if the natural vegetation had not been destroyed, it would be unnecessary to build expensive reservoirs simply to regulate the flow of the Tees.

Some areas of deep peat on almost horizontal surfaces are so extensive that their central parts have been little affected by erosion and a more or less continuous cover of bog-moss survives. It is in these situations that two species of bog-moss, *Sphagnum imbricatum* (Plate 16) and *S. fuscum*, which both tend to form large hummocks, still occur. It is evident from the frequency of the very distinctive remains of *S. imbricatum* in peat throughout the Pennines that this species was formerly widespread. Unfortunately, several large bogs where these species occurred lay beside the Weel and were drowned by the reservoir.

The survival of these species in Upper Teesdale and their disappearance from almost the whole of the rest of the Pennines suggest that the sheer size of the bogs has been a factor in their resistance to change. It is possibly for the same reason that some other species have survived in Teesdale which grow in otherwise undistinguished peaty situations. The most remarkable is dwarf birch (*Betula nana*), for which the occurrence in Teesdale is the southern limit of the species in Britain. Until the construction of the reservoir, the sedge *Carex paupercula*, which also occurs in the Lake District and Scotland, grew with beaked sedge (*C. rostrata*) in a broad natural soakway between the great bogs beside the Weel. A more problematical species for which upper Teesdale is the most southerly occurrence is the moss *Haplodon wormskjoldii*. This species also occurs in the central Scottish Highlands but is otherwise an Arctic species. In Teesdale it has been found a number of times, usually in peat bogs, but on the decaying bones of sheep; certainly a very specialized substrate but one which is widespread in the Pennines.

These few species seem to constitute a special group and the majority of the rare plants of Upper Teesdale are quite absent from the widespread peaty gleys and acid peats. A few grow on the dolerite of the Great Whin Sill, but the majority occur, not only in Upper Teesdale but throughout their range, on soils which are never strongly acid and contain plentiful calcium and often calcium carbonate. Such species are conveniently described as calcicoles, implying simply that they normally grow on calcareous soils, but the reasons for their restriction are more complicated. Most calcicoles sown on strongly acid soils show severe stunting, especially of the roots, which later die. Similar injury is caused by dilute solutions of aluminium salts and aluminium can also be shown to be present in solution in soils of pH below 4.2. In contrast, species which naturally grow on very acid soils show no injury on these soils and are relatively insensitive to aluminium salts. For example, the sedge *Carex lepidocarpa*, which is common in wet calcareous sites in Teesdale, is very sensitive to aluminium, while *C. demissa* which often grows in flushes of acid water is relatively insensitive (Clymo, 1962). This will not explain the absence of calcicoles from less acid soils and, in fact, most will grow healthily on such soils experimentally and sometimes do so naturally. However, in regions of high rainfall there is a marked tendency for soils to be either calcareous or strongly acid. This is because the large quantities of water which move down through the soils (p. 105) carry away calcium, so that most soils become acid, and often strongly acid at the surface, except for those with large reserves of calcium, such as soils developed over limestone. Soils of intermediate pH do occur but they tend to surround areas of calcareous soil or be maintained by seepage of water containing calcium in solution. They are also sometimes associated with outcrops of igneous rocks such as dolerite and basalt.

SOILS DEVELOPED ON THE GREAT WHIN SILL

Upper Teesdale owes much of its special character to the extensive outcrops of the Great Whin Sill, and it is a variety of features associated with this massive intrusion of igneous rock which distinguish this part of the Pennines from all the country to the south and, save for a few small outcrops, from Weardale. Further north there are extensive outcrops at lower altitudes along the Roman Wall and on the coast of Northumberland. The sill also forms the spectacular semicircle of cliffs at High Cup Nick on the western escarpment immediately beyond the head of the Maize Beck.

Development of soil directly on the Great Whin Sill is almost confined to ledges and fissures on the cliffs with their prominent columnar jointing, and to the steep screes of fallen blocks below. Where there are horizontal surfaces, these are usually covered by drift or blanketed with peat.

Although dolerite is described as a basic igneous rock and chemical analysis of whin-stone shows it to contain about 6% of calcium, 3% of magnesium and significant quantities of potassium, sodium and phosphate, the hardness of the rock, its slow rate of weathering and the high rainfall combine to allow acid peaty humus to accumulate, so that heather and bilberry usually dominate the ledges.

Where mineral soils have formed directly on Whin Sill, they have a quite distinctive character. On the southerly aspect of Dine Holm Scar, for example, there are soils varying from 20–40cm deep which consist of a shallow layer of litter overlying a stony loam which is dark brown at the top but becomes a striking orange rusty-brown below. The colour is related to the high concentration of iron in the rock. Analysis shows that such soils are particularly rich in soluble potassium and contain higher concentrations of calcium and magnesium than would normally occur in, for example, soils developed on sandstone cliffs. Such brown soils free of calcium carbonate are immature forms of brown forest soils. This particular example supports vegetation characterized by the presence of bear-berry (*Arctostaphylos uva-ursi*), bell-heather (*Erica cinerea*), bitter-vetch (*Lathyrus montanus*) and bushes of juniper. All the localities of bear-berry in Teesdale are on Whin Sill, but in the south Pennines it occurs in similar vegetation of south-facing slopes of Millstone Grit.

A number of other rare species occur on Whin Sill in Teesdale but are associated with seepage of calcareous water from the adjacent limestone, and they also occur on calcareous soils away from the immediate influence of the sill. However, the small fern, *Woodsia ilvensis*, possibly now extinct in Teesdale, apparently grew in crevices in dolerite and this is in keeping with its localities in the Lake District which are all on similar rocks of the Borrowdale volcanic series.

SOILS DEVELOPED ON SUGAR-LIMESTONE

The special importance of the Whin Sill in relation to the unusual features of the vegetation of Upper Teesdale is not in the soils formed directly from dolerite but in those developed on crystalline marble which was produced by contact metamorphism when the sill was injected. The marble is exposed in cliffs below the sill and in both cliffs and outcrops above the sill.

The structure of the marble is described on p. 128 and among the significant features for soil-development is its breakdown on weathering to release separate crystals of calcite whose diameter up to about 0.5mm is that of coarse sand. This produces a material which has both the consistency and appearance of coarse granulated sugar, so that it is well described by the name 'sugar-limestone'. Disintegration of exposed surfaces of the marble occurs quite slowly although as crystals become detached they are readily washed away. However, when buried under a layer of decalcified glacial drift, the material holding the crystals together in the marble dissolves, leaving them free to separate so that layers of calcite-sand can form which may be as much as 3m deep (Johnson, Robinson & Hornung, 1971). If the protective cover is subsequently eroded away, then the sand is exposed and readily eroded unless colonized by vegetation.

The soils present on the sugar-limestone are related to topography in so far as this determines the distribution of drift and the vulnerability to erosion (Plate 7). On Widdybank the outcrop of sugar-limestone is a relatively narrow band with a low escarpment facing south-west and very much exposed to wind and rain. At the northern end it formed the slopes of the small valley of the Slapestone Sike (Plate 6), but this is now below the water-level of the reservoir. On Cronkley Fell there is a similar west-facing edge of sugar-limestone (Plate IV), but a much more extensive exposure on Thistle Green which is almost horizontal with occasional knolls.

On both Widdybank and Cronkley the sugar-limestone, which is permeable to water, rests directly on the upper surface of the impermeable dolerite or over thin layers of metamorphosed mudstone and, as a result, springs emerge at these junctions at intervals along the edges of the outcrops (Fig. 23). These are important in two respects: they undercut the limestone causing erosion at the spring-head so that there are steep edges to the outcrops, and the calcareous water flows out over the impermeable surface to form quite extensive areas of wet gravel.

At the present time the edges of the outcrops are also very much influenced by wind-erosion. To judge from old photographs this has been active for at least 70 years, but was often initiated by destruction of the turf around the burrows of rabbits. Wind-erosion destroys the thin soils developed on the loose calcitic sand and particles are deposited in more sheltered positions. It is on those parts of the outcrops susceptible to erosion that very shallow grey or almost black soils, known as rendzinas, have developed (Plate IV).

Away from the eroding edges the limestone has varying depths of drift overlying it (Fig.23). Where the drift is very shallow it is generally well-drained and greatly influenced by the limestone to give brown rather than black loamy soils with stones of sandstone which reveal the origin of the material. These soils are described as mull rendzinas or brown calcareous soils. Earthworms are usually plentiful and assist in the mixing of the limestone particles throughout the soil. They also attract moles to the soils and these often cause quite extensive disturbance.

As the drift becomes deeper, the influence of the underlying limestone diminishes until on deep drift drainage is impeded and typical peaty gleys or organic soils occur. There is therefore a sequence of soil types from wet gravels below the outcrops, an abrupt change to very shallow and discontinuous rendzinas along the edges, then a gradual increase in depth and brownness in the brown calcareous soils and, finally, a transition to peaty gleys (Fig. 23).

The vegetation of the shallow rendzinas is described on pp. 73–4. It is in this vegetation that some of the most remarkable of the Teesdale species are found, including Teesdale violet (*Viola rupestris*, Plate VIII), mountain avens (*Dryas octopetala*, Plate 9), hoary rock-rose (*Helianthemum canum*, Plate VIII), dark-red helleborine (*Epipactis atrorubens*), rare spring sedge (*Carex ericetorum*, Plate 12), hair sedge (*C. capillaris*, Plate 13) and in damper places kobresia (*Kobresia simpliciuscula*), Plate 12). Although all but the last mentioned of these species occur elsewhere in the Pennines and on adjacent hills in the southern Lake District, usually on very shallow soils developed in crevices or on ledges on unaltered limestone, it is only in Teesdale that they grow, if not together, then at least in what seems to be a

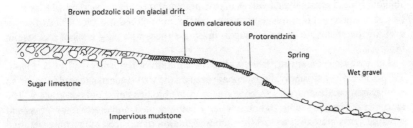

FIG. 23. Section across an outcrop of sugar limestone showing the characteristic relation of soil-types to topography and geology.

more or less similar type of vegetation: a short and often discontinuous turf of sheep's fescue (*Festuca ovina*), blue sesleria (*Sesleria albicans*) and crested hair-grass (*Koeleria cristata*).

All these species are small and relatively slow-growing so that it might reasonably be supposed that their presence could depend on the stunted and sparse nature of the turf. The opportunity to discover whether this, in fact, is the case arose in 1967 when it was known that the slopes of sugar-limestone beside the Slapestone Syke would eventually be destroyed. On this area experiments were set up which would normally have been unacceptable because of the disturbance and possible destruction of the vegetation which they would cause.

Two areas were selected, one on the well-drained south-facing slope above the Slapestone Syke and the other on an area of wet sugar-limestone at the foot of the steep slope. In both sites a grid of 12 square plots was marked out and in July 1967 the vegetation was analysed by recording the numbers of contacts of all species on a thin wire placed vertically into the vegetation at random. Some plots were then left untreated and to others were applied either ammonium nitrate (10g of nitrogen/m²), or calcium dihydrogen phosphate (5g of phosphorus/m²) or a combination of both. The whole areas were subsequently surrounded by a fence of wire-netting to prevent sheep having access to them. A similar method of analysis was used in 1968 on some of the plots, and in 1969 on all the plots to record the changes in the vegetation. The advantage of a method of analysis which does not damage the vegetation is that the same sample-areas can be studied on each occasion.

In 1969 the responses of the vegetation to the treatments had become very clear. Surprisingly there was very little effect of stopping grazing by sheep. The sward inside the enclosures which had no addition was only a little taller than outside, there was a slight increase in the proportion of blue sesleria, but no tendency for the bare patches to become overgrown. This is in marked contrast to the response of grassland both on the brown calcareous soils on sugar-limestone and on unaltered limestones. In both, enclosure usually results in a considerable increase in the biomass of shoots of the order of ten to fifty-fold. Grazing is apparently not the immediate cause of the very stunted growth of the grassland on sugar-limestone.

The shallow rendzinas on sugar-limestone have also been shown to differ from soils on unaltered limestone in Upper Teesdale in the frequency with which they become dry (Welch & Rawes 1969). Because of their large pores and low capacity to hold water, the surface layers can dry out during the summer to the point when most shallow-rooted plants would wilt (a matric potential more negative than -15 bars). It has been suggested that this may at least partly explain their low biomass. However, even in the enclosure on moist sugar-limestone there was only a slight increase in biomass.

The really significant response was to the addition of fertilizers (Jeffrey & Pigott, 1973). The effect of supplying phosphate even on the well-drained site was to cause an almost immediate and very large increase in the biomass of shoots of grasses. The amounts of sheep's fescue and blue sesleria both doubled, and crested-hair grass and quaking grass increased almost four times. Addition of nitrogen alone, however, had almost no effect but when combined with phosphate an even greater increase of grasses occurred. The vigorous vegetative growth of grasses was accompanied by much more profuse flowering. The amount of bare ground diminished and, not surprisingly, some of the smaller plants, including Teesdale violet and especially purging flax (*Linum catharticum*), decreased.

The vegetation on the wet site was dominated by kobresia, with small sedges and sheep's fescue. Again the response was almost entirely to addition of phosphate; nitrogen had almost no effect unless supplied in the presence of phosphate. The effect of supplying phosphate was to cause a ten-fold increase in the biomass of sheep's fescue but, even more surprisingly, red fescue and creeping bent, which were so rare they had not been recorded in most plots in 1967, became co-dominants with the addition of phosphate. A quite dense grassland developed and kobresia, the original dominant, decreased to a tenth of its former abundance. As it benefits from addition of phosphate when grown alone, this decrease seems to be simply the result of being shaded by the taller grasses.

There can be little doubt that the exceptionally low biomass of grasses on the shallow rendzinas is largely caused by deficiency of phosphate. This may not be a simple deficiency because the soil itself contains an ample supply of phosphate, partly held as insoluble organic compounds in the humus, and partly as insoluble inorganic phosphates. The layer of dark humified material which has the texture of soot consists predominantly of small faecal pellets of small invertebrates such as spring-tails and pot-worms (Enchytraeids). To what extent the release of phosphate from this organic material is slowed down by low temperatures is not clear, but these dark, often almost black, rendzina soils are characteristic of the uplands. However, they also form on unaltered limestones so that this feature alone is not peculiar to sugar-limestone.

Another characteristic of the sugar-limestone is that it is closely associated with intensive hydrothermal mineralization, so that veins of galena and barytes are widespread and have been extensively worked. High concentrations of lead occur in the soils, not only close to workings but also over much of the outcrops. Experimentally it has been shown by Dr David Jeffrey that the presence of basic lead carbonate in soil, or lead in solution, reduces uptake of phosphate by roots so that this could be another complication, although evidence that it is significant in natural conditions has yet to be obtained. The presence of vernal sand-wort (*Minuartia verna*), thrift (*Armeria maritima*) and sea-plantain (*Plantago maritima*) is characteristic of soils contaminated with metal ores and these three species all occur on sugar-limestone, but also elsewhere in the Pennines, often on the spoil heaps of old mines.

BROWN CALCAREOUS SOILS

The vegetation of brown calcareous soils on sugar-limestone is described on p. 76. In many respects this vegetation closely resembles that of similar soils developed over unaltered limestones, both in Upper Teesdale and elsewhere in the north Pennines. Although sheep's fescue and blue sesleria remain important species they grow more densely and are usually mixed with sweet vernal grass (*Anthoxanthum odoratum*), heath grass (*Sieglingia decumbens*) and common bent (*Agrostis tenuis*). Spring gentian (*Gentiana verna*) is especially plentiful on these soils but it occurs elsewhere in Teesdale on similar soils developed over unaltered limestones and calcareous drift. Bitter milkwort (*Polygala amara*) is confined to sugar-limestone in Upper Teesdale but it too grows on calcareous drift in the Craven Pennines and near Orton. Alpine forget-me-not (*Myosotis alpestris*), on the other hand, occurs on shallow brown calcareous soils on unaltered limestones only.

The impression gained from the vegetation that there is no clear distinction between brown calcareous soils on metamorphosed and unaltered limestone is confirmed by analyses. On both parent rocks, the depth varies from about 10cm to as much as 50cm of brown loam. Sometimes the colour is reddish, where the limestone itself contains iron-rich minerals. The upper part of the profile, which is densely exploited by roots, is generally darker. Calcium carbonate may either be present throughout the profile, or absent from the upper part and this is then reflected in the vegetation by an increase in the proportion of common bent and the presence of species which are markedly calcifuge. The pH may be about 7.0 throughout the profiles, but is often lower in the upper part. Calcium is the predominant exchangeable cation and the greater vigour of the grasses suggest that these soils are better sources of both phosphate and nitrogen than the shallow rendzinas.

Brown calcareous soils are also characteristic of the better-drained parts of much of the enclosed land in the dale itself. This includes meadows which are cut for hay and many of these contained, until recently, a very beautiful vegetation in which globe-flower (*Trollius europaeus*) and wood cranesbill (*Geranium sylvaticum*) were often plentiful and were accompanied by melancholy thistle (*Cirsium heterophyllum*) in the poorly-drained areas.

The soils of the meadows are developed on calcareous drift or alluvium near the river or its tributaries. The profile consists of an almost uniform brown or greyish-brown loam, often with stones, and sometimes no deeper than 25cm. Frequently the lower part of the profile shows the rusty flecks and greyish patches characteristic of gleying. These soils have probably had lime and farmyard manure applied to them for many centuries to make good the losses of minerals, not only by leaching but also as a result of removal of hay. To that extent the soils have been modified agriculturally and this, combined with the longer growing season and higher temperatures at 300–400m, allows a considerably higher biomass to be achieved by midsummer than on similar soils in the uplands.

Larger crops of hay can be obtained from these meadows by applying greater amounts of chemical fertilizers, especially nitrogen, but this is accompanied by a significant change in the composition of the meadow. At the highest rates of application there is a loss of almost all dicotyledons except ribwort (*Plantago lanceolata*) and dandelion (*Taraxacum officinale*), which become very abundant. The initial increase in native grasses is followed by a spread of soft brome (*Bromus mollis*), which is a relatively worthless species.

WET CALCAREOUS SOILS

Limestones are present at several different levels in the sequence of Carboniferous rocks which form the north Pennines, outcrops are widespread and occur at many different altitudes. The high rainfall and low evaporation leave a large excess of ground-water and this may enter beds of limestone either directly, or indirectly through so-called shake-holes or water-sinks along the lower edges of outcrops of shales or superficial deposits of drift. Limestones are very permeable rocks and water flows freely through them following channels formed by solution of the rock along both its joints and bedding planes. When this water encounters impermeable beds of shale it moves laterally to emerge at the lower edge of the limestone as springs.

Ground-water normally contains carbon dioxide in solution and, although calcium carbonate is only sparingly soluble, it dissolves as the bicarbonate, so that springs which issue from limestone contain quite high concentrations of calcium ions. The sites where springs emerge are a very characteristic feature of the whole of Upper Teesdale and are associated with several different types of vegetation and a corresponding variety of wet calcareous soils.

The springs which emerge from the sugar-limestone either at its contact with the dolerite or where there are impermeable beds of metamorphosed calc-silicate rocks, have already been mentioned. Some of these springs are conspicuous because water flows out at the surface and is surrounded by a large mound of the bright yellowish-green moss *Cratoneuron commutatum*, which becomes encrusted with calcium carbonate to form a weak tufa. The water then spreads out across the impermeable surface and the substrate, which is scarcely a soil, consists of wet sand and pieces of rock, often encrusted with lime. The vegetation consists of scattered tufts of the yellow sedge (*Carex lepidocarpa*) and jointed rush (*Juncus articulatus*), patches of the brownish-yellow moss *Drepanocladus revolvens* and hummocks about the size of ant-hills but formed of the dark olive-green moss *Gymnostomum recurvirostrum* (Plate 16). On these hummocks, and particularly around their bases, grow some of the most remarkable of the Teesdale species, notably hair sedge (*Carex capillaris*), alpine rush (*Juncus alpinoarticulatus*), three-flowered rush (*J. triglumis*), bog sandwort (*Minuartia stricta*, Plate VI) and Scottish asphodel (*Tofieldia pusilla*, Plate 13). All these plants are small and slow-growing, but the vegetation is extremely sparse and much of the gravel is bare. The water is calcareous but contains only traces of other minerals and concentrations of phosphate are often close to the limit of detection. Nitrogen, on the other hand, may not be deficient because blue-green algae, including species of *Nostoc* capable of fixing atmospheric nitrogen, are characteristic of these sites. The soil is not only saturated with water but often extremely shallow and resting directly on solid rock.

Areas of boulders and wet gravel are also characteristic of sites where springs emerge in areas of glacial drift and there are also hummocks, but these are formed of mineral soil. Close to the spring the hummocks are widely spaced with wet gravel between them, but they gradually lose their identity with increasing distance away. The origin of this structure is not clear: possibly the drift is eroded by the spring to leave residual patches which form the hummocks, and erosion may be partly caused by treading of cattle or sheep. Alternatively the hummocks may gradually grow up by pressure generated under them when the surrounding wet gravel freezes. The core of the hummock is usually boulder-clay and it is capped by a shallow dark grey soil which is calcareous. Mosses and liverworts clothe the sides and Scottish asphodel, alpine rush, broad-leaved cotton-grass (*Eriophorum latifolium*), bird's-eye primrose (*Primula farinosa*, Plate VI) and alpine bartsia (Plate 11) grow on the hummocks. A detailed description of this type of vegetation is given by Pigott (1956). The site described was enclosed in 1956 by a wire-fence to prevent grazing and trampling by cattle. With this protection, sedges and marsh horsetail (*Equisetum palustre*) gradually spread over part of the bare gravel, but even after 20 years there has been little change in the composition of the vegetation although, in the years following enclosure, the number of flowering-shoots of alpine bartsia increased from fewer than ten to over two hundred.

Vegetation of very similar structure occurs on steep slopes of boulder-clay which are eroded at their base by the river Tees. In addition to the species already mentioned shrubby cinquefoil (*Potentilla fruticosa*) occurs on some of these sites, as well as on the banks of shingle and alluvium being deposited by the river. There is little evidence of grazing on the steep banks but fresh boulder-clay is constantly being exposed by land-slips and the downward movement of large boulders. No true soil forms, and the subsoil is calcareous but deficient in phosphate and inorganic nitrogen.

A different type of vegetation from those already described occurs where springs emerge at higher altitudes on the eastern slopes of the western escarpment. The characteristic feature of these sites are the pale green spongy 'lawns' of the moss *Philonotis fontana* which grows over an often quite deep deposit of bluish-grey silt. The water is cold and weakly acid, but with significant quantities of calcium in solution. Several arctic-alpine species occur in these sites. Some, like starry saxifrage (*Saxifraga stellaris*, Fig. 19), are widespread in the Scottish Highlands and in the Lake District, but yellow marsh saxifrage (*Saxifraga hirculus*), alpine foxtail (*Alopecurus alpinus*, Fig. 1) and the moss *Splachnum vasculosum* (Plate 15) are of very restricted distribution.

CHAPTER 7

Man and Land in Upper Teesdale

MAN'S influence on the landscape in the vicinity of the Cow Green reservoir is clearly evident today only in the structures associated with the vast dam above Cauldron Snout and, to the more discerning eye, in the relict features of former lead-mining activity. Other traces are surprisingly absent and it is only along the valley of the Maize Beck that stone enclosure walls are visible and traces of former sheep folds are seen on the nearby unenclosed fell lands. One has to move some distance to the east and north to find tamed, farmed landscapes. To anyone familiar with the Pennines this relative absence of traces of former activity, the cairns of the Bronze Age dead, earthwork enclosures or the long stone walls of march-dykes dividing the grazings into large blocks, is notable. The questions so raised are strengthened by a careful examination of the first Ordnance Survey 6-inch to the mile map of the area surveyed in 1858; the fells of the upper dale around Cow Green, Widdybank and Cauldron Snout are rich in place-names, and each ridge, each little sike or stream, and each major feature of the course of the river Tees possesses its own distinctive name; Cow Green itself is a precisely delimited area, while Weelhead, Falcon Clints, Tinkler's Sike, and many others, are all precisely named (Plate 1). The density and completeness of this pattern is unusual and careful study reveals that they are all applied to topographical features (see front endpaper). Apart from the lead mines, shafts and hushes (or early mining channels, following the veins of ore) and a single sheepfold at Weelhead none of these names even hints at earlier human settlement; none, with the possible exception of Dora's Seat (GR NY 886330), incorporates such key words as *shield*, *set* or *erg*, respectively of Middle English, Norse and Irish-Norse derivation and implying the presence of former temporary settlements, shielings, occupied only during the summer months, traditionally between April and August, to take advantage of the rich grazings on the sugar-limestones. It is difficult not to conclude that the surveyors of the area, Lieutenant O'Grady of the Royal Engineers and his men, derived the names they plotted so carefully from the lead miners and shepherds of the mid-nineteenth-century. These names, and this is the telling point, reveal no clear traces of great antiquity. Does this mean that man's hand has always rested relatively lightly on the upper dale?

At this point one meets a practical difficulty: the earlier documents relating to Teesdale tell not of the fell lands but of the settled lands. In all of the Pennines a fundamental distinction must be made between the *inby* lands, the settled, enclosed lands around the villages and outlying hill-farms, and the *outby* or fells, the rough, unimproved, unenclosed hill grazings (Plate 5). The inby lands spread along the dale floor, dale sides and tributary valleys and are separated from the fells by the carefully maintained *head-dyke* or boundary wall. This line has not, of course, been permanently fixed. The tide of settlement has risen in good times and fallen in bad, but the documents have always been largely concerned with the inby lands; only those materials relating directly to lead mines, or to the creation of new intakes or enclosures, speak directly of the fells and the story of man in Upper Teesdale must therefore be told indirectly: it is a story of the links between uplands and lowlands told from the viewpoint of the lowlands. Furthermore, the evidence for man's long occupation of Teesdale is variable in character, in temporal and spatial distribution and in quality, so that there are practical problems of integrating surviving detail and inferred general trends into a single coherent story. However, the landscape of the dale emerges as a vital thread to which other evidence from palynological, archaeological and documentary sources can be related, and the tripartite division of dale floor, dale sides and associated tributary valleys, and swelling upland surfaces forms a constant background motif against which to review man's activities during the last 10,000 years.

For the purposes of discussion it is convenient to recognize four phases of occupation, each characterized by the nature of the evidence available and the degree to which a clear picture can be reconstructed. In practical terms the whole of prehistory, the Roman period and the post-Roman centuries up to the end of the eleventh century may be considered as a single phase, definable in terms of the relative poverty of evidence but nonetheless vital in that it saw the creation of landscapes and the establishment of patterns of occupation and activity which are still to some degree visible in Teesdale to this day. A second phase embraces the medieval and post-medieval centuries, between about 1100 and 1600; many of the details of the present landscape of villages, farmsteads and fields were formed during this period. Concrete, certain evidence for this phase is indeed slight, but much may be inferred from a surer knowledge of the content of the landscape after 1600. The third phase is characterized by richer evidence, maps, surveys, estate records and private documents such as wills; falling between 1600 and 1900 this period saw the maturing of the earlier landscape into something approaching its modern form, and the rise of that complex blend of agriculture and industry best described by the term 'dual economy', with farming and extractive industry occupying equally important places in the livelihood of the ordinary dalesman. The final phase, spanning the period between the end of the nineteenth century and the present, becomes rich in records created by the national government, by the great landed estates, by industrial concerns and by private individuals. This phase blends gradually with the real world of the present and with the memories, lives and personal experiences of the present folk of Teesdale.

Prehistoric, Roman and Post-Roman Occupation

The present cultural landscape of the dale, that is to say the man-created landscape as opposed to the natural endowment of sub-surface rocks, drainage patterns, relief and climate, has been evolving under man's influence since Mesolithic hunters first established themselves in the proximity of the deer-haunted forest glades and streamside clearings, but already at this stage it is possible to postulate the emergence of a fundamental dichotomy that has remained a constant theme in the life and economy of Teesdale. Throughout the dales of west Durham, flints of broadly Mesolithic provenance are found in two distinctive locations: a group of lowland sites occurs, generally below 183m (600ft) in altitude, adjacent to or within the main river valley, while a second series of finds occurs in the uplands, generally above 305m (1000ft), and indeed in the nature reserve at Moor House finds occur as high as 686m (2250ft). There are slight variations in the character of these flint assemblages, but it is possible that we are seeing evidence for a pattern of economic life that extended from lowland to upland, with group territories embracing a variety of terrains so as to take advantage of their varied seasonal plant and animal life. Such 'reciprocity of resources' is a recurrent theme in man's occupation of the earth: human territoriality, within both prehistoric and historic time, can normally be shown to have involved terrain contrasts. This generalization has important repercussions; while there is little direct evidence for the development of Widdybank Fell, West Common and Dufton Fell, it is nevertheless possible to see these areas as part of a wider pattern of economic activity embracing villages and farmsteads, fields and fells, quarries and mines, upland and lowland. In this wider context one can identify important threads of continuity.

The phase of human occupation commencing during the prehistoric period and ter-

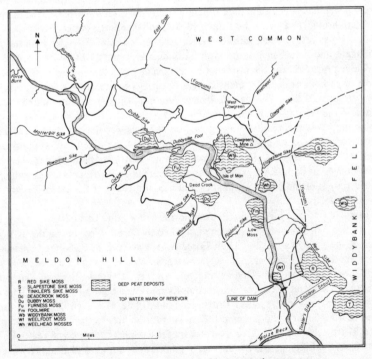

FIG. 24. Cow Green basin before impoundment.

minating in about AD 1100 saw in Teesdale two vitally important transitions, first the transition from forest to a landscape largely cleared of woodland, and secondly the transition from settlements which were only of limited duration to those permanent settlements which are still occupied to this day. The pollen diagrams from Upper Teesdale, prepared by Judith Turner and her students and discussed in Chapter 4, have largely been considered from the viewpoint of the botanical changes, with little reference to the degree to which these were man-induced. Radio-carbon dates are available from only two sites, Red Sike Moss and some 1000m up the valley at Weelhead Moss (Fig. 24, p. 143), and in both cases a sharp transition from an oak-alder assemblage to a grass-plantain-heather assemblage has been dated. This botanical transition clearly represents the point at which major woodland clearance occurs. At Weelhead Moss this appears to have taken place about 1000 years before the birth of Christ, while at Red Sike the radio-carbon date is approximately 400 years younger, about 600 BC. At both sites, as Dr Turner has shown, the proportion of tree pollen declines sharply and a permanent change occurred in the dominant vegetation types.

The vegetational changes from open woodland to blanket peat and grassland would appear to indicate the appearance of varying intensities of human interference during what in archaeological terms can be termed the late Bronze Age. These peat bogs lie over 457m (1500ft) above sea-level in an area that today is inhospitable upland; it is fair to ask why woodland clearance was taking place? At Weelhead Moss cereal pollen has been found intermittently from a level radio-carbon dated to about 3370 BC through to a level substantially higher, and therefore younger, when it ceases. Roderick Squires, working with several sites in the vicinity of Cronkley Fell, was able to detect some disturbance of the natural woodlands during the Mesolithic period and concluded that fire was the prime tool, the burning being undertaken either to drive game or perhaps even deliberately to create clearings within which grass would grow and attract wild deer. During the Bronze Age in particular the intermittent disturbance of the vegetation on the fells continued and by the Iron Age, a phase during which the valley woodlands were opened up, the fells were largely deforested and a pattern of usage based upon hunting and summer grazing was firmly established. A measure of regeneration was experienced during the Roman period but the succeeding centuries, as population expanded and pressure upon land increased, saw the continued retreat of the valley woodlands and a continuation of the extensive land-use upon the uplands.

Tangible evidence for activity in the dale during the latter part of the Iron Age and the Romano-British period has been discovered by Dennis Coggins on the hillslopes around the great waterfall at High Force, where a series of embanked enclosures represent the sites of former enclosed farmsteads. Even when excavated, and two sites have been examined by Dennis Coggins and K. J. Fairless, these can prove remarkably difficult to date and each comprised in effect a group of circular huts and a small farmyard in the native British tradition (Plate 19). Even in Roman times, however, few luxury goods found their way into the hills to provide clear proof of date. There is, in fact, little direct evidence for the Roman occupation of Teesdale. The road from Eggleston across the hills *via* Stanhope in Weardale and ultimately to Corbridge may be Roman, but Upper Teesdale must be seen as a relatively remote hill-

PLATE 13. Three plants of Upper Teesdale with their main distribution-areas in the mountains of Scotland: *above left*, hair sedge (*Carex capillaris*); *right*, Scottish asphodel (*Tofieldia pusilla*); *left*, alpine bistort (*Polygonum viviparum*).

PLATE 14. *Right*, dwarf birch (*Betula nana*) photographed in Iceland. *Below*, leaf or dwarf birch found in peat on Widdybank Fell.

area, the haunt of native farmers, pastoralists and huntsmen, not free of the Roman yoke, but rarely accepting it wholly and necessitating constant patrolling by the cavalry and infantry units based on forts such as *Longovicium* (Lanchester), *Vinovia* (Binchester), *Verterae* (Brough), *Bravoniacum* (Kirby Thore), *Lavatrae* (Bowes) and *Maglona* (Greta Bridge).

The Romans had immense difficulties in subduing the hills, even after the building of Hadrian's Wall, begun in AD 122, and it is worth asking what the uplands might have produced to compensate for the expense of holding them as part of a series of defences in depth. The most valuable product was probably men, auxiliary troopers to serve throughout the Empire, skilled in guerilla warfare and hardened to the warrior's path. More immediately the uplands could supply the forts of the lowlands and the Wall (the largest single market of Roman Britain being the army) with cattle for meat, tallow and hides, sheep for meat, skins and wool, horses, timber, together perhaps with locally produced iron and lead. There is precious little direct evidence for any of these, but the inferences are reasonable and the dales of west Durham have continued to supply these products for 2000 or more years. In parenthesis, a glance at any local telephone directory will reveal the extent to which the Teesdales, Wardles (Weardales) and Tindales (Tynedales) have contributed to the lowland populations, and while extractive industries have tended to dominate both the employment structure and the landscape within the last century, the hill farms of the dales still produce sheep, cattle, and small numbers of hardy hill-ponies, the latter used in warfare as late as the First World War when they drew the guns into action. There are real links here between the horse tackle of the Bronze Age smiths found in Heathery Burn cave at Stanhope in Weardale, the German auxiliary trooper serving with a cavalry unit of the Roman army and alternately freezing and sweltering as he patrolled the misty heights of the dale heads (for the watersheds traditionally provided corridors for cattle thieves and invading armies), and the stout black dales ponies of modern hill shepherds.

Two more things can be said of the Roman dales: some grain must surely have been grown? Market economies were insufficiently developed to bring in large quantities of imported grain (this did not occur until the seventeenth century) and in any case certainly in Weardale and possibly in Teesdale areas of small, square 'Celtic' fields are known, the corn plots of the hillmen, and pollen diagrams from the fells near Stanhope produce the evidence of cereal grains in dated Iron-Age and Romano-British levels. More tangible evidence for another form of economic activity comes from a series of Roman altars, two from Weardale and two from Teesdale, put up in honour of Silvanus, a woodland god, beloved of hunters, indeed at Bollihope in Weardale the dedication is remarkably specific:

SILVANO. INVICTO. SAC	Sacred to the unconquered god Silvanus
C. TETIUS. VETURIUS. MICIA	C. Tetius Veturius Micianus, prefect of
NUS. PRAEF. ALAE SEBOSIA	the *Ala Sebosiana*, freely sets up this in
NAE. OB. APRUM. EXIMIAE	fulfilment of a vow because of the
FORMAE. CAPTUM QUEM	capture of a boar of outstanding size
MULTI. ANTECESSO RES. EIUS.	which many of his predecessors could
PRAEDARI NON. POTUERUNT	not bag. (After J. Gillam)
V.S.L.P.	

It is worth noting that Micianus had travelled some 60 miles from Lancaster, where his unit was stationed. The chase, in addition to affording a training for the courage and skills of soldiers, provided a welcome contribution to the larder and once again a cross-time continuity can be observed; the flat-hatted 'syndicated' marksman shooting the red hill-grouse today has some links, however intangible, with the huntsmen of the Middle Ages, the pig-sticking Roman officers and even the patient Mesolithic hunter with his flint-barbed missiles. It is, however, fair to enquire what impact this activity had upon the landscapes and vegetation of the dale. The available pollen diagrams are unanimous; the woodlands were destroyed and their survivors, along steep slopes, in tributary valleys and where preserved in the lower areas, became a precious resource, to be husbanded and jealously guarded, so that by the Middle Ages the surviving timber was all in the hands of the manorial lords.

The earliest documentary reference to settlement in Teesdale is at once ambiguous and illuminating: in a document compiled in 1050, but using an original of about 1017–1035, we learn that Canute granted to the church of St Cuthbert the village called Staindrop with its hamlets Shotton, Raby, Wackerfield, Ingleton, West Auckland, Eldon, Thickley and Middleton. The author would argue that this Middleton is likely to be Middleton-in-Teesdale: certainly this portion of St Cuthbert's estates passed, after the Norman Conquest, into lay hands and was held of the Cathedral Priory by the lords of Raby and Staindrop. Parts of Teesdale are also included in an earlier grant recorded in 1050 but dating between 830–845 which shows that St Cuthbert had another estate, Gainford, with 'that which pertains to it', from the Tees to the Wear, and from the Dere Street in the east (the Roman road from Catterick to Corbridge via Lanchester) 'as far as the hills to the west', an infuriatingly vague description but perhaps implying that the boundary ran to the main watershed of the Pennines?

Whatever the precise details of interpretation it is clear that Teesdale was divided in some way between estates whose chief villages lay in the lowlands and whose upland territories contained small hamlets, some of which were later to evolve into the dales villages. To these were attached summer pastures and hunting grounds in the hills. On the Yorkshire side of the Tees we have the evidence of Domesday Book: William the Conqueror granted vast areas of land to his most dependable generals, such as that of Count Alan focussing upon Gilling, and these men received estates that were already in existence, estates formerly held by Saxon lords and which normally embraced both upland and lowland territories. There is a pattern here and Jones and Barrow have pointed out that these large estates, made up of scattered settlements, are extremely ancient. Some of their rents and renders are pre-Saxon, indeed there may even be pre-Roman roots, and we are seeing evidence for a deep-rooted territorial and economic reciprocity with villages in the lowlands having lands in the hills, the lowlands producing grain, the uplands supporting stock and providing a hunting ground for the lord of the estate.

It is reasonable to postulate a number of points concerning Teesdale settlement after 1100. Most of the present-day villages were already in existence, either as small clusters or single homesteads, and while some of these may have had Romano-British origins (for Roman pottery has been found in the grounds of Eggleston Hall) they bear in their place-names the imprint of Old English and Scandinavian settlers (Fig.

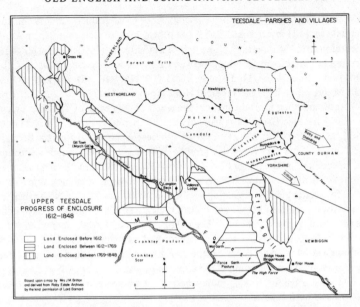

FIG. 25. Progress of enclosure in Upper Teesdale, 1612–1848.

25, p. 147). Middleton (the 'middle village'), Eggleston ('Ecgel's village'), Mickleton (the 'large village') and Staindrop (the 'valley with stoney ground'), are all of Old English derivation, while others, Romaldkirk ('St. Rumwald's church'), Hunderthwaite ('Hunrøthr's clearing') and Raby ('the village by the boundary mark'), all show the influence of the Scandinavian folk who may have penetrated the dale, possibly from Cumberland, during the tenth century or somewhat later. By 1086, however, disaster had struck many of these places for on the Yorkshire side of the Tees Domesday Book records in settlement after settlement, 'It is waste'. There were two reasons for this; the area had experienced Scottish raids in 1070 when King Malcolm is recorded as devastating Romaldkirk and slaying English nobles at Hunderthwaite, while, even if the harrying of the north by the armies of William the Conqueror in 1072 did not affect the dale, the decade between this and Domesday Book's compilation saw many manorial lords moving their men from upland settlements and concentrating them in the more easily controlled and potentially prosperous lowland villages, a policy with a chilling contemporary ring to it.

In the upper dale Newbiggin is a place-name which suggests that the 'new building or house' was a product of settlement after 1100 and it is surely significant that in Upper Teesdale, above High Force, hamlet and farm names bearing undisputable Old English or Scandinavian settlement names lie thinly; *Cronkley* has as a second element *'leah'* meaning 'a clearing', but names such as Ettersgill, Langdon Beck, Widdybank and Birkdale, all refer to topographical features, while Harwood, in the tributary valley of the Harwood Beck (Plate 5), means simply the 'grey wood'. The evidence for little settlement in Upper Teesdale before 1100 is cumulatively rather than individually convincing. When Rievaulx Abbey was granted extensive pasturage in the dale in 1131 by Bernard Baliol (who held his Teesdale lands from Durham Cathedral priory, the inheritor of one half of St Cuthbert's lands), he included rights to grazing on Middleton Common between *Egleshope* (Eggleshope Beck, GR NY 965305) and *Hodeshope* (Hudeshope Beck, GR NY 946285), an area still called Monks Moor, with a building (possibly Hope House, GR NY 984279), pasture rights for 60 mares and their foals throughout the whole of the Forest of Teesdale and, more particularly, a house 10 perches (probably the 20ft perch) in length and 20ft (1 perch) in width at the 'head of *Kaveset* next to Etheresgilebec' (i.e. Ettersgill Beck). The element *set* is clearly the Old Norse *saetr* 'a shieling, a hill-pasture', the site probably being represented by the present Friar House (GR NY 883285). With Kaveset went, 'five acres of land enclosed with hedges and ditches' to be used by the monks from the feast of St Martin till the beginning of the month of April (11th November to 1st April) to depasture their horses and colts. Other clauses in the grant involve animals (probably cattle), cows, bulls and sheep. This specialized establishment at Kaveset probably included a dwelling section, stables and hay-storage facilities and was no doubt manned by *conversi* or lay brothers. We have the interesting picture of part of the more favoured lower portion of the upper dale, just above High Force, being used for winter pasturage for nursing mares, and this documented circumstance is hardly likely to have been unique.

The general picture is clear: by 1100 the dale was settled with small clusters and perhaps isolated single farms, housing folk of mixed British, Anglo-Saxon and Scandinavian origin. Each settlement, we may conjecture, was surrounded by a patch of cleared ground, sometimes worked by one family, sometimes by a group of families. This land was used for producing grain and hay, and the precious fields were protected from the depredations of domestic stock and wild animals, largely deer, by earthwork enclosures topped with a live or dead hedge. Beyond lay the fells with areas of green where beasts were collected for milking, for gelding, for marking and for doctoring at the sites of the summer shielings. By 1100 the Norman lords had placed much of the upper dale under forest law, that is to say land outside the ordinary law of the realm, where beasts of the chase and the surviving woodlands were rigorously protected, although these measures did not necessarily exclude permitting other beasts to graze or indeed the creation of actual farms. Within this 'Forest of Teesdale' were set aside areas where even the deer were not hunted, where they could be left at peace, and to these parts the Old English word *frith*, 'peace', was applied, hence Forest and Frith. Man and land alike were bound to the Anglo-Scandinavian-Norman lords of Staindrop, Raby and Gilling by a network of rents, obligations and services collected as coin, payments in kind and as work or services performed upon his lands or due directly to the lord.

Early Twelfth Century to Late Sixteenth Century

Teesdale has for most of its history been divided between two counties, Durham and Yorkshire, and the final unification of the dale has been brought about by recent local government re-organization. By 1100 the foundations of the settlement pattern had been established and this section must carry the story through four centuries of

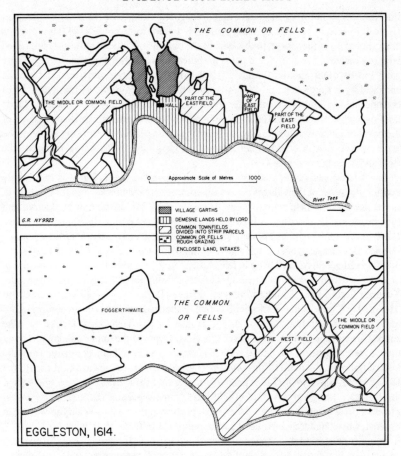

FIG. 26. Eggleston, 1614, showing common fields and enclosures.

development, many traces of which are visible to this day. The basis of settlement was the village, utilizing the varied terrains of the dale sides for communal arable fields, the dale floor as meadowland, and the fells for a variety of purposes, primarily grazing animals but also taking peat for fuel, stone for building and for grindstones, and bracken for bedding-down beasts. Figure 26 is based upon the earliest known detailed map of a dales settlement, Eggleston in 1614. The village, like most dales villages, comprised two rows of farmsteads with their associated outbuildings facing each other across an area of open green. The end fences of the gardens formed a defensible line around the rear of the settlement, but the green was a convenient area for collecting together the village stock, for grazing tethered horses, cows, hand-reared sheep and chickens, and geese. Around the village lay the fields, divided into dozens of narrow strips; these are not shown in 1614, but a map of the west field in 1786 survives, and in this particular case the actual strips are visible on the ground fossilized as the lynchets forming a giant stairway climbing the valley side. In 1614 the fields of Eggleston were in process of being enclosed, a point to be considered later, but it is clear that at an earlier stage, in this part of the dale at least, the boundary of improved land lay between the communal fields and meadows and the unimproved fell. There were indeed other enclosed areas in Eggleston, single farms, surrounded by fields enclosed by a ring-fence and generally known as *intakes*. Some of these may be of considerable antiquity, for immediately to the west of the Eggleston enclosed lands lay Foggerthwaite, an island of improvement in a sea of waste, whose place-name is of medieval origin, possibly meaning the 'clearing distinguished by the long grass' or the 'clearing where cattle could be depastured on long grass', the term 'fog' being Middle English for long rank grass.

There is no such clear picture of the dale above Eggleston, but it is reasonably certain that most of the villages possessed communal 'townfields', and fossil traces of these, preserved in field-patterns, can be seen around Middleton and Mickleton, and they occur as far up-valley as Newbiggin and Holwick. Within the upper dale above High Force settlement in about 1600 seems to have comprised a series of intake farms. Friar House, whose origins have been noted earlier, consisted in 1612 of some 48.6ha (120 acres) of land lying in five closes, four of meadow (i.e. mown) and one of pasture. A crown survey of 1612 appears to list only three farms in the upper dale; Vallance Lodge, in all 224ha (554 acres), Brigge House, in all 176ha (435 acres) and 'Hendfelloe House' some 280ha (693 acres). Vallance Lodge, however, comprised no fewer than 18 separate houses, Brigge House 14 and Hendfelloe House 17. The survey provides a stylized view of the dispersed farms of the upper dale by grouping them together beneath the names of those tenants who held them as a group from the lord of the manor – in 1612 this was the Crown. Mrs Britton argued that the Brigge House group (GR NY 893286) probably represent the farms of the Ettersgill valley, the Vallance Lodge group (GR NY 585313) must represent the area today called Middle Forest extending from Force Garth pasture in the west to Widdybank farm in the east, while 'Hendfelloe House' (a corruption of 'Endfelloe' or 'Hindfelloe House'?) is an appropriate name for the remaining high farms of Harwood. These farms were enclosed by banks and ditches, and extensive traces of these earlier landscapes can be found in the Ettersgill valley where the older bank and ditch enclosures are discordantly overlain by more recent stone walls. The approximate extent of these early intakes can be detected upon an estate map of the upper dale, drawn in 1769, where they stand out as zones of highly irregular small fields which contrast markedly with the rather large intakes which were reclaimed between 1612 and 1769; this is the logic beneath Fig. 25 which summarizes the progress of land reclamation between 1612 and 1848.

The picture in the Upper Teesdale of the early decades of the seventeenth century is one of islands of small farms set in the wider sea of waste; it can be argued that these represent settlements won from the wild during the centuries before 1600, but the situation is indeed even more complex than this for, if Upper Teesdale is not wholly atypical, the great surge forward leading to the permanent occupation of sites originally occupied only on a temporary basis may have taken place between 1100 and 1300, a period when the climate may have been drier and less windy and more favourable to settlement above 366m (1200ft). These settlements must have brought in their wake more grazing animals and more interference with the upland habitats of the high fells of the Tees valley. The fourteenth century must surely have seen a retreat from the upland margins, for the onset of stormier less favourable climatic conditions, the economic decline on a European scale, the Black Death and renewed Scottish raiding (following the defeat at Bannockburn in 1314) must have combined to discourage the survival of marginal footholds, although no doubt a few hardy souls may have clung on grimly.

No details can be given of the stocking of farms before 1600, but between 1600 and 1640 probate inventories, the surveys of property attached to wills, provide revealing details; it is quite clear that farms and individual prosperity varied greatly. Thus, in 1607 Robert Bainbrigge of Langdon Beck died in possession of household stuff and farm stock worth £25 7s. 0d while his cousin (?), Guy Bainbrigge of Hendfelloe House, had goods and chattels worth no less than £508 15s. 10d., and in addition owed debts of £400 14s. 4d., with £133 0s. 6d. being owed to him. The main items of value in all of the probate inventories for Upper Teesdale were the cattle, followed by sheep and horses, but numerically sheep were dominant. The most important crop was hay, produced on the inby land while, during the summer months, Guy Bainbrigge's beasts would have grazed the fells, for the survey of 1612 records that he had right of common within the Forest of Teesdale, that is to say he could graze his beasts by virtue of his possession of a tenancy in the improved lands. The Bainbrigges, or Bainbridges to give them their modern spelling, were in the early seventeenth century dominant in the upper dale and Vallance Lodge, Brigge House and Hendfelloe House were all in the hands of members of this family, who had descended from the hereditary forester of the Forest of Teesdale.

The division of the dale between two counties is reflected in the patterns of lordship found throughout the last 1000 years: the north bank lands are today in the hands of Lord Barnard whose family have held the estate since the mid-seventeenth century, but he is the ultimate successor to the Nevilles, the de Beauchamps, the Baliols and the Fitz Meldreds, although during the period before the Reformation the ultimate over-lord was the Cathedral Priory of Durham. On the south bank the present Strathmore estate can be traced back via the Bowes-Lyons, the Bowes, and the Fitz Hughs to an award by William I to Count Alan; before the Conquest it was held by Torfin. This pattern of lordship is important, for from it flowed patterns of decision-making which had the power to alter the landscape, to encourage or discourage settlement, to specify clauses in leases designed to stimulate better farming, the power to rebuild and re-model both fields and farms. Too often these decisions are not documented and too often we must make guesses concerning their presence and impact, but lordship, as the white-washed farms of the Raby lands attest (see below), is a real and vital force in controlling what is done with land. Governments may restrict, limit and forbid, but the local landlord has the power to take positive decisions concerning his estates and the realities of this power are demonstrated by the changing landscapes of the next phase of occupation.

Changing Landscapes 1600–1900

The period between 1600 and 1900 was, in west Durham as a whole, a time of changing landscapes, quickening economic activity and rising population. Figure 26, the map of Eggleston, indicates the beginning of radical change in the form of the partial enclosure of the East Field. The arable strips were in process of being consolidated, enclosed and converted to meadowland, i.e. grassland for mowing to produce hay. The reasons for this are complex, but briefly by the late sixteenth and early seventeenth centuries it was increasingly possible to import Baltic grain relatively cheaply; this freed the farmers of the North-East from complete dependence upon home-produced grains and encouraged increasing specialization; coupled to this was a growing demand for the products of animal husbandry amongst the rising population of the Durham coalfield. In the dales this encouraged increased hay production so that more sheep-flocks, more cattle and more horses could be carried through the winter months, a desperately hazardous proceeding in that a very late spring could spell disaster. The impact of these trends can be seen in probate inventories, lists of property associated with wills; if gross numbers of cattle, sheep and horses are taken from inventories relating to farms in the Forest of Teesdale, farms such as Ettersgill, Langdon Beck, Forcegarth and Watgarth, then a clear pattern emerges: the number of farm animals (cattle, sheep and horses) increases significantly when the inventories of the period 1600–1640 are compared with those for 1660–1700, indeed the number of sheep kept more than doubles.

Such figures of course mask the variations in the size of individual farms, ranging in 1769 from as little as 2.8ha (7 acres) to as much as 162ha (400 acres), the seasonal variations depending upon when the inventory was compiled (after or before lambing), the honesty or otherwise of the good and true neighbours who did the compilation (for no one is above suspicion), and no doubt also conceal the powerful feeling that it is unlucky for a hill-farmer to count his sheep! Nevertheless, the overall trends are clear, and by 1700 there were rather more than twice as many sheep upon the hill grazings as had been present in 1600.

These changes were accompanied by others, notably an increase in the actual number of farms, the enclosure of large tracts of newly reclaimed land and, although we have no exact measure before 1801, an increase in population. Mrs Britton has demonstrated from surveys and rentals relating to the Raby estates that between 1612 and 1758 the number of farms in Upper Teesdale remained constant; the period 1758 to 1769 saw some small increases, while between 1769 and 1847 the number of farms virtually doubled, a development indicative of both changing economic circumstances and an expanding population. Some of these increases can be attributed to the fission of farms, sometimes between father and son and sometimes between different families (perhaps related by marriage). This need not have meant that individual farms grew smaller, although this could and did occur, because reclamation and intaking went hand in hand with population growth and fission. In Harwood, for example, there were two farms at Marsh Gill (Gill Town, GR NY 825324, Plate 19) in 1769, by 1803 there were three, and by 1848 the field books list no fewer than four, held respectively by Elizabeth Dixon, Jonathan Raisbeck,

William Toward and Jeremiah Dowson; all of these folk were alive in 1851 and the detailed census returns of that year record that Elizabeth Dixon was a widow, with two other males (her sons) living in the house; they and the other occupiers and three further males are all described as lead miners. The individual farms ranged in size from 12.5ha to 8.5ha (31 acres to 21 acres). We are seeing here that intimate and complex relationship between agriculture and extractive industry generally termed the 'dual economy'. The characteristics were neatly defined by Joan Thirsk: 'In bestowing minerals, Nature has made its most generous gifts to the highland communities of England, and so compensated them for the disappointments of their farming. Thus there was hardly a county in the highland half of England without a considerable mining or quarrying industry, carried on for the most part by small family groups or by the partnership of two or three individuals . . . Most miners were part-time farmers and while neither occupation by itself yielded them an adequate living, they managed to fit their industrial and agricultural occupations into a satisfactory workable whole'.

This 'dual economy' has been the basis of Dales life since the seventeenth century and is, to a surprising degree, still present to this day although it is now less a question of a single individual being engaged in both occupations at once than of undertaking work in mineral extraction at particular stages in life (when a young man for instance, while the father can still work the farm), or of the members of a single family, whose social and economic fortunes may be inextricably interwoven, being variously involved in the two enterprises. Many a dalesman still has a brother who is a mining engineer, and though he be working in the ice of Canada or the heat of the Gulf we can once again see here echoes of the ancient tradition. Mrs Britton has been able to demonstrate by means of the grant book of the mines held from Lord Barnard's predecessor, the Duke of Cleveland, that many of the mines in operation between 1833–1845 were worked by small groups of men, men who can be proved to be tenant farmers because their names appear in the farm books of 1847 as holders of small farms in the Forest of Teesdale. In the Census returns of 1851, of the 180 males recorded in Harwood, no fewer than 101 were lead miners, and 3 were smelters. Wives and children could manage the small holdings, except at peak work times, notably lambing in the spring and haymaking during the early summer.

Two threads then have to be followed, agriculture and lead mining, threads which interlace like the well-known patterns on northern Old English crosses. A corollary of the agricultural changes outlined earlier in this chapter was that from the seventeenth century onwards, the prime use of improved land was as hay-meadow and as late as 1803 the Lord Barnard's estate surveyor was recommending an increase in the amount of meadow 'to guard against bad winters'. As Mrs Britton emphasizes there was a marked degree of stability in the general character of land usage within the dales from 1600 onwards.

There were of course some changes and Fig. 23 illustrates successive stages of reclamation in the upper dale, reclamation that was often piecemeal in character; this was in contrast to both sides of the river down valley from Newbiggin where systematic and large-scale enclosures of the fells by Act of Parliament took place between 1764 and 1867. In effect these lower fells were regarded as 'more improvable' and when enclosed were appropriated to specific farms. In the upper dale the relatively small scale intakes dealt only with such lands as were considered susceptible to improvement while the less improvable fells were left as commons. It must be emphasized that this was not simply a forward and upward movement of the head-dyke, the boundary between improved land and fell has fluctuated considerably, at times advancing and at times retreating. Furthermore, a study of the surviving estate maps and modern maps reveals one remarkable point: between 1769, when Greenwell mapped the entire upper dale, and the present day, there have been substantial alterations in individual field boundaries; and after a careful evaluation of the evidence Mrs Britton concluded that this was indeed real, rather than the product of bad mapping, and took place between 1803 and about 1850.

This same period saw extensive alterations to the estate farmhouses; the traditional farm of the dales is the long-house, with house, hay barn, byre and stables being placed in a long row, all under the same roof, although terrain difficulties do sometimes encourage the construction of an irregular cluster. In 1803 the buildings of the Raby estates were described as being in 'bad repair' and accounts survive recording the construction of new farmhouses and byres and the repair of older structures throughout the middle of the nineteenth century. Similar trends can be observed on the Streatlam estates and it is quite clear that the old dales landscapes were given, so to speak, a face-lift at this time and these improvements extended to the re-building and re-furbishing of the characteristic stone walls, sheep folds and stells (circular windbreaks for providing shelter for sheep – reputedly invented by George Napier, one of Nelson's captains, who eventually farmed in Northumberland), and the provision of various types of underdrain. At this time (1856) Marsh Gill (Plate 19) was provided with a new dwelling house. The tradition of whitewashing the Raby farms can certainly be traced back to 1848 for Francis Cockshott in *A Journey on foot through Teesdale* (1848) notes 'the houses are for the most part rude in their construction, but their being whitewashed partly redeemed the poverty of their aspect, and this operation is said to be always performed, with becoming loyalty, on the approach of the Duke to the moors in the hunting season'. More prosaically it was written into the leases, the estate providing the lime, the tenant the not inconsiderable labour. Although it was formerly done once yearly the estate now asks for it to be done every second year, and during the summer of 1975 a characteristic Teesdale scene was the pile of white lime, dumped from a lorry, near all the farms and cottages. Such improvements in farm structure and farm fabric were associated with a multitude of adjustments in the tenurial patterns, with farms being amalgamated and subdivided. The trend was towards more convenient, more compact units, and the visible living landscape of today is a complex palimpsest still in process of adaptation and slow transformation under the caring hands of great estates.

There appear, in Upper Teesdale at least, to be no traces of deliberately created small-holdings for lead miners; rather there was a complex but natural interaction between well-established farms, the possibility of new intakes and the presence of lead mines. The lead mines in fact stimulated population growth; they kept, indeed attracted, more people than could be supported by the hill-farms alone. Between 1801 and 1851 the populations of Middleton itself and Forest and Frith show marked increases, virtually doubling over the half century; significantly in Newbiggin and Eggleston these trends are far less marked, while on the Yorkshire side of the dale, in

Lunedale and Holwick, the population remained virtually static, although Mickleton and Romaldkirk increased somewhat.

Of the earlier history of lead extraction in the Dale little need be said: there seems to be no tangible proof to demonstrate conclusively that the Romans ever worked local deposits, the frequent references in the literature to Roman activity probably being speculation rather than fact. By the sixteenth century, however, there is clear evidence for lead extraction in the lower part of the dale around Eggleston, and by the seventeenth century the Flakebridge Mine in the Eggleshope valley was of considerable importance and the map of 1614 records 'Leade Mylls' in the valley of the Eggleston Beck. In Humberston's survey of 1670 there is a reference to the Grass Hill Mine, set at 610m (2000ft) in Harwood (GR NY 816354). It may be that the view of the history of metalliferous mining as 'not one of steady, uninterrupted progress' is valid but it is perhaps too easy to lay emphasis upon 'the primitive techniques, very limited geological knowledge' and the 'transitory and shifting character of the activity'. Primitive techniques can be surprisingly effective, local geological knowledge had been acquired and transmitted by centuries of accumulated experience, while the small-scale organization of the industry together with its close links with farming meant that the vicissitudes of changing economic climates could be considerably ameliorated.

The productive flats and veins of the Pennine orefield, the horizontal sheets and vertical or inclined sheets of lead-bearing mineralization, are intruded into the Carboniferous rocks and the principal producing area during the eighteenth and nineteenth centuries has concentrated within the upper valleys of the South Tyne, the Allen, the Wear and the Tees. Most of the veins are occupied by gangue materials, notably fluorspar and barytes, in which strings of ore occur, but the flats, which are the result of lateral spread of mineralized solutions, are much purer bodies of ore with little gangue material. Thus, lead mining tends to be a matter of luck: a vein yielding well during one week, month, year or decade may suddenly fail to produce ore at all, and it was this characteristic above all others which favoured a system of extraction based essentially upon small scale enterprises comprising groups of miners operating within a system of crushing, washing, transporting and smelting organized by large enterprises such as the London Lead Company and the Blackett-Beaumont concern. This characteristic also helped to maintain the tradition of close links with hillfarming. It is surely one of the supreme ironies of Pennine history that the fluorspar and barytes, part of the waste products of mining to the early miners, are now eagerly sought by contemporary industrial giants and are bringing yet another transitory industrial boom to the dales.

The veins are richest near the surface and there has been little mining in excess of 100 fathoms (183m) in depth. The usual practice was to sink short shafts to the vein or to drive adit levels into the hillside to reach the ore, extending the workings by means of a warren of levels and cross cuts. This had repercussions by the 1860s and 70s when the industry faced increasing foreign competition; the easily won resources of the dales had already been extracted, and between the peak of production, in about 1860, and 1900 there was a catastrophic slump. The first clear picture of lead mining in Teesdale, however, is provided by a map in Lord Barnard's collection dated 1732. It shows that the visible traces of mining in the Cow Green area must pre-date 1732, for two worked veins are shown near the head of Weelhead Sike. The overall impact of lead mining upon the dale in terms of farming and population trends has already been emphasized, but the physical effects of mining were widespread and may be conveniently divided into three categories, the landscapes of prospecting and extraction, the sites associated with processing, and the more general impact of improvements in transportation.

The landscapes showing the characteristic effects of lead mining tend to lie beyond the limit of the present head-dyke but nevertheless there are areas where stone-walled enclosures seem to be superimposed upon old workings, as for instance at Skears, to the north of Middleton-in-Teesdale (GR NY 950283). According to Raistrick horse levels were generally used, i.e. adits, driven into the hillsides, rising slightly so as to effect drainage. It is possible, however, that some of the earliest visible traces of mining are to be seen in the 'hushes' or great channels running down or across hillsides. The conventional explanation of these is that they were a means of exploiting surface outcrop of veins by using a reservoir to release a torrent of water to remove surface soil and rock. The author must admit to a certain scepticism. The great Red Grooves hush (GR NY 930289) cuts through a watershed and, although water did undoubtedly find its way into hushes and there may even have been deliberate flushing from reservoirs, it is surely likely that careful preparation by means of blasting was an essential preliminary, and hushes are in effect surface quarries following veins: it would be unwise to overemphasize the role of water in actually carving out these immensely deep channels cut through solid rock. Traces of hushes can be seen near the present car-park by Cow Green reservoir, as can areas of characteristic 'dead ground', spoil from adits and shafts still distinguishable because of the extent to which the ground has been poisoned. Another fine example of this can be seen at Flakebridge, over 457m (1500ft) above the valley of the Little Eggleshope Beck. Characteristic flat-topped spoil dumps, abandoned reservoirs and dams and chaotic gravel washes, still bleak, grey and unvegetated, scar the green hills; while collapsed adits, their sides still showing signs of timbering or stonework, and sealed or partially sealed shafts can still form traps for the unwary visitor (Plate 20). Near to many mines traces of buildings can be found – 'offices', incorporating a smithy, and, in the case of the more remote mines, a 'shop' or dosshouse. Many miners left their wives and families to fend for themselves throughout the week, or sometimes all the summer months, and went to live in the hills by the mines, an activity known as *walletin'* i.e. 'walleting', from the long cloth wallets or bags in which were carried clothes, personal items and some tools. These were gripped in the middle and slung over the shoulder so as to produce a balanced load.

The processing of lead need not concern us in detail. While mining was concentrated in Teesdale above Eggleston the smelt mills tended to be at nodal points where the ore from widely scattered enterprises could be brought together for processing. In 1732 there were smelt mills in Newbiggin, Middleton and Hudeshope Beck near Middleton, and by the early nineteenth century Bailey lists mills in Eggleston, Langdon (probably Langdon Beck) and Gaunless, in the Gaunless valley outside the dale. During the seventeenth century smelting relied largely upon charcoal, probably drawn from coppice woodlands in the foothills of the Durham uplands where tracts of parkland preserved some timber, but by the eighteenth century, according to a manuscript cited by Raistrick, a mixture of peat and coal was used. From 1745 onwards the London Lead Company began to acquire the leases of mines throughout the dale and this company remained a dominant force until they surrendered their leases in the late nineteenth century. Middleton-in-Teesdale was in fact virtually a company town, and they brought an element of stability to the area and the industry, based on 'very sound technical processes in mining and smelting constantly kept up to date, and a readiness to spend money on experiment and development'. Their paternalism spanned education, recreation, health and cleanliness and their undoubted pride was Masterman Place in Middleton, built to plan in 1833, and consisting of neat uniform rows of cottages and gardens within which they placed 'their most deserving workmen'. In addition the Company provided 'baths, company schools, chapels and all the social amenities that the old village did not possess'.

David Alexander has emphasised the importance of transportation in the lead industry. The bulk of lead produced was taken from mine to smelt mill by 'galloways', pack-ponies, usually travelling in trains of about twenty accompanied by a man and a boy, together with a dog thrown in as a 'heeler' to assist keeping the teams on the move. The lead was carried in panniers each weighing about one hundred weight, slung over a wooden saddle. Between 1800 and 1830 the London Lead Company constructed a number of significant roadworks, notably the present main road up Teesdale, but also a myriad of smaller feeder roads between mines and mills. The London Lead Company claimed that though they 'must never expect to see any direct return on the capital they advanced towards making and repairing roads and bridges (between 1815 and 1865 they invested over £12,000 on road schemes) yet they would derive an ample return for the outlay in the reduction in the rates of carriage of lead, stores, (including, no doubt, coal for fuel) and in keeping down the rates of wages by facilitating the ample supply of provisions and necessities for the work people and by economising the time of the agents in their journies from mine to mine and district to district'. This investment is still paying dividends to the inhabitants of Teesdale.

Lead was not of course the only mineral won in the Teesdale mines; zinc, silver and graphite were also extracted while building stones, some grindstones and even an inferior local coal ('crow coal') was taken from the land. Furthermore, the valley above High Force contains numerous small slag heaps, some of which have produced medieval pottery, suggesting that there is a long tradition of small-scale iron working in the area. The peak of mineral production lay in the 1850s and 60s, a period of peak population, but increasing difficulties in local mines because of depth, led to a decline during the final decades of the nineteenth century. The hills, tortured and torn apart, returned to silence, the old tracks grassed over, the mine-shops, pumps, mills and washing floors fell into picturesque ruin and the landscape was left once again to the sheep, the grouse shooter and the curlew, lapwing, plover and skylark.

1900 to the Present Day

Lead mining has disappeared from Teesdale as an industry, and although whinstone is still extracted (Plate 20), the present pattern is one of scattered hill-farms. In considering the present-day landscape it must be remembered that the rainfall in Upper

Teesdale falls in the range 1000–1500mm per annum and rises to over 2000mm per annum on Cross Fell. This means that the soils of the area tend to be leached of plant nutrients and rather acid in character so that peat forms on the higher areas. In practical terms the Teesdale soils, in order to grow grass successfully and avoid reverting to the heather, coarse grasses, rushes and rare plants of the unimproved fells, need two things, drainage and fertilizers. Drainage schemes were undertaken in the mid-nineteenth century and many of the fields were then provided with underdrains. These can be startlingly visible during the summer months, for the drains, with the wetter soil around them, show up as green lines etched on the golden fields of buttercups, lines which are more regular, more geometric, than marks left by the plough. Certainly by 1866 most of Ettersgill had been underdrained and it is quite clear that this process continued during the second half of the nineteenth century throughout the whole of the Upper Teesdale estate of Lord Barnard. Today pipe drains are still functioning on most of the farms although the less expensive form of open drains, dug with a small digging machine, can be seen scarring the surface of marginal pastures that have a tendency to heavy rush-infestation.

To counteract the leaching effect of the rainfall upon the soils frequent applications of lime and basic slag are desirable, and Mr H. L. Beadle has drawn attention to the large numbers of lime kilns. These can be documented as early as 1856 and here we are seeing a further facet of the improving movement that led to the restructuring of field patterns and the rebuilding and repair of farm buildings, and indeed Mr Beadle concludes 'taking into consideration all the information available it would appear that in the early days a large number of holdings had their own kiln, however small and primitive'. The meadows of Upper Teesdale, as seen today, are the product of at least 125 years of intensive care, and many have roots that go back twice or three times this time. How future trends in farming and taxation will affect the area is a matter of speculation, but there is a tendency to create larger units whose tenants obviously concentrate on the best lands allowing marginal lands and indeed marginal farmhouses to decay. The moorland is gradually creeping back over hard-won acres. The advent of the tourist, the 'country-cottage', and the motor-car is placing new pressures upon this old environment although in Teesdale these pressures are still relatively light and proximity to Birmingham or Manchester would have produced greater strains! The view that upland landscapes offer recreational facilities for more than a chosen few is one that has been gaining ground steadily during the last 50 years and the provision of public access by means of footpaths, including the important Pennine Way, and a public car park adjacent to the new reservoir, are a reflection of these new demands.

Finally, what can the historical geographer say of the rare Teesdale arctic-alpine flora and the distinctive hay-meadows, rich in herbs more at home in the field layer of birch woodland? The short answer is little or nothing, but this is hardly satisfying nor should it be accepted. Upper Teesdale, that portion of the Tees valley above the High Force and more particularly the Cauldron Snout, appears to have experienced sustained but relatively light interference from man once the woodlands had been cleared. This generalization would apparently pertain from the Iron Age to the eighteenth century, but the second half of the eighteenth and the whole of the nineteenth century saw intense but localized activity in the vicinity of the lead veins.

Furthermore, these high moors were only moderately suitable for grouse production and so may have escaped the persistent burning to maintain the low, young growth of heather so characteristic of grouse moor management on the fells between 305m and 457m (1000ft and 1500ft). The grazing intensity was never sufficiently high to warrant stinting until the nineteenth century, and today the Raby estates permit grazing only between 1st March and 20th November. There are indications that during the nineteenth century the hills were normally grazed between these two dates but on the Harwood moors the terminal date was 30th September. These rules meant effectively that in the uplands grazing was eliminated through the colder half of the year and the Rievaulx charter cited earlier surely hints that this practice was followed as early as 1131. During the months between September and April it seems to have been the age-old tradition to winter the cattle (if not the sheep) partly in byres and partly on the aftermath of the meadowland for Bailey records that 'In the vale of the Tees they have a singular and very ancient practice of stacking their hay in the middle of the field and foddering the cattle through the winter all over the field'. The site of the stack was moved each year. As Dr Margaret Bradshaw has pointed out this practice may account for the high densities of *Alchemilla* species (lady's-mantle) found within many Teesdale meadows. A lease relating to a Harwood farm in 1875 cited by Mrs Britton makes the point that the tenant should 'not mow the meadowland oftener than once in any year during this agreement, (and) not have the same in meadow two successive years without being sufficiently manured to the satisfaction of the said Duke or his agent'. This foddering would have taken place between 30th September or 20th November and 1st April. The time between the end of the hay harvest, the end of July or the beginning of August and the introduction of increased numbers of beasts on or after September 30th, may well be critical in terms of the survival of the unusual hay-meadow plants, giving them time to mature and reproduce. In these reciprocal arrangements, whose ultimate roots may lie in the Iron Age or even earlier, we see the essence of man-to-land links in Teesdale and a context in which floristic rarities, preserved and maintained by a fortunate combination of climatic, terrain and geological circumstances, were also sustained by a fortunate combination of locational and economic conditions. It is surely no accident that the arctic-alpine plants survive in that part of the Tees valley that is the most isolated, the most inhospitable and which, if the absence of evidence is indeed a sufficient guide, has consistently experienced 'high-costs' in terms of accessibility. Human interference has never been sufficiently intense to eliminate the natural variety of the habitat and produce a heather-grassland mosaic such as is more normal over the fells of west Durham.

CHAPTER 8

The Terrestrial Animals

UP to the present, 1454 species of animals have been recorded from Upper Teesdale, about 7% of all species known to occur in the British Isles, excluding marine animals. Nematodes and several minor groups have not been included, and more detailed future research on certain groups is likely to increase the list considerably. The numbers are given in Table 7 together with the totals for Britain, and a comparative list is shown for Wytham Woods near Oxford, perhaps the only other area which has been studied with equal intensity.

It is evident that certain groups (indicated by * in the table) are well represented in Teesdale. These include stream-living stoneflies, mayflies and caddisflies as well as the animal group characteristic of upland and tundra regions, the true two-winged flies (*Diptera*). Other groups are under-represented (indicated by † in the table). These include several which have many species in Britain, such as moths, butterflies, beetles, bees, wasps and ants.

A Typical Teesdale Animal: The Rush-Moth and Its Interrelationships with Rushes

The rush-moth, *Coleophora alticolella*, is probably the commonest and yet the least known moth in Upper Teesdale. The caterpillar is only 3mm long when fully grown and the adult is small and inconspicuous. Nevertheless, the ecology of this moth illustrates many of the problems encountered by animals living in an upland area such as Upper Teesdale.

The rush-moth emerges as an adult in June and lays eggs on the inflorescences of rushes, normally of the moor rush, *Juncus squarrosus*, but also of the common rush, *J. effusus*. The eggs hatch while the seed-capsules are swelling, and the caterpillars bore into them and feed on the ripening seeds. In the last two instars the caterpillar spins a silken case and this can be seen protruding from seed-capsules between August and October. The caterpillars then drop to the ground where they overwinter in the litter and eventually pupate in the spring. The caterpillars are so abundant in some areas that they consume a great part of the total seed production.

Both the moth and the moor rush are influenced by the decrease in temperature related to increasing altitude. On average the temperature falls by 1°C for every 200m increase in altitude (pp. 104–5), a difference which persists throughout the year. There is thus a nearly constant 3°C difference between the extreme altitudes in Upper Teesdale. The moor rush is found throughout this range, but each plant produces

PLATE 15. `Above, *Splachnum vasculosum*, a rare moss which usually grows on animal excrement in wet places on mountains. *Below, Rhytidium rugosum*, a moss of calcareous rocks and short grassland in scattered localities from South Wales and East Anglia to North-west Scotland and in one locality in Northern Ireland. Note the rosette of Teesdale violet.

PLATE 16. *Above*, the uncommon bog-moss *Sphagnum imbricatum* which forms brown hummocks on raised bogs. Note the slender pointed stem-tips. *Below*, hummocks of the moss *Gymnostomum recurvirostrum*, dark brown and of irregular shape, very characteristic of the calcareous sikes.

TABLE 7. The number of species of animals recorded in Upper Teesdale in comparison with the British List and the fauna of Wytham Woods, Oxford. Modified from Coulson and Whittaker (1977)
* indicates relatively abundant in Teesdale. † indicates relatively poorly represented.

	Teesdale	Wytham	Britain
Pot worms	26	?	?
Earthworms	15	?	27
Insects			
Springtails	56*	56	305
Grasshoppers	1†	9	38
Earwigs	0	1	9
Stoneflies	27*	6	33
Mayflies	16	5	46
Dragonflies	3†	19	42
Plant bugs	75	273	1411
Lacewings and alderflies	3†	21	60
Scorpionflies	1	2	4
Caddisflies	31*	23	188
Moths and butterflies	121†	532	2187
Beetles	141†	1074	3690
Bees, wasps, ants	95†	774	6191
True flies	510*	638	5199
Fleas	9	?	56
Centipedes	6	28	90
False scorpions	1†	8	26
Harvest spiders	3	17	20
Spiders	84	219	580
Mites and ticks	111	260	1700
Snails, slugs	16†	65	188
Fish	3†	20	45
Amphibia	2	4	6
Reptiles	1	2	6
Mammals	14	24	47
Birds (breeding)	83*	73	226
Total:	1454	4153	22420

Nematode worms, booklice, and one or two minor groups omitted.

fewer inflorescences each year and each inflorescence contains fewer developing capsules as the altitude increases (Fig. 27c).

The rush-moth is rarely encountered above 600m (2000ft) and up to that altitude there is a progressive decrease in the degree of infestation of rushes by the moth. This is clearly shown in Fig. 27b, presenting data collected in the Langdon Beck area. Two factors are important in determining this relationship. First, the moth is small and probably never flies further than 200m and then only in calm and warm conditions such as occur infrequently, so that its potential rate of spread is slow. Secondly, there

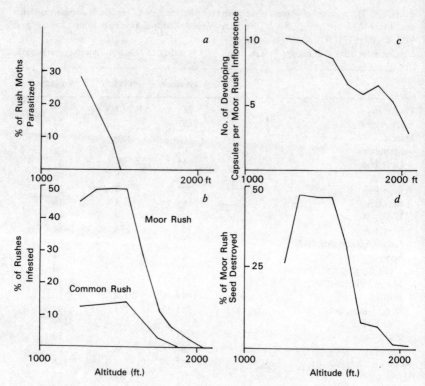

FIG. 27. The inter-relationships between the rush-moth, *Coleophora alticolella*, the common and moor rush and altitude: *a*, the percentage of rush moth caterpillars parasitized; *b*, the percentage of inflorescences infested by the rush-moth; *c*, the reduction in ripening capsules per moor rush inflorescence at higher altitudes; *d*, the effects of the rush-moth on seed production of the moor rush.

is considerable year-to-year variation in the altitude above which the moor rush sets no seed. In years when this limit is low, caterpillars of the rush-moth hatching at higher altitudes die from lack of food, and the life-cycle is completed only at lower altitudes. The higher areas are recolonized slowly during a series of years in which the rush sets seed successfully. Consequently the altitudinal distribution of the moth ebbs and flows in relation to the number of years since the rush last failed to set seed. This simple interaction is, however, modified if the common rush occurs in the same area, for although this is not the preferred food of the rush-moth, it is much less affected by temperature than is the moor rush and sets seed annually over the whole of the altitudinal range. Each year a few caterpillars of the rush-moth succeed in developing on its seed-capsules and these act as a reservoir for reinfection of the moor rush after years in which it fails to set seed. This last situation clearly shows the advantage to the rush-moth, as to other animals, of possessing alternative food supplies.

The rush-moth is parasitized by at least seven species of parasitic wasps

TABLE 8.

Zone	1	2	3	4	5
Altitude	Over 2500ft	2000–2500ft	1600–2000ft	1400–1600ft	Below 1400ft
Moor rush	Rarely sets seed	Seed set irregular	Seed set in most years	Seed set annually Most consumed by moth	Seed set annually Much consumed by moth
Common rush	Absent	Annual seed set	Annual seed set	Seed set annually	Seed set annually
Rush-moth	Absent	Present only occasionally	Present in most years	Present and abundant	Present and common Numbers regulated by parasites?
Parasites	Absent	Absent	Absent	Usually absent	Present

(*Ichneumonoidea*). Just as the rush-moth is unable to exploit seed production by the rush over the whole of its altitudinal range, so these parasites decrease markedly in numbers with increasing altitude, eventually disappearing completely at 460m (1500ft), leaving the moth wholly unparasitized above this altitude (Fig. 27a). This decrease at higher altitudes appears to result from two factors. First, there is a lower density of host caterpillars at higher altitudes; secondly, the lower temperatures at greater heights reduce the searching efficiency of the female parasites to a point at which they cannot find sufficient hosts to ensure their survival in the next generation. These interactions are summarized in Table 8.

This study illustrates four factors which influence the rush-moth or its food supplies and which have been shown to influence many other animals in areas such as Upper Teesdale where there is a wide range of altitude. The four are:

  i. the distribution of suitable food;
 ii. the distribution and abundance of parasites and predators;
iii. the influence of the lower temperatures at higher altitudes and
     of other climatic effects associated with altitude, and
 iv. the impact of plant-feeding animals on the vegetation.

Each of these will now be considered in more detail.

i. THE DISTRIBUTION OF FOOD PLANTS

Although several factors restrict the number of animal species in Upper Teesdale, amongst the most important are undoubtedly the relatively small number of different plant species and the scarcity of trees. Most plant species have a set of animals which feed exclusively or mainly on them, so that a restriction in the number of plant species implies a restricted diversity in the animals. There are few animals which feed on only one plant species but very many are restricted to a group of closely related plants. Thus at least five moorland animals depend on heather for their own food supply. *Strophyngia ericae*, a sap-sucking bug, and *Lochmaea suturalis*, the heather beetle, feed exclusively on heather and it forms the major part of the diet for the red grouse and the caterpillars of two moths, the northern eggar and the emperor (Plate 22).

Trees are particularly important in that they not only offer a variety of ecological niches for different animals on trunk and canopy, but they also influence the surrounding environment and thus contribute considerably to the diversity of habitats.

ii. THE DISTRIBUTION OF PREDATORS AND PARASITES

The situation for the rush-moth, in being found at higher altitudes than any of its parasites, appears to be common to many of the species which have been investigated. J. B. Whittaker has for many years studied froghoppers in Upper Teesdale and, although they are heavily parasitized in the lowlands, he has failed to find any evidence of infestation at high altitudes. Similarly cranefly larvae (leatherjackets) are

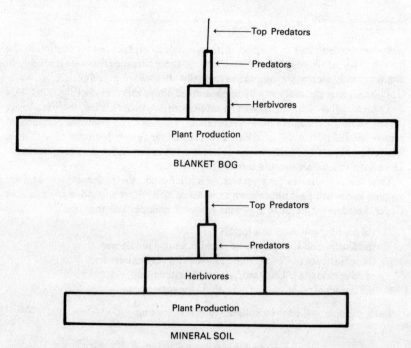

FIG. 28. 'The pyramid of numbers' based on the plant production, numbers of herbivores, predators and 'top' predators (predators which usually feed on other predators, e.g. merlin which feeds on meadow pipits). These figures have actually been calculated on energy values, but similar figures are obtained if weight is used. Note that, although the plant production is less on the mineral soil, there are more herbivores and predators there than on the blanket bog.

PLATE 17. *Left*, peat-profile on Widdybank Fell. *Below*, peat-profile showing wood at the base of peat on the high ground between Teesdale and Weardale.

PLATE 18. *Above*, search for rare plants by students of Durham University Extra-Mural Department. *Below*, reproductive units of spring gentian (*Gentiana verna*). To the right are two vegetative rosettes in late juvenile stage. Of the six very young rosettes the one on the extreme right is dead.

but rarely attacked by the fly *Siphona* in upland areas although attacks are common at lower altitudes. Several investigators have commented on the scarcity of hymenopterous and dipterous parasites in Upper Teesdale and only one moth, the emperor, has been found to be frequently parasitized. This extends even to the cuckoo. Although its major host, the meadow pipit, is one of the most common birds of high moorland, the cuckoo rarely lays its eggs at altitudes above 300m (1000ft).

Many vertebrate predators occur in Upper Teesdale but, in relation to the densities of their potential prey, these also are much less frequent than would be expected in lowland sites. The meadow pipit, for example, encounters very little nest predation in Upper Teesdale and most clutches fledge successfully, unlike the situation on lowland heaths. Although birds of prey are well represented, their numbers are low. In a three-year study of meadow pipits at Moor House not a single merlin, the pipit's main predator, was seen on the Reserve. It seems likely that the scarcity of voles in the upper part of the dale accounts for the small numbers of short-eared owls. Accordingly, the 'pyramid of numbers' (Fig. 28), in which the herbivores (e.g. craneflies) form the base, small predators (e.g. meadow pipit) the next layer, and their predators (e.g. merlin) the top, is very broad-based.

iii. INFLUENCE OF ALTITUDE ON CLIMATE

In Teesdale the temperature throughout the year tends to be 1°C lower for each 200m (650ft) rise in altitude. This may appear to be a small change, but the mean annual temperature at Moor House is only 5°C so that the altitudinal effect is quite important. For warm-blooded animals the lowered temperature requires only a little more food to counteract the greater heat loss, but for cold-blooded animals living at higher altitudes presents greater problems. Body processes in animals are temperature-dependent, and growth can be expected to be slower at lower temperatures. Thus very few, if any, insects go through more than one generation a year in Upper Teesdale and some take considerably longer to complete a generation than at lower altitudes. For example, the small plant bug found on heather, *Strophyngia ericae*, takes two years to complete a life-cycle in Upper Teesdale but only one year near sea-level. Similarly, the large cranefly *Pedicia rivosa* extends its life-cycle to two years in Upper Teesdale, whilst another cranefly, *Tipula rufina*, goes through two generations a year in the lowlands but has only one a year in Upper Teesdale and in Iceland.

Another type of adjustment to temperature is seen in two species of cranefly, *Molophilus ater* and *Tipula subnodicornis*, in which larval growth-rates vary so little with change in temperature that the time taken to complete larval development is little longer in the higher and colder sites than at lower levels. This mode of adaptation may well be found in other cold-blooded animals when information on their growth-rates in different environments has been fully collated.

With increasing altitude in Upper Teesdale there is more rain and less direct sunlight as well as lower temperatures. The climate may be described as sub-arctic but the summers are wetter, cooler and much more cloudy than in most tundra regions of the sub-arctic. It has been suggested that these conditions may account for both the lack of mosquitoes and the small numbers of Hymenoptera (wasps, bees, ants and parasitic wasps) compared with their abundance in true tundra. It may well be that their flight is drastically limited by the lack of direct sunlight so that they are often unable to warm their bodies sufficiently to fly in search of their food and hosts.

iv. THE EFFECT OF ANIMALS ON THE VEGETATION

Although the effects of sheep, rabbits and other large vetebrates on the vegetation are well documented (pp. 50–1, 63, 82–3), there is a tendency to underestimate the role of invertebrates in consuming plant material and influencing the composition of plant communities. The larvae of craneflies (leatherjackets), for example, consume almost as much of the grassland vegetation in Upper Teesdale as do sheep, whilst on the blanket bog and other peaty areas they ingest twice as much as sheep. Other examples of the influence of invertebrates include the consumption of almost the entire liverwort production by a single one (*Tipula subnodicornis*) of the 68 species of cranefly found in Upper Teesdale, and by the impact of the rush-moth on the seed production of the moor rush (Fig. 27d). Much has still to be learnt in this field, but it must be borne in mind that most of these animals, though small, are extremely abundant.

Rare Animals of Upper Teesdale

The presence of a number of rare plants in a restricted area of the dale raises the question whether there are similarly rare animals in Upper Teesdale and, if so, whether they have the same distribution as the plants. This is difficult to answer because much less is known about the distribution of animals than of higher plants. This comparative ignorance is chiefly due to the difficulty of identifying the very much larger number of animal species. Few animals are as easily recognized as birds and butterflies, and the large number (1454) of animal species known from Upper Teesdale represents about 7% of the total known from the British Isles.

There is a consequent doubt for some animal groups as to whether species are genuinely rare or merely appear so because the group is little collected or the taxonomy not fully worked out. For instance, the pot-worm *Cernosvitoviella briganta*, a species new to science, was found to be common on the blanket bog in Upper Teesdale. Pot-worms are not attractive to the collector or taxonomist and the moorland species in Britain have been worked on by only two zoologists, both working in Upper Teesdale. Examination of other moorland localities might well reveal that this new species is widely distributed. For these reasons the present analysis is restricted to well-worked groups of spiders and insects: there are no rare vertebrates in Upper Teesdale. The 22 rare species in Table 9 are allocated to groups according to their habitats. There are, of course, others almost as uncommon as these, but it is essential to draw an arbitrary limit for inclusion. It is clear that there are many rare insects in Upper Teesdale and that they occur in many different habitats, though there tend to be more on the blanket bog than elsewhere. Present information gives no indication that more rare species are associated with the sugar-limestone in the Cow Green area than with other areas, so that the factors influencing the distribution of the plant rarities do not appear to affect insects and spiders.

TABLE 9. Rare animals (insects and spiders) recorded from Upper Teesdale

High altitude streams; above 600 m

Blood-sucking blackfly	*Simulium dunfellense*	new to science
	Simulium naturale	new to science
	Prosimulium latimucro	first British record
Stonefly	*Capnia vidua*	
	Protonemeura montana	

Streams below 600m

Cranefly	*Dicranota gracilipes*	first British record
	Dicranota guerini	second English record
	Dicranota exclusa	first English record

High altitude grassland; above 600m

Sawfly	*Pachynematus clibrichellus*	first record from England
Cranefly	*Tipula gimmerthali*	second record from Britain
	(restricted to flushes)	

Grasslands below 600m

Sawfly	*Pachynematus glabriceps*	new to science
Cow Green – sugar limestone		
Spider	*Hilaira nubigena*	second British locality
Ground-beetle	*Notiophilus aestuans*	first record in northern England
Rove beetle	*Xantholinus clarei*	first British record
Rove beetle	*Atheta strandiella*	second British record

Blanket bog

Cranefly	*Tipula limbata (= vafra)*	second English locality
Horse-fly	*Hybomitra montana* and *H. flavipes*	
Bluebottle	*Calliphora alpina*	second British record
Plant bug	*Teloleuca pellucens*	
Parasitic wasp	*Acanosema productus*	first British record
Bird flea	*Ceratophyllus borealis*	
Northern dart moth	*Amathes alpicola*	first English record

Affinities of the Teesdale Fauna

The contrast between peat and mineral soils results in major differences in the vegetation of Upper Teesdale. This marked distinction is also found in the faunas of the two types of substratum, though a few groups, such as the mites, have species inhabiting both types.

A study of the geographical distribution of the animal species, where this is known, shows that they fall into two major groups, one composed of species with sub-arctic or alpine distributions and the other of species distributed across central Europe. The former dominates the peat fauna, the more temperate animals being found mainly on the mineral soils. There are, for example, very high densities of earthworms on the mineral soils with few penetrating to the blanket bog, and all the species found in Teesdale are also known from lowland regions of this and other European countries: there are no sub-arctic earthworms.

Mineral soils provide the agricultural land in the lower parts of Teesdale. At higher altitudes they lie alongside the Tees and even its smallest tributaries (Plate 3) and are also found wherever limestone outcrops. Almost all the animals of these mineral soils are also found in grasslands at low altitudes in Britain, although the converse is not true, since many lowland species fail to reach areas at higher altitudes. The fauna of upland grasslands is essentially, therefore, a species-poor lowland grassland community, restricted to those species that can survive the harsh climate of Upper Teesdale. The animals include several species which are agricultural pests, such as click-beetles and the common cranefly, *Tipula paludosa*, so that the upland areas act as a reservoir from which agricultural land can be reinfected.

In contrast the fauna of peat contains relatively few species found at low altitudes in this country. The exceptions are usually species that also occur round the edges of ponds and streams or in lowland fens. Typically the fauna of peat soils has very close affinities with that of northern Scandinavia and the species-poor fauna of Iceland.

In summary, then, there is in Upper Teesdale a juxtaposition, with little overlap, of two distinct faunas. That on the peat, of sub-arctic origin, is close to its southern limits, whilst the grassland fauna has penetrated from the lowlands and most of its species are at or near their northern or altitudinal limits.

The Seasonal Abundance of Insects

The short summer, long winter and very short spring and autumn characteristic of the sub-arctic result in a single large emergence of adult insects, initiated by the spring rise in temperature and the increasing day-length. These large synchronized emergences are notorious because many of the insects are blood-sucking flies.

In Upper Teesdale the emergence of insects associated with the peat areas has a similar large spring peak, and the blanket bog can shimmer with flying insects in late May and early June. The summer, however, is longer than in the true sub-arctic and, since the peat species are mainly of sub-arctic origin and adapted to utilize the spring rise in temperature, there is a long summer period when the blanket bog is virtually devoid of flying insects. The situation on the mineral soils is very different. Here the species of temperate lowland origin are adapted to emerge in spring, summer or autumn. The numbers of flying insects are at a much lower level than on the blanket bog in spring but are maintained throughout the warmer part of the year. This contrast is shown in Fig. 29.

Despite the large area of peat in Upper Teesdale, most of the insect-feeding animals cannot support themselves on it throughout the summer. The common and pygmy shrews, frogs, large ground beetles and meadow-pipits, although they take full advantage of the spring bloom of insects on the blanket bog, have to move to the mineral soils or the banks of streams to find food during the rest of the summer. The heterogeneity of soil and vegetation is consequently of major importance in enabling insect-feeding animals to survive in these upland conditions. The insect predators have either to be highly mobile, like the meadow pipit, or restricted to a more or less broad band along the interfaces between peat and mineral soil, as are the two species of shrew and the common frog.

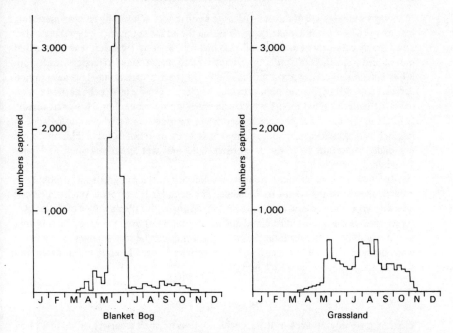

FIG. 29. The numbers of insects (and related groups) captured in standard traps on blanket bog and grassland throughout a year. Note the huge spring peak on the blanket bog and the smaller but more consistent numbers of the grassland. The average weight of each animal on the grassland is larger than on the blanket bog, so that the bulk of available food for predators is larger on the grassland than would appear from the figure. After Coulson & Whittaker (1977).

The Birds of Upper Teesdale

In recent years 83 species of birds have been recorded as nesting in Upper Teesdale, not a large number for so extensive an area. However, the list includes several uncommon species and the abundance of certain groups, such as the waders, makes Teesdale of considerable interest. It is not possible in this account to deal with each of the breeding species in turn, and those have been selected which are of particular importance in Upper Teesdale.

GAME BIRDS

Two game birds, the red and the black grouse, are especially noteworthy. The former is the more abundant, large areas of moorland being managed specifically for red grouse. Although heather is not the sole food of red grouse, it is the most important component of the diet and breeding birds are restricted to areas where heather is well represented. A burning regime producing heather stands of different ages ensures that the young growth of high nutritional value is always available to the birds.

These upland moors are wetter than those at lower altitudes and, perhaps because of this, grouse bags are not usually as large as on moors at lower levels. An interesting feature of red grouse in Upper Teesdale is that the adults supplement their diet in May and June by eating large numbers of craneflies (daddy-long-legs). It is well known that parent birds take their offspring to wet flushes and stream-sides to feed on insects, but it has been assumed hitherto that the adults are strictly vegetarian. This assumption can be explained by the fact that previous studies on grouse have been carried out on lower or better drained moors where craneflies are not abundant. However, insects contain up to ten times the concentration of nitrogen and phosphorus present in heather and therefore provide an important extra nutrient source. This might be especially important to birds in exposed, cold and wet situations such as Upper Teesdale.

The black grouse, although numerically inferior to the red grouse, is probably of greater interest to the visitor to Teesdale. The cock birds aggregate on a traditional area known as the 'lek' and indulge in prolonged and active display. One of these 'leks' is recorded as the largest in England and can be observed from the road. On this area displaying males with tails fanned and bowed wings can be seen rushing to and fro at most times of day. On smaller 'leks' such activity is usually confined to dawn and dusk in the few months before breeding.

WADING BIRDS

There is probably no area in Britain which harbours such a variety of wading birds during the nesting season. In recent years, eleven species nested in Upper Teesdale and seven of these breed abundantly. Most of these species advertise themselves by conspicuous aerial displays prior to nesting and some like lapwing, redshank and curlew (Plate 21) agitate noisily when man, or other potential predator, intrudes into an area where they have young. Few people can visit Upper Teesdale in the spring without encountering the tumbling display flight of the lapwing. The liquid call of the curlew, given when gliding on arched wings, is equally familiar, and the 'drumming' of the snipe diving over its territory is not infrequent. The 'creaking gate' call which accompanies the aerial display of the golden plover and the trilling chatter of the common sandpiper are, perhaps, less well known; the first as it occurs in early spring, the second because the bird confines itself to the stream-sides.

The lapwing is the commonest of the Teesdale waders and, typically, nests in pastures and meadows although it has been found nesting as high as the summit of Cross Fell. An intriguing problem is why lapwings nest in certain fields but not in others immediately adjacent. In many cases the difference persists from year to year. Susan Taylor, who made a study of breeding lapwings in the neighbouring Weardale valley, found that the distribution of nests was related to the abundance of food in the area immediately surrounding the nest. Due to natural factors, such as the mineral content of the soil, or to management, some fields supported much greater densities of invertebrates such as earthworms. It was these fields which proved attractive to the nesting birds, although other factors such as the presence of human habitation, presence of trees, and gradient, also influenced the bird's choice.

The redshank occurs over much the same area as the lapwing but its distribution is more restricted and it appears to nest where the water-table is close to the surface.

Snipe are even more restricted, nesting in marshy fields and also in a few wet places on the high fells.

Golden plover, curlew and, less frequently, dunlin nest on the high fells and grouse moors. The first is associated with limestone outcrops where the turf is heavily grazed by sheep. These areas do not have a greater density of potential food but it is probable that such as there is is both more visible and the more easily obtained on short turf than it would be on blanket bog or among the moor rush. If this is the case, sheep grazing must play an important part in determining suitable feeding areas for the plover.

Until this century dotterel nested regularly in Teesdale on the fell crowns. The birds are still seen in the area but are usually in passage to more northern breeding grounds. It is amazing that the dotterel, which is the highest nesting, and apparently least adaptable, of the waders in Teesdale, should in recent years have colonized the polders in Holland where it breeds below sea-level.

Two wading birds nest on stream-sides. The oystercatcher has arrived only recently in Teesdale and reflects the trend from coastal to inland breeding which has occurred in the species in recent years. In England the spread inland appears to have followed up the course of rivers such as the Lune and the Eden which drain into the Irish Sea. This can be inferred from the fact that oystercatchers nested by the upper stretches of the river Tees several years before they appeared on the lower reaches below Barnard Castle.

The common sandpiper spends almost all of its time on or alongside river banks and nests almost to the source of the Tees and its tributaries. Although it is the last wading species to arrive each year, it is the first to leave the high moorland streams. Within hours of the chicks hatching the nests are deserted and it appears probable that the parents start to lead the young downstream at a very early age. By the time the chicks are half grown, the upper nesting area is empty of sandpipers.

WAGTAILS AND PIPITS

The grey, pied and yellow wagtails all nest commonly in Upper Teesdale, but the most abundant bird is undoubtedly the meadow pipit. All four species feed on invertebrates, mainly insects, but there are marked habitat differences between them. The grey wagtail feeds predominantly along stream sides and takes a very high proportion of aquatic insects, such as mayflies, stoneflies and caddisflies, in its food. The yellow wagtail and pied wagtails overlap somewhat in their feeding, but the former occurs more commonly in hay-meadows, whilst the latter is often more frequent in pastures and, of course, they use quite different nesting sites. The meadow pipit favours longer vegetation and is the dominant species on the heather moors where it tends to feed on slow-moving insects, particularly craneflies, picking these up whilst it walks over the moor: it does not adopt the rapid rush employed by the wagtails to capture fast-moving insects.

Few bird species remain in Upper Teesdale in the winter and under conditions of snow and zero temperatures only red grouse and the dipper are regularly encountered. Most other birds have moved either to lower altitudes (for example, golden plover and curlew moving to the coast), or have left the country completely

TABLE 10. Information concerning the breeding of the meadow pipit in Britain, Scandinavia and Iceland.

	Britain		Scandinavia (Norway)	Iceland
	Lowlands (below 152m; 500ft)	Highlands (over 305m; 1000ft)		
Mean clutch size	4.46	4.07	5.55	5.42
Total nest mortality	30%	4%	—	—
Broods	2.0	1.6	1.0	1.0
Young reared per pair	6.2	6.3	c 5	c 5
Peak of laying	4th week April	2nd week May	2nd week June	1st week June

and migrate back in the spring (common sandpiper, yellow wagtail). Meadow pipits which nest in Teesdale have been shown to winter in Spain and Portugal and return in late March and April, leaving again in August and September.

The meadow pipit nests from sea-level to over 900m in Britain and over 14 days'

TABLE 11. The food brought to nestling meadow pipits on the Moor House Nature Reserve

FIRST BROOD(late May)

Cranefly *Tipula subnodicornis*	83%
Other craneflies	2%
Other adult flies	4%
Stream insects (stoneflies, mayflies)	11%
Total	100%

Percentage of food from blanket bog = 86%
Percentage of food from grasslands = 3%

SECOND BROOD(early July)

Cranefly *Tipula paludosa*	40%
Other craneflies	1%
Other adult flies	11%
Fly larvae	5%
Moths	10%
Stream insects	33%
Total	100%

Percentage of food from blanket bog = 2%
Percentage of food from grassland = 65%

PLATE 19. *Left*, Iron Age homestead, Force Garth. *Below*, Gill Town in the Harwood valley, showing a farm-hamlet.

PLATE 20. *Above*, rake with old lead-workings, Widdybank Fell. *Below*, Whinstone quarry, Force Garth.

difference has been found in the start of the breeding season at different altitudes. Thus the breeding season is noticeably later in Upper Teesdale than in lowland areas, presumably as an adaptation to the later emergence of adult insects at higher altitudes. Further differences occur between the pipits nesting at low and high altitudes which result in a lower clutch size, fewer second clutches, less parasitism by the cuckoos and lower nest predation in the upland areas. In Norway and Iceland the meadow pipit is single-brooded, breeds even later, but has a distinctly larger clutch size. These differences are summarized in Table 10.

A study of the food brought to the young meadow pipits in Upper Teesdale shows a marked difference between the food of the first and second broods (Table 11). Almost all of the food brought to the first brood is collected from the blanket bog and peat soils, where there is a large spring emergence of insects which coincides with the pipits' eggs hatching in late May. By the time the second brood is in the nest, this emergence has finished and little available food is present on the moor and the meadow pipits change to collecting food from the streams and the mineral soils. It is noticeable that the meadow pipit and several other insect-feeding vertebrates, such as the common and pygmy shrew and the common frog, all rely on the soil and vegetational mosaic to ensure suitable food availability throughout the time of year that they are active in Teesdale (see p. 168).

Herbivores

Since prehistoric times, the uplands of Teesdale have been grazed by a series of mammals. The wild ox *Bos taurus primigenius* certainly occurred in the area and remains of horns still come to light as peat is eroded. Red deer roamed the fells but the last herd disappeared shortly after 1747. Mountain sheep were probably introduced into the area by Norsemen in about AD 900. The Norse influence still persists in the local names and sheep-marking systems and the terms *gill* and *beck* are also of Norse origin. When parish boundaries were defined, the communities living on the west side of the northern Pennines extended their areas up and over the fell tops into Teesdale, and similar extensions appear to have occurred from the Alston area and from lower Teesdale. Thus parts of Upper Teesdale have probably been used for sheep-grazing for over a thousand years. However the high intensity now encountered is probably relatively recent.

During the last century domestic geese were grazed extensively on the fells during the summer but this practice died out many years ago. Cattle are restricted to lower pastures and the only other vertebrate grazer of consequence, apart from the rabbit, is the red grouse.

SHEEP

Although not native to the country, sheep, more than any other animal, have influenced the landscape and vegetation of Upper Teesdale. Much of the area is managed for sheep and the effects of sheep-grazing on the vegetation are considerable, resulting in close-grazed grass swards and the lack of trees over much of the area. Most of our knowledge of the behaviour and effects of sheep in Upper Teesdale stems from the detailed studies of Michael Rawes and David Welch on the Moor House National Nature Reserve and this account relies heavily on their information.

The practice of grazing sheep has changed little in the past 100 years. The sheep are driven to the high moors in the spring, visited occasionally, but otherwise left to wander free until November when they are gathered for wintering on lower pastures. Despite the lack of walls or fencing on the fells, the sheep remain within a well-defined home range, known as the heaf, and a shepherd will know where to find the flock. Usually the knowledge of the heaf is acquired while the young animal is running with its mother, and for the flock as a whole it will be an area of long-standing tradition. Consequently, the flock is normally sold with the farm and establishing new flocks on the fells requires a great deal of shepherding until the home range is acquired.

Swaledale (Plate 22) are the commonest sheep, followed by Cheviot, both hardy upland sheep. The hill-farmer derives income from his flocks in three different ways. First, the ram lambs which run with their mothers during the summer are fattened on lower ground in the winter and then sold for meat. Second, the ewe lambs which are not kept as replacements in their own flock are sold in the autumn for cross-breeding with Teeswater, Wensleydale or Blue-faced Border Leicester rams and the production of fat lambs on lower pasture. Third, the stock sheep produce good quality wool which is taken from them in July. It is normal practice to breed from a ewe three times but a number of ewes will evade the annual round-up each year and thus may survive for a longer period.

The removal of most of the sheep from the fells during the winter is necessary, not only because of the severe weather but also because, once the growing season has ended, there is little for the animals to eat. Even during the summer, upland areas do not provide good pasture, and the stocking rates, 2 or 3 sheep per hectare as opposed to about 6 per hectare throughout the year on lowland areas, reflect this. The average density, however, obscures what is actually happening on the area. Sheep are highly selective feeders and choose to feed on limestone grasslands where there is a high proportion of grasses such as common bent and sheep's fescue. This preference for grasses leads them to aggregate on the few limestone areas where densities five times the average are often observed. In contrast, the neighbouring areas of blanket bog, where heather and cotton-grass (a sedge) are the dominant plants, commonly support one sheep only per 100ha. Plate 3 shows sheep on areas of riverside alluvium.

This range of grazing preference by sheep has two effects. First, Agrostis-Festuca grassland is closely grazed and these areas are characterized by a very short sward. Secondly, the sheep utilize only a very small proportion of the plant growth on the large areas of blanket bog. Each sheep consumes about 1kg wet weight of vegetation daily and selects this from the mineral soils in restricted areas. Exclosure experiments carried out by David Welch on the Moor House Reserve have clearly indicated the effects of grazing on the vegetation composition of upland grasslands. In particular, areas left ungrazed for as little as five years show a greater plant species diversity. A further major effect of sheep-grazing is found in the effects of flowering and fruiting of many plant species. In an enclosure on Cow Green the spring gentian flowered and fruited much more freely than on neighbouring grazed areas. The vegetation of Teesdale must consist of species which can both withstand grazing and can succeed in producing viable seed or reproduce by vegetative means. It is likely that many plant species have already been 'lost' from Upper Teesdale by their inability to co-exist with sheep.

Soil Animals

As recently as 1951 W. H. Pearsall, in his book *Mountains and Moorlands*, commented on the paucity of the fauna of moorland soils. We now know this to be incorrect. Most animals that are found in the soil are necessarily small to allow them to move through the spaces between soil particles and, until efficient techniques were developed to separate them from the soil, their abundance was not realized. Even today, almost the entire information concerning the soil fauna of moorlands has been obtained in Upper Teesdale and little is known about the species composition and abundance of the soil fauna in other regions of Britain.

Large soil animals, such as earthworms and leatherjackets, are familiar to the gardener or naturalist, but the great majority of soil animals are much smaller and less easily recognized. The smallest animals, the nematode worms (which include eelworms), are seen readily only under a microscope. Most soil animals live in the top 6cm of the soil where food and, in the case of moorland soils, oxygen are more abundant. Because of this, it is usual to express the density of soil animals in numbers per square metre of ground surface and not in numbers per unit volume of soil which

TABLE 12. The mean population density (numbers m^{-2}) of animals on the four main habitat types in Upper Teesdale

| | | | Numbers per sq metre | | |
| | | | Mineral soils | | Peat soils | |
			Limestone grassland	Alluvial grassland	Moor rush	Blanket bog
Earthworms	(Lumbricidae)		390	390	4	0.1
Pot-worms	(Enchytraeidae)	soil fauna	80,000	160,000	200,000	80,000
Nematodes	(Nematoda)		3,300,000	3,300,000*	3,900,000	1,400,000
Springtails	(Collembola)		40,000	45,000	23,000	80,000
Mites	(Acarina)		33,000	36,000	41,000	33,000
Craneflies	(Tipulidae)		120	87	2,500	700
Ground-beetles	(Carabidae)		3	3*	2	1
Spiders	(Araneida)	above ground	40	370	300	130
Moths	(Lepidoptera)		<1	<1	<1	<1
Plant bugs	(Hemiptera)		100	50	250	3,500
Grouse			0	0	0	0.00011
Small mammals			0	0.00001	0.00010	0.00001
Sheep			0.00056	0.00026	0.00013	0.000014

*No direct measure — assumed to be equal to limestone grassland

might at first seem more appropriate. Table 12 shows the average densities of animals on four different types of moorland soil. It is obvious that birds and mammals are much less abundant than the invertebrates and should, were the purpose of the table other than comparative, be expressed as numbers per hectare or acre for practical purposes. The nematodes are exceedingly abundant and have well over a million individuals per m^2 on all four soil types, whilst mites, springtails and pot-worms are

TABLE 13. Average weight (g dry wt m^{-2}) of animals on four main habitats in Upper Teesdale (after Coulson & Whittaker 1977).

		Mineral soils		Peat soils	
		Limestone grassland	Alluvial grassland	Moor rush	Blanket bog
Earthworms	(Lumbricidae	23.20	23.22	0.04	neg.
Pot-worms	(Enchytraeidae)	4.10	5.15	4.60	2.16
Nematodes	(Nematoda)	0.14	0.14	0.18	0.17
Springtails	(Collembola)	0.12	0.15	0.05	0.10
Craneflies	(Tipulidae)	4.10	6.10	1.96	0.58
Mites	(Acarina)	0.35	0.66	0.32	0.40
Soil fauna sub-total		**32.01**	**35.42**	**7.15**	**3.41**
Ground beetles	(Carabidae)	0.007	0.007	0.004	0.002
Spiders	(Araneida)	0.003	0.047	0.039	0.017
Moths	(Lepidoptera)	neg.	neg.	neg.	neg.
Plant bugs	(Hemiptera)	0.010	0.007	0.029	0.025
Above-ground invertebrate sub-total		**0.020**	**0.061**	**0.072**	**0.044**
Grouse		0.0	0.0	0.0	0.023
Small mammals		neg.	neg.	neg.	neg.
Sheep		14.00	6.50	3.20	0.35
Vertebrate sub-total		**14.00**	**6.50**	**3.20**	**0.373**
Grand Total		**46.00**	**42.00**	**10.40**	**3.83**

present in tens of thousands per square metre. For every animal seen above ground on moorland soils, there are at least 10,000 more in the soil below! The soil is literally alive and teeming with animals.

Several factors contribute to the abundance of the soil fauna in upland soils, which is equal to or in excess of that found in many lowland soils. Obviously there must be sufficient food to support this number of animals, but equally important is the high rainfall in Upper Teesdale and the almost permanent wetness of the soil. The small size of most soil animals renders them particularly susceptible to desiccation, but the summer droughts, which cause heavy mortality in lowland areas, rarely occur in Upper Teesdale.

The importance of a group can be assessed not only by a number of individuals but

PLATE 21. *Above*, curlew on nest. *Below*, redshank on nest.

PLATE 22. *Above*, Swaledale sheep, Widdybank Fell. *Below*, emperor moth (*Saturnia pavonia*) on heather.

also by the weight of these living organisms. Table 13 shows the total dry weight of each group present in a square metre of each of the four soil types. This way of looking at the information reveals a different picture; nematodes become less important and earthworms become the dominant animal on both mineral soil areas, with pot-worms and cranefly larvae (leatherjackets) making appreciable contributions to the total. These last two groups are also important in the peat soils, but earthworms are virtually absent and contribute little. Above ground, sheep contribute the only appreciable weight and their preference for limestone grassland and dislike of blanket bog is clearly shown.

On the mineral soils there is just over 40g dry weight of animal material per square metre, and three-quarters of this is soil animals. The peat soils support a smaller total weight of animals and the blanket bog (which covers much of Upper Teesdale) has less than a tenth of the weight of animal material that is found on the mineral soils. It is instructive to compare the weight of soil animals with that of sheep. On limestone grassland, and areas dominated by the moor rush, the weight of the soil animals in twice, on alluvial grassland five times, and on blanket bog nine times, that of the sheep.

The difference between the fauna on the blanket peat and on the mineral soils contributes largely to the different natures of the two soils. The absence of earthworms and the reduction in the total weights of pot-worms, cranefly larvae and sheep on the bog accounts for much of the peat accumulation; if these areas had a comparable soil fauna to that on the mineral soils, there would be little plant material left unconsumed. On mineral soils, it has been estimated that at least 80% of the annual plant production is eaten by animals and the remainder (and the animals' droppings) are consumed mainly by bacteria and fungi. In contrast, less than 10% of the plant production on the blanket bog is ingested by animals and the proportion which is not consumed by bacteria and fungi enters a zone without oxygen and accumulates as peat.

The reasons for the much smaller soil fauna on blanket bog are under investigation. Animals have up to ten times the concentration of minerals, including nitrogen, phosphorus and calcium, that is found in plants. These higher concentrations are essential for the function of the nervous system and in the use of muscles in locomotion and feeding. Blanket peat isolates the root system of bog plants from the underlying bed-rock, which is the normal source of minerals, and since the heavy rainfall leaches minerals out of the peat, the plants which grow on the peat have low concentrations of minerals such as nitrogen and phosphorus. Consequently, animals on blanket bog, and perhaps other areas, have to be highly selective feeders, and although there is an abundance of energy foods, they select those plants or parts of plants which are relatively high in minerals, and ignore the rest. Sheep and grouse have already been demonstrated as being highly selective feeders, choosing those plants with above average mineral content, and there is reason to believe that the same is true of many invertebrates. Further evidence for this contention has been obtained by fertilizing vegetation with nitrogen or phosphorus and this treatment has resulted in significant increases in the soil fauna and the rate of consumption of plant material.

The relatively unproductive (to man) nature of much of Upper Teesdale may be one reason why so many unusual and interesting animals still survive there. One day, man may learn to use such areas for more intensive food production and this will undoubtedly bring changes. Before this occurs, we have much to learn about the large number of animals found in Upper Teesdale and similar areas.

CHAPTER 9

The Freshwaters of the Cow Green Area Before and After Impoundment, with Special Reference to the Fauna

Introduction and Brief Description of the Impoundment

THE Cow Green dam was completed in June 1970 and the reservoir began to fill during July of that year. By the spring of 1971 the water was only about 3.5m below top water level, and the first overflow from the reservoir took place in January 1972.

Detailed descriptions of the river Tees and its tributaries within the Cow Green area before impoundment have been published by members of the Freshwater Biological Association's Cow Green team. It is a stony upland stream subject in times of heavy rainfall to very severe spates during which the river carries large quantities of suspended solids, chiefly eroded peat, probably amounting annually to several million kg dry weight. In consequence of the 'flashy' nature of the river, macroscopic aquatic vegetation is sparse (p. 191) and consists chiefly of streamers of filamentous algae which develop on the river bed in the slower-flowing reaches during dry periods and are quickly scoured off in times of spate. The chemical composition of the river water varies considerably with discharge (volume flowing per unit time).

The invertebrate fauna of the Tees before impoundment consisted chiefly of larvae of stone-flies (*Plecoptera*) and may-flies (*Ephemeroptera*) with a population density of about 1000 animals per square metre.

A survey of fish populations revealed the presence of brown trout (*Salmo trutta*), minnow (*Phoxinus phoxinus*) and bullhead (*Cottus gobio*, Plate 31). As expected, no migratory species such as salmon or sea trout were found, these species being unable to negotiate large waterfalls such as High Force and Cauldron Snout. Prior to dam-construction the trout was widespread throughout the Tees and its tributaries, whilst the minnow was confined to the Tees and the lowermost reaches of a few tributaries and was nowhere found above top water level of the projected reservoir. The bullhead (Plate 31) was most abundant in the main river. It also occurred within the lower reaches of some of the tributaries entering at Cow Green, but always below the proposed top water level of the future reservoir, though it was found in some heads-treams on the Moor House National Nature Reserve up to an altitude of 628m.

Other features of the pre-impoundment fish populations, as compared with lowland populations, were the slow growth of the trout, the relatively low population-densities (0–0.06 trout per square metre in the Tees, 0.10–1.4 in tributaries), and the low annual production (0.7g fresh weight of trout per square metre in the Tees,

4.4–10.9 in tributaries). In addition both bullhead and trout had a high annual survival rate. In Trout Beck the fraction of the trout present at a given time which were
still alive one year later was estimated at 0.52, compared with 0.095 for a southern
chalk stream. Another notable feature was the considerable year-to-year variation in
the numbers of trout and bullhead fry present in midsummer. This appears to reflect
variation in survival during the egg or alevin stages rather than in the success of the
spawning process. The relatively high survival rate of these fish probably reflects a
low metabolic rate. This is likely to be of considerable value to the species, since
growth in weight is spread over a number of year-classes, giving a more efficient
utilization of available resources. It also ensures that, in any given year, several year-
classes participate in reproduction and this can be regarded as an insurance against
the effects of a succession of years of poor or negligible recruitment.

Physical and Chemical Changes Resulting from Impoundment

Following impoundment the total surface-area of water within the Cow Green basin
was increased about twenty-fold, and it is important to examine the physical and
chemical consequences of the creation of this large man-made lake (312ha) before
considering the effects upon the aquatic fauna. Basically it constitutes a 'buffer zone'
in which the large and often rapid environmental fluctuations observable in the
natural river are appreciably smoothed out.

   i. Figure 30a shows the manner in which the impoundment modifies the annual
cycle of water temperature in the Tees immediately downstream of the dam. The rise
in water temperature in spring and early summer is delayed by about one month and
the fall in autumn by about two weeks. In addition, the summer peak of water
temperature is reduced by almost 2°C. The monthly means of daily temperature range
(maximum–minimum) are shown in Fig. 30b and the effect of impoundment in reducing short-term temperature fluctuations is very striking.

   ii. Within the Tees system the concentrations of most of the common elements in
solution in the water change with varying rates of flow. Thus the calcium concentration in the natural Tees at Cow Green varied from at least 37 parts per million in dry
weather to about 3.5 during spates. Passage through the reservoir reduces the range
of variation to 6.4–8.1 parts per million.

   iii. Downstream of the dam the severe flash spates and the very low dry weather
flows, typical of the natural Tees, are eliminated. In addition to any direct influence
which this more even flow may have on the aquatic fauna, it has also permitted the
development of a permanent vegetational cover, chiefly of algae and mosses, on the
river bed. This in its turn provides additional cover for the fauna.

   iv. Most of the suspended solids brought into the reservoir will settle there, so that
the impoundment will markedly reduce the amount carried by the Tees downstream
of the dam. It is also likely that such suspended solids as do pass through the reservoir
will undergo qualitative changes before they are finally discharged.

   Within the reservoir itself the effects of impoundment have been even more
marked. The following points are noteworthy.

   i. Creation and filling of the reservoir led to the submergence of large quantities of
terrestrial vegetation which can be expected to take some years to decompose. In the

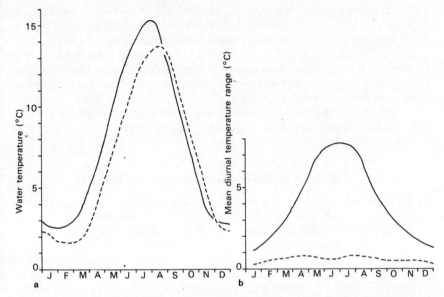

FIG. 30. The effect of impoundment upon water temperature regime in the River Tees below the site of Cow Green dam: *a*, annual water temperature cycle (based on monthly means) in the natural Tees (solid line) and the regulated Tees (broken line); *b*, annual cycle of daily temperature range (maximum–minimum), based on monthly means.

meantime this is a potential source of food and mineral nutrients for the aquatic flora and fauna. Large quantities of terrestrial animal material were also inundated (p. 183).

ii. Few, if any, elements of the aquatic fauna, least of all the fish, are capable of increasing their numbers at a rate matching that at which new aquatic habitats were being produced during the filling of the reservoir. The population-density of aquatic animals was therefore initially low and, as will be shown below, the fish populations took several years to increase in response to the increase in the available habitat. There is the further complication that the change has been from a stony upland river to a large body of standing water.

iii. As already noted, a quantity of suspended solids settles out within the reservoir, the amount probably being about 4 million kg each year. This material will gradually alter the nature of the bed of the reservoir, and, since most of the suspended solids are organic, they will form a potential source of food for detritus-feeding invertebrates.

iv. In many large and relatively deep lakes 'thermal stratification' occurs during the summer, an upper warm layer of water floating upon a colder and denser layer throughout the warmer part of the year. During this period the cold lower layer (hypolimnion) becomes rich in mineral nutrients but depleted of dissolved oxygen, whilst the upper layer (epilimnion) has adequate dissolved oxygen but may become depleted of mineral nutrients. In many lakes thermal stratification occurs annually and is so stable that it does not break down until the onset of cooler and more windy weather during autumn and early winter. The Cow Green reservoir, however, is relatively shallow (maximum depth 23m) and in an exposed position. Thermal stratification occurs comparatively rarely and lasts only until the arrival, usually within a fortnight, of a spell of cooler and more windy weather. For most practical purposes, therefore, Cow Green reservoir can be regarded as a body of water which is almost uniform, throughout the depth range and at all times of year, in ionic composition, temperature and concentration of dissolved oxygen. In ionic content and temperature the water is very similar to that of the Tees below the dam (p. 180), particularly in that short-term fluctuations are considerably smaller than in the natural river.

Effects of Impoundment on Aquatic Invertebrates

Data collected by P. D. Armitage show that within the reservoir the typical fauna of a stony upland river, chiefly of the may-flies *Rhithrogena semicolorata* and *Baetis rhodani* and the stone-flies *Leuctra moselyi* and *L. inermis*, has been largely replaced by other species and groups and in particular by aquatic worms, the water-shrimp *Gammarus pulex*, the leech *Glossiphonia complanata* and non-biting midges (*Chironomidae*). There has also been an appreciable increase in the population-density and total weight of the bottom fauna compared with that of the river. In addition, impoundment was quickly followed by the development of zooplankton (chiefly *Daphnia hyalina*) within the reservoir.

Further work by the same author shows that there have also been major changes in the invertebrate fauna of the Tees immediately below the dam. Notable features are increases in numbers of may-flies of the genus *Baetis* and of non-biting midges, and corresponding decreases in may-flies of the family *Ecdyonuridae* and of stone-flies. The coelenterate *Hydra vulgaris* and small worms of the genus *Nais*, formerly absent or scarce, now contribute substantially to the total fauna. Armitage lists seven species, including five stone-flies and a may-fly, found in this portion of the river before impoundment but not seen since. He also lists eleven species of various groups which have appeared only since impoundment. It is important to note, however, that all these species have been recorded elsewhere in the district and most of them are of widespread occurrence, and that all seven species lost from this part of the Tees are known from other localities in Upper Teesdale. One aquatic species seems to have been lost from the reservoir basin. A small isolated population of the large may-fly *Ephemera danica*, whose larvae burrow in the stream-bed where there is sand or fine gravel, occurred in the lower reaches of Dubby Sike but has not been seen since they were covered by the reservoir. Deposits of sand or fine gravel are scarce in the Upper Tees and Butcher, Longwell & Pentelow noted in 1937 that *Ephemera danica* was uncommon in the Tees and that larvae had been found by them only near Eryholme, about 83km downstream from Cow Green.

As zooplankton developed within the reservoir, quantities were discharged in the water passing the dam. Armitage & Capper estimated the annual output at about 150kg dry weight, chiefly of *Daphnia hyalina*, and found that it rapidly settled, only 1–2% remaining in suspension at a point 6.5km downstream from the dam. They also estimated that within 0.4km downstream from the dam, and during the period of maximal concentration in August and September, the material settles out at a daily rate of 0.19g dry weight per square metre. This is probably a negligible input of animal material to the river as a whole but is an appreciable addition of potential food material for detritus-feeders over several kilometres just below the dam.

Effects of Impoundment on Fish Population

As already noted, fish populations may take several years to complete their response to environmental changes. Observations on the fish at Cow Green by the Freshwater Biological Association's team are still in progress and no comprehensive account of the effects of impoundment can yet be given, but there is already information on certain points.

THE FOOD OF FISH

Over 300ha were submerged by the filling of the reservoir, including a good deal of limestone and alluvial grassland on soils with fairly abundant earthworms. It is estimated that about 95,000kg fresh weight of earthworms and 35,000kg of larval craneflies were submerged, together with smaller quantities of other terrestrial invertebrates. Earthworms have been shown by Roots to survive immersion for 8–12 months and could therefore have provided food for fish for considerably longer than the time taken for the reservoir to fill, as Campbell showed from the presence of earthworms in the stomachs of trout in two Scottish lochs after artificial raising of the water level. The stomachs of trout in the new Cow Green reservoir were packed with terrestrial invertebrates, chiefly earthworms, from the latter part of 1970 until the early spring of 1973. During this period there was a steady development of both the planktonic and the bottom-dwelling invertebrate fauna of the reservoir and, from 1973 onwards, aquatic organisms formed the greater part of the food of the trout.

Downstream from the dam most of the observed changes in composition of the invertebrate fauna were reflected in the stomach contents of the fish, but there were a few interesting exceptions. First, although Armitage found large numbers of *Hydra* and small aquatic worms in the Tees below the dam, they were not identified in any fish stomachs after impoundment. It is known, however, that small aquatic worms rapidly become unrecognizable in fish stomachs, and the same is probably true of *Hydra*. Secondly, although the presence of zooplankton and other small crustaceans within the reservoir was reflected in the stomach contents of all three species, in the river downstream of the dam the trout have been shown to consume drifting zooplankton but the bullheads do not appear to do so. A satisfactory explanation of this cannot be expected until more is known about the feeding behaviour of the bullhead in flowing water.

FISH FECUNDITY

In general, the number of eggs developed each year by a sexually mature female fish of a given species within a stable environment is a function of the size of the fish, though there will, of course, be some variation between individual fish and also some year-to-year variation. A large environmental change such as an impoundment might, however, bring about a change in fecundity. This could take either or both of two basic forms. First, the relationship between fish length and egg number may remain the same, but a change in growth-rate may lead to a change in the average size of the spawning females and hence to a change in the average number of eggs laid by each female. For example, the size of trout in the reservoir is now much greater than in the Tees and the average number of eggs laid per female is consequently considerably greater. Secondly, fecundity can change through a change in the number of eggs produced by a fish of given size. This will modify the egg output of the population even if there has been no change in the average size of the spawning females. This type of change is exemplified by the bullheads in the Tees below the dam. Their fecundity appeared to be falling during the years 1971–1973, and in 1974 and 1975 it was significantly lower than in the pre-impoundment period. During the years of transition a substantial proportion of the breeding population may be supposed to have been present before impoundment, their fecundity being determined, at least in part, by conditions during the early part of their lives. Figure 31 compares the calculated

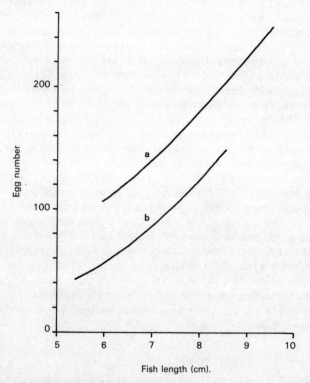

FIG. 31. The relationship between length (cm) and egg number for female bullheads in the River Tees between the foot of Cauldron Snout and the confluence of Maize Beck: *a*, before regulation; *b*, during 1974 and 1975.

relationships between fish length and egg number during the pre-impoundment period and during 1974 and 1975. It will be seen that there has been a great reduction in the number of eggs laid by a fish of any given size, this being about 39% for a fish 7cm long. J. C. L. Edwards has observed a very similar reduction for minnows in the reservoir basin following impoundment.

SPAWNING TIME OF FISH

Within the reservoir basin before impoundment there was little year-to-year variation in the mean length of minnows in the Tees at any given time during the first year of

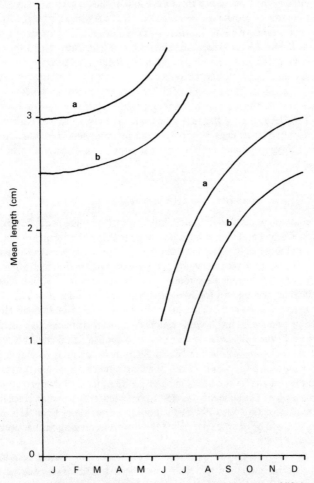

FIG. 32. Observed mean length (cm) of minnows during their first year of life in a, the River Tees and b, in Cow Green reservoir.

life, and this was also true of fish hatched during the transitional year 1970. During 1971–1975 there was again little year-to-year variation in the growth of minnow fry but the mean length on any particular date was appreciably smaller than in the years before 1971 (Fig. 32). More detailed studies by J. C. L. Edwards have shown that this reduction results from later oviposition, possibly in response to the delayed temperature-rise in spring. There is also some reduction in growth during the later years of life, probably due again to the changed temperature regime.

FISH GROWTH

The growth-rate of fish might be expected to vary considerably with large changes of environment, and the Cow Green trout have in fact shown such a change. A marked increase in the rate of growth and average length of the reservoir trout was apparent as early as the autumn of 1970, but there was only a slight decrease during the period 1972–1975. Figure 33 compares the growth of two fish, one entering the river Tees from a nursery stream at 1-year old and 7.5cm long, the other entering the reservoir at the same age and length. It can be seen that the reservoir fish may be expected to reach a length of 34cm (and a weight of about 454g or 1lb) when 4 years old, while the river trout would be less than 20cm long (and only c. 100g in weight) at the same age. Because of the large size of the reservoir trout the average sexually mature female now lays more and larger eggs. A parallel trend since impoundment has been towards smaller year-to-year variation in the summer population-density of trout fry in the afferent becks.

DISTRIBUTION AND MOVEMENTS OF FISH

Before impoundment, as already noted, bullheads in the small becks flowing directly into the Cow Green basin were confined to reaches below the future top water level of the reservoir. Immediately after impoundment, therefore, a breeding population of bullheads was present in the reservoir but there were none in the small afferent becks. By 1972, however, bullheads were found from time to time in most of the becks, and in Lodgegill Sike they are now found regularly at 0.24km and in Red Sike (Fig. 24, p. 143) have been recorded at 0.30km upstream of top water level. In Near Hole Sike a small breeding population has become established, but this appears to be exceptional: in all other becks the bullheads are very largely older fish and there is no evidence of successful reproduction within the becks. Such evidence as is available suggests, indeed, that these fish form part of the breeding population within the reservoir in spring and that they enter the becks in early summer, most of them returning to the reservoir in autumn. The bullhead has clearly extended its distribution since impoundment and may have developed a hitherto unobserved migratory habit. It is difficult to see why this should be or what prevented the fish from ranging further up the becks before impoundment.

Within the Cow Green system the trout have always shown a degree of migratory behaviour. Before impoundment each small beck had its own resident stock of sexually mature fish and most of those in the Tees itself at Cow Green spawned within the afferent becks or in the headwaters. Recruitment to the river population was

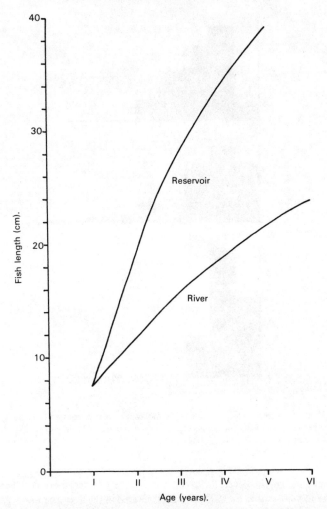

FIG. 33. Growth of hypothetical trout in the River Tees (before impoundment) and in Cow Green reservoir. Note that both fish have been assumed to live in an afferent beck, reached a length of 7·5cm at one year old, and then migrated to the river/reservoir. The growth is based on population averages.

chiefly through beck fish entering the main river. After impoundment there were similar interchanges of trout between the reservoir and the becks. Careful reading of the scales can often show when an individual trout left a beck and entered the river or reservoir, and it seems usually to have taken place in winter, at the end of the year's growth. Figure 34 shows results for the Tees before impoundment and for the reservoir during 1971 and 1973. Before impoundment fewer than 10% moved into the Tees from becks during the first year and over 85% in the second to fourth years.

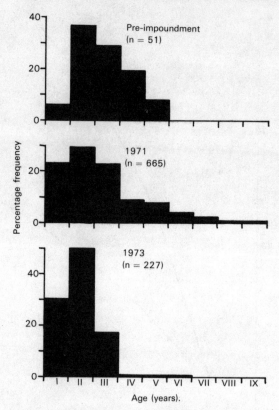

FIG. 34. Percentage frequency distributions of the ages at which trout entered the River Tees during the pre-impoundment period, and the reservoir during 1971 and 1973. n = number of fish upon which each distribution is based.

After impoundment, however, the average age at entry to the reservoir fell gradually from year to year so that by 1971 over 20% entered in the first year and 75% by the third year. By 1973 over 30% entered in the first year and only a negligible number in years after the third.

FISH NUMBERS

Estimates of trout numbers within the reservoir are being obtained from a tagging programme (Plate 23), but it will be some time before recoveries are sufficiently numerous for reliable estimates to be made. Some idea of the changes taking place can meanwhile be obtained by using a standard method of capture. Figure 35 shows the average catch taken in 100 hauls of a seine net on two occasions each year, only fish of 15cm or more in length being included because smaller fish can escape through the net and are therefore not sampled efficiently. The data suggest that the numbers of

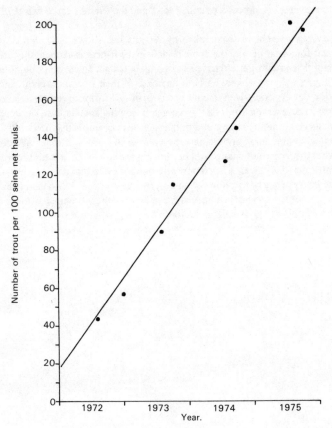

FIG. 35. The average number of trout with length 15cm or more caught in 100 standard hauls of a seine net in July and September of each of the years 1972–1975 inclusive. A calculated line has been fitted to the points.

large trout have increased about five-fold between July 1972 and September 1975 with, as yet, no sign of levelling off, though this must take place eventually. It is likely, too, that this change in numbers will lead to reductions in growth-rate, fecundity or survival-rate.

Cow Green Reservoir as a Sporting Fishery

Before impoundment the river Tees at Cow Green had a sparse population of slow-growing trout. The average size was small, few surviving to attain 18cm in length. The reservoir has never been stocked artificially but the indigenous trout have so increased in numbers and growth-rate as to make it a viable sporting fishery. Visits by anglers rose from 357 in 1971 to 1083 in 1974. The total catch during these four years was

1917 trout averaging almost a pound (446g), and the average catch was 0.72 fish per angler-visit.

The average weight of trout taken by anglers has shown little sign of decrease during this four-year period, but some decline in the fishery is likely in the future. The number of fish caught per angler-visit is unlikely to fall, since the population is still increasing, but there is likely to be a decrease in their average weight. Increasing population-density could lead to either or both of two forms of response: a reduction in growth-rate, reservoir trout of a given age becoming smaller than at present; or a reduced survival-rate, resulting in a population with younger fish predominating, so that even without a fall in growth-rate the average size will be smaller. We do not yet know what the pattern of change will be, and it is the aim of the present programme of the Freshwater Biological Association at Cow Green to maintain quantitative surveillance of the trout population for some years to come. If a decline of the fishery becomes obvious, it should then be possible to analyse the mechanisms at work and to suggest ways of remedying the situation.

CHAPTER 10

The Vegetation of the River Tees above Middleton

Changes in the Large-Aquatic Flora of the Cow Green Basin

BEFORE inundation more than half of the bottom of the Cow Green basin consisted of alluvial flats (in black in the map, Fig. 36, below) over which the river changed its course from time to time, leaving ponds in abandoned channels, and through which

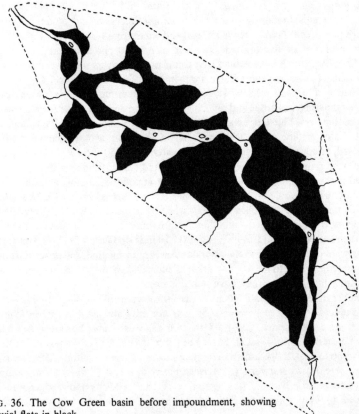

FIG. 36. The Cow Green basin before impoundment, showing alluvial flats in black.

191

the lower courses of the tributary becks lacked the impetuosity characteristic of upland streams. Here, free from the savage scouring which made most of the Upper Tees seem almost barren botanically, some large aquatic plants were able to establish themselves. Just above Cauldron Snout the lowest 2km of the main river, the so-called Wheel (or Weel) of the Tees, was also slow-flowing and free from severe scouring and here too there was some conspicuous aquatic vegetation. This stretch was still recovering from an earlier period when the aquatic flora had been sparse and species-poor.

The aquatic vegetation of Upper Teesdale had until quite recently (p. 193) received little attention apart from publications by R. W. Butcher in 1933 and 1937, but a book attributed to a Mr Garland and believed to have been published in 1804 has an interesting small map in which the lower half of the Wheel is shown as of uneven width, widening in two places to make room for islands. In 1933, when the present writer first saw it, it was everywhere about 35m wide, had no islands, and was indeed rather a dull place. Butcher, nevertheless, noted it as exceptional. Elsewhere in the upper 65km of the Tees he found only four species of macroscopic plants, none of them flowering plants; but in the Wheel he saw marsh horsetail (*Equisetum palustre*), a starwort (*Callitriche intermedia*), spiked water-milfoil (*Myriophyllum spicatum*), unbranched and floating bur-reed (*Sparganium emersum* and *S. angustifolium*), reddish pondweed (*Potamogeton alpinus*) and willow moss (*Fontinalis antipyretica*): seven species in all, five of them flowering plants and one a horsetail.

A few years later Butcher would have found nothing except thin marginal fringes of bottle sedge (*Carex rostrata*). The barytes mine on Cow Green (Fig. 24, p. 143) had reopened and in 1937 a heavy sludge began to reach the river, burying all plants between the fringes of sedge and reducing the average depth of water from 1m to only a few centimetres. The sludge was not toxic, but nevertheless all the buried plants were killed. Later settling-ponds were installed at the mine and the sludge gradually dispersed, restoring the original depth of water. By 1950 there were signs that the Wheel was returning to its condition in Garland's day. Bottle sedge ceased to be limited to the margins, a thin growth of it appearing off the left bank at the lower end. A kilometre upstream, at Black Brae Corner, a shoal formed and by 1953 had almost reached the surface. The following year, when the mine closed, it had grown into an island and continued to grow until, just before inundation, it was 2000sq m in area with the river widened at this point as at the islands on Garland's map. Two further shoals were developing upstream and downstream of the first, the uppermost being almost certainly due to the accumulation of silt round submerged reddish pondweed, suggesting that all three may have had this origin.

Butcher noted that aquatic plants in the Wheel were only in 'small quantities', but at the time of submergence vegetation was not only abundant but twice as many species were represented. By 1968 the full list was: water horsetail (*Equisetum fluviatile*) and marsh horsetail, lesser spearwort (*Ranunculus flammula*), common water-crowfoot (*R. peltatus*), alternate-flowered water-milfoil (*Myriophyllum alterniflorum*), two starworts (*Callitriche platycarpa* and *C. intermedia*), common floating-leaved pondweed (*Potamogeton natans*) and reddish pondweed, unbranched bur-reed, common spike-rush (*Eleocharis palustris*), bottle sedge and two stoneworts

PLATE 23. *Above*, bullhead (*Cottus gobio*). *Below*, release of young tagged trout into the reservoir.

PLATE 24. *Above*, margin of Cow Green reservoir showing erosion by wave action. *Below*, rafts of dead bottle sedge (*Carex rostrata*) becoming detached from the margin of the reservoir.

(a *Chara* and a *Nitella*). The mouths of tributary becks and frequently submerged ground adjoining the river provided additional species which included blinks (*Montia fontana*), marsh arrow-grass (*Triglochin palustris*), bog pondweed (*Potamogeton polygonifolius*) and flote-grass (*Glyceria fluitans*). The downstream kilometre of the Wheel, the part shown on Garland's map, was still of even width and void of islands. Soundings, however, showed some shallowing half-way along and off the right bank, where water horsetail had appeared with floating-leaved pondweed outside it; and the sedge off the left bank at the lower end was now mixed with water horsetail and had developed into a large mat of vegetation joined to the bank and blocking a quarter of the channel. About 100m upstream there was a bed of the two stoneworts. Opposite this, off the right bank, was a shoot of water-milfoil and another had found its way down the rapids into a comparatively quiet pool at the head of Cauldron Snout: the main mass was upstream of Black Brae Corner. Further evidence that regeneration was proceeding downstream was provided by the water-crowfoot which had previously been no nearer than Wheel Head but in 1966 jumped a kilometre to colonize the shoal just below Black Brae Corner.

An explanation of these changes since Garland's day is not hard to find. During the nineteenth century some of the miner-smallholders in the upper dale pastured geese in the Cow Green basin, and 60 or 70 of the voracious birds were taken to the Wheel each May and left there until October. Over the years this must have resulted in a depletion of the vegetation and a consequent washing away of the islands of plant-trapped silt. But the sludge that was fatal to the plants in 1937 was also injurious to the geese, and after that year they were no longer summered in the basin. It is unfortunate that the Wheel has been lost just when its vegetation was recovering from this period of impoverishment.

In standing water on the alluvial flats, often at some distance from the Wheel, there were to be found not only the species listed above but, in addition, Lenormand's water-crowfoot (*Ranunculus omiophyllus*), marsh cinquefoil (*Potentilla palustris*), common starwort (*Callitriche stagnalis*), bog-bean (*Menyanthes trifoliata*), marsh speedwell (*Veronica scutellata*), jointed rush (*Juncus articulatus*) and bulbous rush (*J. bulbosus*) and also, in one of the ponds in an old channel of the river, northern water sedge (*Carex aquatilis*). This last is an exclusively northern species, common in arctic and sub-arctic Scandinavia and extending eastwards through northern Russia into Siberia. Its discovery at Cow Green, almost at its southern limit, was an interesting addition to the list of plant species whose Teesdale sites are at some distance from their nearest localities elsewhere. Like the common water-crowfoot, the water-milfoil and the reddish pondweed, this sedge seems to have been lost from the Cow Green area since the filling of the reservoir, but it has happily been found again recently near Middleton (p. 194). Of the 26 species of large aquatics listed for the Cow Green basin before impoundment only 11 could still be seen in the reservoir in 1973, but the marsh speedwell had returned by 1975 and 8 others, though missing from the reservoir itself, are still growing not far away, as is the floating bur-reed, recorded by Butcher but not seen in 1968.

Finally, Plate 32 shows some of the rafts of bottle sedge that rose to the surface soon after the reservoir had filled, drifting in the wind until they finally stranded. This seems to have taken place where the sedge was growing in a shallow organic soil over clay impenetrable by its roots and where rhizomes and roots were consequently matted together more or less in one plane.

The Macroscopic Vegetation between Cow Green and Middleton

The impounding of the Tees above Cauldron Snout and the resulting partial regulation of its flow, coupled with the proposed transfer of water from the Tyne, stimulated a long overdue survey of the river's macroscopic vegetation in the summer of 1975. A brief account is given of a few of the 66 species found with at least their basal parts permanently submerged, even during periods of lowest flow, within the 10km stretches upstream and downstream of High Force (see map 37 below). Of 24 species

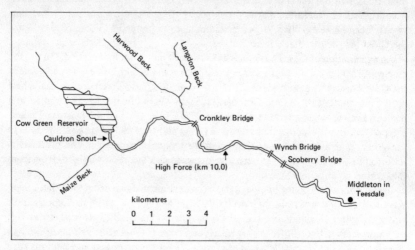

FIG. 37. Map showing the upper 20km of the stretch of the Tees surveyed for large aquatic plants in the summer of 1975.

totally or almost totally confined to submerged habitats, all but two were algae or bryophytes, these two being an encrusting lichen of the genus *Verrucaria*, which was very abundant and found in every half-kilometre of the surveyed stretches, and the alternate-flowered water-milfoil, found rarely and only above High Force. The algae ranged from small encrusting forms to the long filamentous growths of the abundant red alga *Lemanea fluviatilis* and of several green algae including species of *Cladophora*, *Oedogonium* and *Ulothrix*. The standing crop of algae fluctuates markedly from season to season, but the bryophyte population seems more stable. Four mosses were particularly frequent: *Hygrohypnum ochraceum*, *H. luridum*, *Eurhynchium riparioides* and *Fontinalis antipyretica*, all typical of similar habitats in other rivers of north-east England and south-east Scotland. In contrast, of the 21 species only rarely found submerged and more frequent in periodically submerged habitats, 15 were emergent vascular plants, including bottle sedge (*Carex rostrata*), carnation sedge (*C. panicea*) and glaucous sedge (*C. flacca*), soft rush (*Juncus effusus*), water-cress (*Rorippa nasturtium-aquaticum*), lesser spearwort (*Ranunculus flammula*), marsh arrow-grass (*Triglochin palustris*) and water horsetail (*Equisetum fluviatile*).

Three of the species of algae observed merit special mention: *Nostoc parmelioides Rhodoplax schinzii* and *Heribaudiella fluviatilis* have either never or only rarely been recorded previously from Britain. Until 1972 *Heribaudiella*, one of the very few brown algae of fresh water, was known only from a few fast-flowing streams in north Devon. *Nostoc parmelioides* has a globular thallus consisting of a blue-green alga in symbiotic association with a midge larva. It had previously been known to occur only in three rivers in the British Isles. *Rhodoplax* is a green alga with red pigmentation which imparts a crimson colour to all rock surfaces it colonizes. It was found only in stretches of river where the flow is torrential, in agreement with the habitat described for it in continental Europe. Neither *Nostoc parmelioides* nor *Rhodoplax* had been recorded for this country until the recent surveys of rivers in north-east England. All three are often quite frequent in suitable habitats, suggesting that some species regarded here as rare may not have been sought with sufficient diligence.

The one bryophyte worthy of special note is *Grimmia agassizii*, recently found by H. J. B. Birks in central Scotland but hitherto unrecorded in England. This is a species widespread in Scandinavia on wet rocks in streams and lakes and in sub-alpine rivers carrying melt-water in summer. It is almost certainly absent from the upper parts of the Wear, Tweed and Teviot, though almost all other bryophytes found in the Tees are also present in them. It would be interesting to confirm this very restricted occurrence.

The alternate-flowered water-milfoil and the northern water sedge (*Carex aquatilis*) were previously thought to be confined to the Wheel and to have been lost after inundation. The former is abundant only in one site opposite Falcon Clints but seems well established there. The finding of the sedge is important because it is at the southern limit of its British distribution and this is only the third reliable record for it in England.

Butcher (p. 191) listed only four species of macroscopic plants from the uppermost 65km of the Tees, excluding the Wheel, suggesting that he overlooked all but the best known mosses and did not attempt to record algae. The results of the recent survey show the flora of the upper reaches of the Tees to be typical of fast-flowing upland British rivers and very much the same as in the upper Tweed. In both the only non-emergent vascular plants are the starworts (*Callitriche* spp.) and the alternate-flowered water-milfoil. *Grimmia agassizii* is the only species common in the upper Tees which is so far not known from other rivers in England.

Summary, and Consideration
of the Future of Upper Teesdale

IT would probably be true to say that, up to about 1930, much of the biological work on Teesdale was concerned with systematics and plant geography. After that time, though systematists, supported by naturalists, continued to play an important part, other scientists began to take an interest in the remarkable flora and the problems it presented; and this book demonstrates some of the progress they have made. At the same time, zoologists, geologists and geographers have been attracted to work in Teesdale, and have made a contribution to knowledge which is both significant in itself and also of importance in understanding the vegetational history. It should be added that in this book, and hence in this summary, the work of the geologists, which is now very extensive, is only referred to as it bears on the natural history. Nor will any attempt be made here to review in detail the work in biology and geology which has been done on the Moor House National Nature Reserve, though much of this is relevant, and many authors of this book have taken it into consideration. It is upon the Upper Teesdale Reserve and the reservoir area that most of the work reported here has been concentrated.

The review begins with a brief introduction which leads to a summary of the history of the vegetation and flora. This is followed by a description of the geographical origins of the plant species and their mode of variation. The nature of the plant communities is then surveyed, first descriptively then analytically. There is an analysis of individual species in terms of population dynamics and then an account of the main environmental factors – climate, rock and soil – which by their interaction control the ecosystems. This in turn leads to a consideration of the Teesdale flora and the reasons for the concentration of so many rare and disjunct species in such a small area. The animal life is briefly surveyed, and then the biology of the reservoir and the streams that run into it. Finally the questions of conservation and its present and future hazards are discussed.

Introduction

As has been pointed out by Professor Clapham in his introductory chapter, the main seed plants of Upper Teesdale had been recognized by the early years of this century; and though additions continued to be made, of which the most notable was that of dwarf birch (*Betula nana*) in 1965 (p. 97), there was not much more to be done in the

196

way of recording. But the detailed distribution of the plants in the dale was not well known, and some of the first advances in this direction were made by Elkington, who produced a detailed map of the distribution of spring gentian (*Gentiana verna*), and Bradshaw, who mapped the species of lady's-mantle (*Alchemilla*). Intensive work on the distribution of the vascular plants and bryophytes of a single important area, that of Widdybank Fell, were made by Bradshaw and a team of voluntary workers over a number of seasons. The data, now stored in the University of Durham, are of great interest in themselves, and they also formed a base for the phytosociological mapping work which was to follow.

A brief mention may be made of two other activities which formed part of the rescue work before the dam was built and which should be put on record. The first was the formation of a collection of herbarium specimens of the flora of the reservoir basin (which included many of the rarities). The second is the formation of two living museums, one at Durham and one at Manchester University, in which small populations of some twenty of the rarer species have been maintained in cultivation.

Quaternary history

As in so many places, the key to the present in Upper Teesdale lies in the past. It was realized a long time ago that the climatic changes of the ice-age, and the cycles of change involved in the advances and retreats of the glaciers, must have had a part to play. The earlier hypotheses centred on perglacial survival, with the rare arctic-alpine plants perched on refuges (nunataks) on mountain tops or ledges which the ice had not reached. This hypothesis was scotched by the geological evidence; and a new hypothesis, which was to be abundantly verified, was put forward by Godwin in 1949. This suggested that the Teesdale 'assemblage' of relict and disjunct species was the remains of a late-glacial flora, a park-like herbaceous flora which had followed the retreating ice-sheets at the end of the last glacial phase. Over most of England this kind of vegetation had disappeared, having been replaced by woodland in the lowlands and peat bog in many upland areas; but here and there, bits and pieces of it had survived. The most obvious survival areas were the tops of the higher mountains in Snowdonia and the Lake District; but in addition, other areas at a lower altitude retained portions of this vegetation and a few of its characteristic species. Upper Teesdale was such an area, but one which had been favoured by fortune in that the number of survivors was unusually large.

This hypothesis called for two main lines of confirmatory evidence. This first was to demonstrate, by investigation of post-glacial fossils, that a late-glacial flora of the kind postulated had actually existed in Upper Teesdale. Such floras were known from many other places in the British Isles, and indeed in western Europe; could the plants be shown to be present in Teesdale as postulated? The second requirement was to explain how Upper Teesdale had managed to acquire and retain such an unusually large proportion of the late-glacial flora. Were some special features of climate and soil involved, and if so, what were they? These two lines of approach form one of the central themes of this book; we shall deal now with the first.

The conclusive evidence has been supplied by Judith Turner, and it is set out in Chapter 4. She has applied the techniques of pollen analysis and radio-carbon dating to investigate the composition and age of a number of peat deposits in Upper Teesdale. The earliest deposit actually in the reservoir area is dated to about 8000 BC, and its composition is very similar to that of deposits of the same date elsewhere in the British Isles. Willow and juniper are both present, as well as two species of saxifrage. By 6800 BC the numbers of herbs had decreased, and birch, pine and hazel had appeared, and from then onwards the trees continued to increase, in places reaching 600m (2000ft), though not as densely as in the lowlands. As time went on there was some deterioration in climate, leading to leaching and peat growth, but most of the area around Cow Green remained wooded, and the vegetation did not change significantly until about 1000–500 BC. And so far as can be seen, the presence of Neolithic man in the area seems to have had little effect on the vegetation.

After 1000 BC, woodland was replaced, on the better-drained soils, by grassland and on the worse-drained soils by blanket bog. The spread of grassland can be dated to 1200–600 BC, and it seems likely to have been due to man and his grazing animals. After this time, the changes in the vegetation of the uplands seem to have been relatively slight.

Against this background, we can now mention the finding and dating of some of the relict Teesdale species. Fossil remains of the dwarf birch, for example, a typical arctic plant, have been found in more than one place, and can be dated back to 10,000 years ago. Pollen grains of the mountain avens (*Dryas octopetala*) also span the same period of time. Pollen grains of the hoary rock-rose (*Helianthemum canum*) and the spring gentian have been dated back to the full forest period, as has the yellow mountain saxifrage (*Saxifraga aizoides*). These examples will suffice to show the comprehensive and convincing evidence of post-glacial survival of relict species which Dr Turner has demonstrated.

One of the questions which she raises, and has often been discussed, is the nature of the habitats which the plants have occupied. During the forest period, there were no large stretches of limestone grassland such as there are today, so that species such as the mountain avens and the gentian may have been restricted to local limestone outcrops (such as eroding sugar-limestone), or calcareous flush areas associated with the streams. Later, when human interference led to the extension of the treeless areas, opportunities for extension of range must have occurred. The mountain avens has remained in a small restricted area on Cronkley Fell; but the gentian has spread far and wide and now occupies an area many square miles in extent.

Not all the rare species have survived: Jacob's ladder (*Polemonium caeruleum*) is recorded from the Upper Teesdale peat at a number of levels over the last 10,000 years, and it survived into the nineteenth century on Dun Fell. It is now extinct; and it serves as a reminder that other species too may disappear, after a long tenure, if they and their habitats are not carefully conserved.

Recent History

Reference has been made above to the comparatively small changes in the upland vegetation of Teesdale in historic times. This theme is taken up by Dr Roberts in his chapter on Man and Land. He distinguishes three phases of human occupation. The first includes the whole of prehistory, the Roman period and early medieval times up to the end of the eleventh century: there is little historical or archaeological evidence on this period, but the broad patterns of the dale as we know it today were laid down. In a second phase, between 1100 and 1600, the present landscape of villages, farm houses and fields was formed; and in the final phase, from 1600 to the present day, the landscape matured into its modern form, with its complex blend of agriculture and industry.

By 1100, it is clear that the dale was settled with small farms, each with its patch of cleared ground, enclosed by a hedge and used for producing grain and hay. Beyond were the unenclosed fells, where beasts could graze under the care of the farmer. Much of the upper dale at this period was under forest law, and was thus an area where beasts of the chase and the surviving woodlands were protected. In the succeeding centuries, there were advances to and retreats from the fell land, but some of the land at the higher levels was brought into cultivation. The most important crop was hay, and there were considerable numbers of both cattle and sheep.

One of the features of life in the dale since the seventeenth century has been a 'dual-economy', in which farmers or members of farming families divided their time between farming and either mining or quarrying. Thus in the early part of the nineteenth century, there was a marked rise in population in the upper part of the dale, stimulated by increased lead-mining. It is doubtful whether lead was mined in Roman times, but it had certainly begun in the sixteenth century and has been important ever since. It is ironic that fluorspar and barytes, waste products of the early miners, are now highly valued. Mining had a physical effect on the landscape in the form of tunnels, 'hushes', enclosures and the like, and its effects can be well seen on Widdybank Fell, where mining has been going on for more than 200 years. Smelting was done in the valleys, e.g. at Middleton, and there was some road-building for the ponies which carried the ore. The industry declined at the end of the nineteenth century, and has only intermittently been revived in war-time.

It is thus probably no accident that the rare plants of Teesdale are found on the high fells which are most distant and isolated, and where man has had the least influence. The mining has always been local; the grazing has not been intensive, and the moors have not been highly suitable for grouse shooting. As regards the meadows along the floor of the valley, these have been developed by draining and by treatment with lime and basic slag over a period of 100 years or more; and though floristically rich, as are many old meadows which acquire the native species such as cowslip, crane's bill and globe flower over the course of time, they do not harbour many of the Teesdale 'assemblage' of arctic-alpine or disjunct species. The main exception is in the species of lady's mantle, of which four or five are found in the meadows and along the roadsides. Three of these find in Teesdale and Weardale their only English locality; and though some are undoubtedly native (e.g. *Alchemilla glomerulans*), others (e.g. *A. subcrenata*) may possibly have been introduced with fodder in the nineteenth century.

The Seed-Plant Flora

The species themselves (at least the seed-plants and ferns) are analysed and described in Chapter 1. The Chapter begins with a geographical analysis, which classifies the species according to the nature and extent of their geographical range. Of the 390 plants classified, about half belong to the *European-Siberian* and *sub-atlantic* groups, and these form the backbone of the flora, as they would in any part of northern England. It is by the comparatively large numbers of the more specialized groups that the Upper Teesdale flora is distinguished. For example, there are two representatives of the *Eurasiatic arctic-montane* group (e.g. alpine forget-me-not, *Myosotis alpestris*), fifteen representatives of the *circumpolar arctic-montane* group (e.g. mountain avens), and ten representatives of the *European or Siberian continental* group (e.g. horse-shoe vetch, *Hippocrepis comosa*). Altogether, species from sixteen different phytogeographical groups are represented; and this diversity reflects the diversity of the late-glacial flora from which many of them are descended, as well as the special features of the Upper Teesdale climate and soil.

Many of the rarer Teesdale species have a markedly disjunct distribution; that is to say, the Teesdale populations are separated by a large gap from the nearest population in Britain or abroad. The question which naturally arises is whether this isolation has led to evolutionary change, the isolated populations diverging from one another in the course of time, as they adapt, each to its own local environment. The nature and extent of these changes, in a series of species, is described in Chapter 1 by Dr Elkington. One kind of variation which is explored is chromosomal. Thus, are Teesdale populations polyploid, as compared with diploid populations elsewhere, or vice-versa? One example is the horse-shoe vetch, where diploids are found in Derbyshire and south-west England in ungrazed habitats, and tetraploids in north and central England in grazed habitats. The Teesdale population, which occurs only on sheep-grazed grassland on Cronkley Fell, is tetraploid, as expected.

A second kind of genotypic variation is not associated with chromosome change, but is marked by differences in form, habit and soil preference. As regards habitat, several species have prostrate or dwarf varieties which are probably conditioned, at least in part, by sheep-grazing (as in the tetraploid horse-shoe vetch mentioned above). Populations of several species are also adapted to soils rich in lead. Especially interesting are the studies of the variation associated with geographical isolation. Dr Elkington discusses six examples, of which the spring gentian is typical. This species is not found elsewhere in Great Britain, but is known from western Ireland; and Elkington compares Teesdale, Irish and continental populations (from the Alps and Pyrenees). Both field samples and plants in cultivation have been compared; and significant differences have been observed, almost certainly genotypic, in the shape of both the leaves and the calyx. It was found that in the alpine plants there was a progressive change in leaf-form which was correlated with altitude. The Teesdale plants resembled the alpine populations from the highest altitudes, while the Irish plants differed significantly from both, though resembling more the lower alpine populations. It is possible that the differences in leaf shape are related to the amount of heat lost from the leaves in moving air; and this explanation would fit the differences observed, though it is not proven.

Another kind of variation, described as polymorphic, is one in which variants within a population occur in a proportion which may differ from one population to the next. Thus in the out-breeding mountain avens, British populations vary in the number of branched hairs on the veins on the underside of the leaves (Fig. 6). A similar kind of variation is found in the inbreeding species, hoary whitlow-grass (*Draba incana*). Here the variable character is the number of stellate hairs on the leaf, and their distribution between upper and lower surfaces. The Upper Teesdale populations are unique in England in having stellate hairs on the upper surface of the leaves. The variation extends to continental populations. This kind of polymorphism is difficult to explain in adaptive terms, though it is possible that the hair character may be linked with a character of physiological importance which will eventually be revealed by experiment. Physiological variation associated with geographical location has been described by Lloyd, who compared photosynthetic rates in samples from six populations of blue sesleria (*Sesleria albicans*), taken from Upper Teesdale, Malham, Iceland, France, Switzerland and Czechoslovakia. Under uniform conditions, these samples showed significantly different rates of photosynthesis, the lowest being those from the British samples. There were also differences in the stomatal frequencies of the populations, but these were not correlated with photosynthetic rate.

The general conclusion derived from these studies of geographical variation is that, although the Upper Teesdale populations of disjunct species are often slightly different from those elsewhere, the differences in most cases are not great; and in only one case, that of the hoary rock-rose, has the Teesdale population been named as a distinct subspecies. This is in line with the evidence from past history. The Teesdale populations were separated from the general late-glacial flora relatively recently (*c.* 12,000 years ago). It is not to be expected that in this length of time, a considerable amount of evolutionary differentiation would have taken place.

The Plant Communities

Following the discussion of the species of Upper Teesdale comes a description and analysis of the plant communities. Dr Ratcliffe deals first with those well known types of vegetation which are found in many parts of the north of England and which occupy much of the montane areas of the Pennines, including Upper Teesdale (Chapter 3).

Interspersed in these extensive tracts are smaller special habitats often on special rocks and soils, which bear the localized or even unique plant communities which harbour the Teesdale rarities. They are often associated with limestone or the Whin Sill, and in some cases with mineral content of the soil, amount of water movement and other local influences. They are described by Dr Ratcliffe, and also in an interesting survey of Widdybank Fell by Bradshaw and Jones, recently published as a series of vegetation maps with an accompanying booklet. These authors have used the technique of phytosociology to describe a series of named plant associations, both widespread and localized, which cover the Fell. In order to illustrate the types of associations in which some of the rarer species flourish, two (simplified) examples will be quoted here.

The first is from the association named by Bradshaw and Jones *Seslerio-Caricetum pulicaris*, and it is found on Cronkley as well as on Widdybank Fell. It is a grassland with a rather coarse appearance in which blue sesleria and heath grass (*Sieglingia decumbens*) are important as well as sedges and the less conspicuous sheep's fescue and crested hair-grass. They often form a dense vegetation mat underlain by wild thyme and common rock-rose, and various mosses and lichens are also present in the turf. The amount of cover varies greatly, as does the soil, from dry, immature rendzinas to deeper and damper base-rich soils, but always with a high pH, usually 7.0–7.5. This is the association which is found on the sugar limestone and in which Teesdale violet, spring gentian, bitter milkwort and mountain avens are characteristic species.

The second is from the association named *Pinguiculo-Caricetum dioicae*. This includes a range of flush and mire communities of different physiognomies. Some are on flushed calcareous gleys with high pH, others on more peaty soils, with low calcium and lower pH. Cover is rarely complete, often about 80%, and the soils may be stony. One fairly extensive community in this association, which was called by Pigott 'turfy marsh', is characterized by purple moor-grass and broad-leaved cotton-grass, devil's-bit scabious and two rush species. In this community, kobresia and bird's-eye primrose play a large part, and both alpine bartsia and yellow mountain saxifrage occur.

It will be noted that these communities, which between them contain a significant number of rare species, both occur on predominantly alkaline soils, one dry and the other wet, and that both are low-growing and usually open, with less than 100% cover. These features are characteristic of most of the associations in which the rarer species are found.

The phytosociological method of survey used by Bradshaw and Jones has the advantage that the plant communities are named according to a system which is internationally recognized. It is thus possible to identify and compare the Teesdale associations with those in other parts of northern and western Europe. Some years ago a similar phytosociological survey was made of the Moor House National Nature Reserve; and the two surveys taken together present a fairly comprehensive picture of the vegetation of Upper Teesdale. In the interest of both science and conservation, it is much to be desired that the survey be extended to the whole of Upper Teesdale, both inside and outside the reserves.

Population Dynamics

Ecological studies are of many kinds. One of these is population dynamics, which seeks to analyse the composition of a community, not as a static unit, as in phytosociology, but as an ever-changing complex, in which the processes of germination, growth, senescence and death can be followed in detail, and be correlated both with the biology of individual species and the way in which they fit into their environment. A study of this kind, to produce significant results, has to continue for a period of many years; and Dr Bradshaw, in her chapter on this subject (Chapter 2), describes work begun in 1968 which continues to the present day. Her results can be illustrated by reference to three species which reproduce in different ways and have different ecological preferences.

The first is spring gentian. It is surprising to find that, under present conditions, this perennial herb, found mainly on calcareous grassland, reproduces almost entirely by vegetative means. Most flowers and seed-capsules are eaten by grazing animals and seedlings are very rare. The plant maintains itself by producing lateral rosettes from its underground parts. These shoots have a half-life of 3–5 years; and as they die off, they are replaced by new ones at a rate which keeps the populations fairly stable.

Hoary whitlow-grass, on the other hand, is a short-lived perennial which flowers once and then dies; and it is dependent entirely on seed for its reproduction. The reproductive unit, the leafy rosette, has a half-life of 2–3 years, so there is a rapid turnover; and though the proportion of plants flowering in grazed sites is only about 10%, a fair number of seeds is produced, and 10-20% of these develop into seedlings in nature. Dr Bradshaw estimates that for every 1000 seeds produced, there are 8 survivors mature at three years old. This reproductive capacity is sufficient to maintain the populations, which are found on open soils and are often associated with old lead mines.

The third species is the Teesdale violet. Here the reproductive unit for purposes of observation is the vegetative rosette. This species differs from the other two in that it reproduces both vegetatively and by seed (mainly from self-pollinated closed flowers), the two methods contributing practically equal amounts to the stock of new plants. Ecologically also, this species is intermediate between the other two, spanning the gap from closed to open limestone soils.

Quantitative data of this kind, based on careful observation of permanent quadrats over many years, and tracing the history of individual plants, throw a new light on the way in which a species survives the chances and changes of successive seasons. It is also of value in making management plans for the conservation and encouragement of species of special interest.

The Upper Teesdale Flora and Its Environment

The main environmental factors, which are closely related to one another and which interact in a complex way, are those of climate and soil. Soil formation is bound up with the nature of the rock from which it is produced; and Dr Johnson, in Chapter 6, describes geological features of Upper Teesdale, and in particular those which are relevant to soil formation. Thus the combination of Lower Carboniferous clear water limestone, late Carboniferous earth movements and the injection of the Whin Sill produced coarse-grained crystalline marble; and Tertiary and recent erosion, with the Quaternary glaciation, exposed this unusual bedrock. Rendzina soils then developed on the outcropping marble. A geological setting of this type is unknown outside Upper Teesdale in Britain; and this has undoubtedly been one of the important factors in the survival of members of the late-glacial flora, many of which are associated with these rendzinas.

The total range of soils in Upper Teesdale is great; and it includes many which are not unique but are to be found in many parts of northern England. Thus there is a series of podzols, developed from sandstones, shales and non-calcareous boulder clay, and there are extensive areas of peat. Other Teesdale soils have been developed from dolerite, and the acid soils developed from this rock, which may initially contain quite high concentrations of minerals, are of importance for some prominent features of the vegetation, such as juniper heath. The limestone soils have been formed from both altered and unaltered limestone. One notable feature of some of these soils is their deficiency in nitrogen and phosphate. Finally there is an important group of flushed soils developing on calcareous gravels and peats, which form series of habitats for many species. The existence of widespread mining has been described by Dr Roberts in Chapter 7. There are many mine-tips rich in calcite, barytes, fluorite, galena (lead-rich) and sphalerite (zinc-rich) which are important for both vegetation and flora.

A second major factor affecting the vegetation is climate. Systematic observations on climate have been taken at the Moor House Nature Reserve since 1953; and further observations have been made on Widdybank Fell during the past decade. Dr Pigott describes in detail (Chapter 5) the features of this upland climate, with its cool, cloudy, rainy and windy weather, frequently with heavy snow in winter; and he has pointed out its great variability with height, slope and aspect. But it is interesting that the climate of Upper Teesdale is similar to that of other Pennine areas at the same altitude: it has no unique features.

Attention should be drawn to recent experimental investigations on the effects of climate on Teesdale plants. These have included the effects of temperature on leaf area, in which kobresia and sea plantain were used, and the effects of temperature on growth and reproductive capacity. In this series of experiments, a species-pair was used, the lowland orpine (*Sedum telephium*) being compared with the upland rose-root (*S. rosea*).

Also relevant here are observations by Bellamy and his colleagues on productivity. Productivity is controlled by a complex series of factors of which climate and soil nutrients are probably the most important; and it is thus a way of studying the interactions of environmental factors. Bellamy found that some of the flush communities on Widdybank Fell had a low productivity, comparable with that of alpine tundra ecosystems in other parts of the world.

These observations and experiments point the way back to the questions posed in the introduction to this book, viz., how did the rare species reach Upper Teesdale, and why are so many of them concentrated there?

As regards the origin of the rare species, the hypothesis that they are remnants of a late-glacial flora which has persisted to the present day is now well established and authenticated. The other question is a more difficult one to answer. Of course, it should not be forgotten that Upper Teesdale is not the only home of these late-glacial relics, only the most important. Many, such as bird's-eye primrose and mountain avens, are found in other parts of northern England, notably in the Craven district of Yorkshire. This suggests that environmental conditions favouring survival existed over a wide area, but that these conditions were specially favourable in Upper Teesdale; and this hypothesis appears to fit the facts. It would seem that no single factor, by itself, is responsible for survival, but a combination of factors of climate and soil. Thus, as has been pointed out, many of the survivors are sub-arctic species, at the southern end of their geographical range, and possibly limited by summer temperature. It is frequently observed that species at the limits of their climatic range require special conditions of exposure and soil; and as has been shown, in previous chapters, the habitats of the sub-arctic survivors are usually restricted within narrow limits. Again, these species require an unshaded environment with a cool climate; and such conditions are found on the high Teesdale fells, where habitats free of woodland appear to have been present throughout the post-glacial era. Open habitats, too, with not too much competition from other species, are important for many of the survivors; and these are provided in both wet and dry environments (as in the examples cited above, p. 200–1) at places such as Widdybank Fell.

In keeping habitats open, and in limiting the growth of competitors which would interfere with the rare species, soil factors are undoubtedly important. Thus, it has been shown that, on natural phosphate-poor soils on Widdybank Fell, kobresia can compete with sheep's fescue; but addition of phosphate to the soil favours the grass, which may then swamp the kobresia. The occurrence of heavy metals such as lead and zinc in the soils also helps to keep habitats open.

It is perhaps worth emphasizing here that the areas occupied by the rare species in Upper Teesdale are very variable in extent. Some species such as horse-shoe vetch seem to be at the end of their tether, others such as spring gentian are widespread, and could well extend in the future, given the opportunity. At present, grazing restricts the production of seed.

To sum up, it would appear that the survival and persistence of the rare species of the Teesdale flora have been governed by a combination of factors, both historical and environmental. The climate and topography are such that southern species at the northern edge of their range, and northern species at the southern edge of their range, can both survive. In addition the range of habitats, which includes high fells, river banks, marshes and flushes, screes and cliffs, and soils derived from boulder clay, limestone and dolerite, is extraordinarily wide; and it leads to the development of a large number of ecological niches. Perhaps too, the remoteness of the area, in human terms, has played its part. Man has made many changes, but most of the critical habitats have survived; and, by the destruction of woodland and the introduction of grazing animals, some important habitats may well have been extended.

Terrestrial Animals

Upper Teesdale has some 1450 species of animals; the flies (*Diptera*), the characteristic group of upland and tundra regions, form the largest component (500 species). As regards rare species, there are no rare vertebrates, and estimates of rarities in other groups can only be made where they have been well studied; but it can be said that there are 22 rare species of spiders and insects, many to be found in streams or blanket bog and few on sugar-limestone.

When the fauna as a whole is analysed geographically, it is found that two distinct faunas can be distinguished, that on peat being of sub-arctic origin and that of grassland related to the general lowland fauna of the British Isles. This mixture is apparently less diverse than in the plants, though in both there are both northern and southern elements.

A characteristic and frequent insect species is the small moth, *Coleophora alticolella*, whose caterpillars feed on two rush species. The distribution of the rushes, the parasites and the predators have all been studied; and the influence upon them of temperature (associated with altitude) and of plant-feeding animals has been analysed and assessed. These environmental factors are of general importance to the Teesdale fauna and to the insects in particular. As regards distribution of food plants, the relatively small number of plant species, and the scarcity of trees, both limit the animal populations. As regards parasites, it is often found that the host species ascend higher than the parasites and are free from them at higher levels. The density of vertebrate predators is low. The climatic effect of change of altitude has wide significance, as does the effect of grazing by the larger vertebrates; but the role of invertebrates, e.g. the larvae of craneflies, on vegetation is often underestimated. These larvae consume up to twice as much vegetation as sheep.

Among birds of note are the red and black grouse, nine species of waders and four species of wagtails and pipits. Work on the meadow-pipit has shown that the breeding season is noticeably later in Upper Teesdale than in lowland areas, and that at higher altitudes the clutch size is reduced and there are fewer second clutches. Almost all the food brought to the first brood is collected from peat soils where there is a large spring emergence of insects. By the time the second brood is ready there is little available food in the moorland, and food is collected from streams and from the mineral soils.

Although some studies have been made of moorland sheep and their effects on vegetation, much work in Upper Teesdale (including Moor House) has been concentrated on the fauna of the moorland soils; and this is now better known here than anywhere else in Britain. The most abundant groups in terms of numbers are nematodes, pot-worms (*Enchytraeidae*), springtails (*Collembola*) and mites (*Acarina*) in that order, and these are about equally numerous on mineral and peat soils. But in terms of dry weight, the relative frequencies are very different, and the three most important groups are the earthworms, the pot-worms and the craneflies, in that order. The dry weight per square metre is generally higher on the mineral than on the peat soils. One of the factors contributing to the high abundance of microfauna in these moorland soils is the high rainfall, which diminishes the summer mortality found in lower, drier areas.

These faunistic differences are correlated with the nature of the soils; thus a much lower proportion of plant material is ingested by animals on the moorland soils, and thus is available for conversion to the peat. The smaller amount of soil fauna on the peaty soils is probably correlated with its much lower mineral content: experimental addition of nitrogen and phosphorus fertilizers has resulted in significant increases in the soil fauna.

Aquatic Habitats

The most extensive study of the reservoir itself has been made by Dr Crisp and his colleagues (Chapter 9), who have traced the effects of the impoundment of the reservoir upon the river below the dam and have also followed the events within the reservoir itself. The chemical and physical composition of the river below the dam, e.g., the temperature and ionic character of the water, have been significantly affected. The effects on the fauna have been an increase in the bottom-living animals, e.g. *Hydra*; the arrival of zooplankton from the reservoir in the form of water-fleas (*Daphnia*) has also contributed a significant amount of food. Within the reservoir, there have also been significant changes in the fauna, e.g. increases in animals such as *Gammarus*.

The changes in the fish population have been investigated in detail. There are three species, the trout, the bullhead and the minnow. The soil within the reservoir at the time of its filling was estimated to contain 95,000kg of earthworms and 35,000kg of cranefly larvae and these, which were able to survive the submergence for some time, provided an important item of fish food between the time at which the reservoir filled up (spring 1971) until the spring of 1973. After that time, the more normal diet of aquatic invertebrates was resumed. In this new environment, the numbers of trout in the reservoir increased five-fold between 1972 and 1975. There was also a growth in the average size of the fish and in the number of eggs laid. There is no sign yet of a levelling-off in the population. One of the results of this population-explosion is that a sport fishery has developed. The number of angler-visits per year has risen to over 1000, and the weight of the average catch to 1lb.

Some observations on the aquatic seed-plants have been made, in particular those of the Cow Green basin both before and after the construction of the reservoir and of the Tees between Cauldron Snout and Middleton. There have also been studies of the algal flora of the small calcareous streams or 'sikes' by Dr Whitton and his colleagues which have shown a striking abundance of blue-green algae presumed to be nitrogen-fixing.

Conservation, Present and Future

Much of the work which is described in this book is of a basic kind. All is eventually relevant to conservation, but some of it more directly so. Thus detailed mapping and detailed vegetation survey indicate the extent of the rare species and the area of the rare communities. Analysis of plant populations reveals those which are peculiar to the area and those which are widely distributed, and so can guide conservation measures. Studies of the soil in relation to plant growth show why some of the rare species are able to survive and compete and indicate what steps to take, and what to avoid, in conserving them. For example, addition of phosphate to certain soils may encourage common grasses at the expense of rare sedges, and this is clearly not desirable in a Nature Reserve.

The effects of building the reservoir, and its direct effects on the rare plants and communities, have been mentioned by Dr Bradshaw. It was thought that the reservoir might also have an indirect effect through the ecological consequences of changes in the microclimate of Widdybank Fell, but no such consequences have so far been detected. An effect of wave-action (Plate II) on the south-west-facing shore of the reservoir was foreseen but it has proved more serious than expected. When the water level is high and a gale is blowing, 3ft high waves beat on the shore, removing large amounts of turf and undercutting the bank. Turf has recently been removed in this way along 6m of the shore round Slapestone Sike, an area of sugar-limestone with a particularly important flora. A remedy for this most undesirable state of affairs has yet to be found.

As regards activities on the reservoir, there has been a rapid build-up of the trout population, and many of the visitors to the area are now anglers. The bird population has also increased, another welcome feature.

The fells themselves are at present managed partly for sheep grazing and partly for shooting, and conservation measures are agreed in consultation with the owners and their tenants, a procedure that has usually proved successful. One of the most difficult areas is the summit of Cronkley Fell, where there is a rich and important area of limestone pasture. Exclosures have been constructed here to keep out grazing animals or to allow grazing to be controlled; and under these conditions many of the rarer species can flourish, set seed and extend their area. But outside the exclosures there is a large population of rabbits, its size probably increasing as a result of a series of mild winters. The rabbits graze and burrow into the existing turf and are causing most serious erosion and loss of vegetation. Some control measures have been and will continue to be applied, but the problem cannot be solved without large expenditure of money and resources.

Another important part of the vegetation, in which an ecological study is currently in progress, is the meadowland in the lower part of the dale. The meadows are famous for their hay, which is rich in a variety of interesting local species, often northern in their distribution. They have flourished for many years, but are vulnerable to changes in agricultural treatment. Some of these, such as drainage, or cultivation and reseeding, could lead to increases in productivity but a loss of floristic richness. Clearly a compromise has to be attempted here. It is much to be desired that experiments on a few meadows could be arranged, with the consent of the farmer. These might lead to a régime which would conserve the flora without impairing utility and yield.

Comparatively little work has been done on the woodlands of the dale. There are several natural birch woods, three of which have recently been fenced by the Nature Conservancy Council, in agreement with the farmers. Conservation of these interesting woods is much to be desired. Also famous in Upper Teesdale are the woods of juniper, which cover large areas on both banks of the river near High Force. Some recent experiments by Dr O. Gilbert and others suggest that high intensity of sheep grazing is preventing regeneration, and that arrangements for producing germination sites, e.g. the use of fire, need investigation. Though the juniper woodland is on the whole in a satisfactory condition, many of the plants are 60–100 years old, and it is important now to encourage regeneration. One area has recently been fenced.

It will be clear from what has been said that much work remains to be done in Upper Teesdale. Every author in this book has a list of projects which he would like to undertake because of their scientific importance and because, in many cases, they would contribute to good management. Among such projects are studies of the effects of 'gripping' and heather burning, studies of the ecology and population dynamics of species in sensitive river-side and stream-side habitats, studies of microclimate, especially in relation to the influence of the reservoir, extension of detailed vegetation mapping to the whole of the Upper Teesdale Nature Reserve and some of the hay-meadows, and an extension of physiological and biosystematic work to the numerous rare or important species not yet investigated in this way. On the animal side, the ecology of important and species-rich invertebrate groups such as the chironomids and ichneumons needs to be studied; and work on the performance of both animal and plant species at different altitudes, which has already begun, should be extended. It is to be hoped that some of these projects will eventually be put in hand, though to find the necessary support for all of them will take some time.

In the meantime, the day-to-day work of conservation continues. Upper Teesdale is not a natural history museum, nor an outdoor laboratory, though this is what it has sometimes been called. It is, as it has long been, a living community, with its traditional activities of quarrying and farming. All the associations of plants and animals which have been described in this book have developed, during historical times, under the hand of man; and their survival in the future will continue to depend upon human activities. The Nature Reserve is held by the Nature Conservancy Council under special agreements with the land-owners and their tenants; and it is one of the tasks of the Council, through their regional officers, to combine, as far as possible, conservation with farming and sporting management, and to improve understanding of conservation among local people and visitors. There is thus a continuous process of negotiation and agreement. The situation is complicated by the increasing numbers of visitors; at High Force this is of the order of 150,000, and at Cow Green, 50,000. These visitors are attracted by the natural beauty of the dale, and increasingly by the interest of the scenery and the flora. The problem of control of visitors within the Reserve – principally by wardening – has to be faced; but the opportunity is also taken to direct them to the Nature Trail on Widdybank Fell, and to the Durham Conservation Trust's new information centre at Bow Lees.

The world does not stand still; and it is impossible to predict what future activities, industrial or otherwise, external or internal, may yet make their mark on the dale. Nevertheless, there are grounds for hoping that, with informed public interest and goodwill on all sides, the future of Upper Teesdale, in the shape in which we know it today, may be reasonably secure.

Acknowledgments

CHAPTER 1

Investigations by Dr A. Dale and Dr Gillian Fearn reported in this chapter were supported by grants from the Teesdale Trust which are gratefully acknowledged.

T. T. Elkington

CHAPTER 2

The foundation work and recording in 1968 was done by Mrs M. E. Thomas. Most of the field-work and processing of the field data was carried out by J. P. Doody (1969–1972) and R. B. Gibbons (1972–1975) under the supervision of M. E. Bradshaw, who also provided supplementary data. Financial support provided by the Teesdale Trustees (1968–1972) and the Natural Environment Research Council (1972–1975), and laboratory and garden facilities by the Department of Botany of Durham University, are all gratefully acknowledged. *M. E. Bradshaw*

CHAPTER 3

I wish to acknowledge the great value of talks I have had about the vegetation and plant communities of Upper Teesdale with Professor Donald Pigott and with Dr Margaret Bradshaw. *D. A. Ratcliffe*

CHAPTER 4

Much of the research upon which this chapter is based was funded by the Teesdale Trust and by the Natural Environment Research Council and my colleagues and I would like to express our gratitude to them. Also to the staff of the Nature Conservancy and to Mr Tom Buffey for their valuable help in the field. I would also like to thank most warmly the colleagues, students and friends who have been involved with the work for their interest and cheerful practical assistance at all stages.

J. Turner

CHAPTERS 5 & 6

I would like to thank Mr F. H. W. Green and Mr Richard Harding for making available their analysis of the meteorological records from the station on Widdybank, and Professor Gordon Manley for his critical comments on this chapter and for supplying various meteorological records. Several of the investigations reported in these two chapters were supported financially by grants from the Teesdale Trust. *C. D. Pigott*

CHAPTER 7

This account could not have been written without the assistance of two M.A. theses, one by Mrs J. Britton, *Farm, Field and Fell in Upper Teesdale, 1600–1900* (Univ. of

Durham, 1974), and the other by Mr D. A. Alexander, *Settlement, Field Systems and Landownership in Teesdale, 1600–1850* (Univ. of Durham, 1972). The first of these was undertaken with the assistance of Teesdale Trust grant, the second was privately financed. Both studies are largely concerned with the north bank or Durham lands, but Mrs Britton concentrated almost exclusively upon that portion of the dale above Middleton in the possession of the Raby estates, and Mr Alexander's study, while nominally concentrating upon Eggleston, embraces the whole of the dale, both the Durham and Yorkshire sides. Mr Dennis Coggins read and commented upon an early draft of the chapter and provided the enormous benefit of detailed, local knowledge, while many other scholars allowed me access to their researches. Any misinterpretations of their material are mine alone. Grateful thanks are due to Lord Barnard for allowing both myself and my students free access to his archive material. Without such access much of the work would have been impossible. Fig. 24 is based upon the First Edition Ordnance Survey 1:10,560 maps (1855–7, 1888–93) and information provided by Dr J. Turner and Professor A. R. Clapham. Fig. 26 is redrawn from an original consulted by kind permission of Durham County Record Office.

Grateful acknowledgment is made of the debt owed to the technical staff of both the Department of Photography of ICI and the Department of Geography of Durham University for their vital assistance with the illustrations and last, but by no means least, my thanks are due to Mrs Suzanne Eckford for doing the typing.

B. K. Roberts

CHAPTER 8

This account of the fauna of Upper Teesdale relies heavily on the analysis and synthesis of the studies at Moor House which formed part of the U.K. contribution to the International Biological Programme, and particularly on the zoological studies, the review of which was written by Dr J. B. Whittaker and myself and is to be published shortly. In addition to my indebtedness to Dr Whittaker and to the many other zoologists, too numerous to acknowledge individually here but mentioned in the IBP review, I would like to express my appreciation of the extensive taxonomic studies made by Dr J. M. Nelson and the considerable help received from Dr Jennifer Butterfield and Mr Michael Rawes, Officer-in-Charge at Moor House. Most of the zoological studies at Moor House have been financed by the Nature Conservancy, the Natural Environment Research Council and the University of Durham, but additional surveys have been made possible by several grants from the Teesdale Trust.

J. C. Coulson

CHAPTER 9

Financial support for the work at Cow Green was provided by the Teesdale Trust, the Natural Environment Research Council and the Department of the Environment (under contract DGR 480/34). The Northumbrian Water Authority, the Raby Castle Estates, the Strathmore Estates and Mr P. B. Oughtred allowed us to work on their fisheries. Dr J. P. Harding gave permission to reproduce Plate 31a, Mr A. E. Ramsbottom drew the figures for the chapter and also gave permission to reproduce Plate 31b, and Dr P. D. Armitage and Mr J. C. L. Edwards gave access to their unpublished data. The author is indebted to all these organizations and individuals and also to all the members of the F.B.A.'s Cow Green team, upon whose work this account is based.

D. T. Crisp

CHAPTER 10

A grant from the Natural Environment Research Council is gratefully acknowledged, for without this financial assistance the survey of the river could not have been made. To Dr B. A. Whitton, alongside whom I worked, I give my sincere thanks for all his guidance.   *N. T. H. Holmes*

SUMMARIZING REVIEW AND FORWARD LOOK

Dr Helga Frankland and Dr T. J. Bines, of the Nature Conservancy Council, gave valuable and much appreciated assistance during the preparation of this final chapter.   *D. H. Valentine*

The map of Upper Teesdale which forms the front end-paper was prepared for the book by Mr Robin Fenton of the Nature Conservancy Council, and the geological map of the back end-paper by Dr G. A. L. Johnson of the Department of Geology of Durham University, to both of whom the Editorial Committee wish to express their thanks.

The vertical aerial view of the Cow Green reservoir forming part of Plate 1 (facing p. 65) is a composite constructed by Meridian Airmaps Limited from photographs taken by them, and is reproduced with their permission.

We wish finally to thank Mr Brian H. Grimes, formerly on the staff of the Nature Conservancy Council, for his expert assistance in the selection of topographical photographs.

References

I. Accounts of recent research (1967–76).

1. ALEXANDER, D. A. (1972). Settlement, field systems and landownership in Teesdale between 1600 and 1850: A study in historical geography. Unpublished M. A. Thesis, University of Durham.
2. ARMITAGE, P. D. (1976). A quantitative study of the invertebrate fauna of the River Tees below Cow Green reservoir. *Freshwat. Biol.,* **6**, 229–240.
3. ARMITAGE, P. D. & CAPPER, M. H. (1976). The numbers, biomass and transport downstream of micro-crustaceans and *Hydra* from Cow Green reservoir (Upper Teesdale). *Freshwat. Biol.,* **6**, 425–432.
4. ARMITAGE, P. D., MACHALE, A. M. & CRISP, D. T. (1974). A survey of stream invertebrates in the Cow Green basin (Upper Teesdale) before inundation. *Freshwat. Biol.,* **4**, 369–398.
5. ARMITAGE, P. D., MACHALE, A. M. & CRISP, D. T. (1975). A survey of the invertebrates of four streams in the Moor House National Nature Reserve in Northern England. *Freshwat. Biol.,* **5**, 479–495.
6. ARNOLD, S. M. (1973). Interactions of light and temperature on the germination of *Plantago maritima* L. *New Phytol.,* **72**, 583–593.
7. ARNOLD, S. M. (1974). The relationship between temperature and seedling growth of two species which occur in Upper Teesdale. *New Phytol.,* **73**, 333–340.
8. ARNOLD, S. M. & MONTEITH, J. L. (1974). Plant development and mean temperature in a Teesdale habitat. *J. Ecol.,* **62**, 711–720.
9. BEADLE, H. L. (1968). Upper Teesdale lime kilns. *Durham Local History Society Bulletin,* **8**.
10. BELLAMY, D. J., BRIDGEWATER, P., MARSHALL, C. & TICKLE, W. M. (1969). Status of the Teesdale Rarities. *Nature, Lond.,* **222**, 238–243.
11. BELLAMY, D. J. (1970). The Vegetation. In *Durham County and City with Teesside* (ed. Dewdney, J. C.), Brit. Ass. Adv. Sci., 141–152.
12. BIRKS, H. J. B. (1968). The identification of *Betula nana* pollen. *New Phytol.,* **67**, 309–314.
13. BOTT, M. H. P. (1974). The geological interpretation of a gravity survey of the English Lake District and the Vale of Eden. *J. geol. Soc. Lond.,* **130**, 309–331.
14. BRADSHAW, M. E. (1970). The Teesdale Flora. In *Durham County and City with Teesside* (ed. Dewdney, J. C.), Brit. Ass. Adv. Sci., 141–152.
15. BRADSHAW, M. E. & JONES, A. V. (1976). *Phytosociology in Upper Teesdale*: Guide to the vegetation maps of Widdybank Fell. With 5 accompanying maps. The Teesdale Trust.
16. BRITTON, J. M. (1974). Farm, field and fell in Upper Teesdale, 1600–1900: A study in historical geography. Unpublished M.A. Thesis, University of Durham.

213

17. CARTER, J. R. (1972). The diatoms of Slapestone Sike, Upper Teesdale. *Vasculum,* **57**, 35–41.

18. CONOLLY, A. P. & DAHL, E. (1970). Maximum summer temperature in relation to modern and Quaternary distributions of certain arctic-montane species in the British Isles. In *Studies in the Vegetational History of the British Isles* (ed. Walker, D. & West, R. G.), Cambridge, 159–223.

19. COULSON, J. C., HOROBIN, J. C., BUTTERFIELD, J. & SMITH, G. R. J. (1976). The maintenance of annual life-cycles in two species of Tipulidae (*Diptera*); a field study relating development, temperature and altitude. *J. anim. Ecol.,* **45**, 215–233.

19a. COULSON, J. C. & WHITTAKER, J. B. (1976). The ecology of moorland animals. In *The Ecology of some British Moors and Montane Grasslands.* Berlin.

20. CRISP, D. T., MANN, R. H. K. & MCCORMACK, JEAN C. (1974). The populations of fish at Cow Green, Upper Teesdale, before impoundment. *J. appl. Ecol.,* **11**, 969–996.

21. CRISP, D. T., MANN, R. H. K. & MCCORMACK, JEAN C. (1975). The populations of fish in the River Tees system on the Moor House National Nature Reserve. *J. Fish. Biol.,* **7**, 573–593.

22. DALE, A. (1974). Biosystematics of selected species in the Teesdale flora. Unpublished Ph.D. Thesis, University of Sheffield.

23. DOODY, J. P. (1975). Studies in the population dynamics of some Teesdale plants. Unpublished Ph.D. Thesis, University of Durham.

24. EDDY, A., WELCH, D. & RAWES, M. (1969). The vegetation of the Moor House National Nature Reserve in the northern Pennines, England. *Vegetatio,* **16**, 239–284.

25. ELKINGTON, T. T. (1969). Cytotaxonomic variation in *Potentilla fruticosa* L. *New Phytol.,* **68**, 151–160.

26. ELKINGTON, T. T. (1971). Biological Flora of the British Isles: *Dryas octopetala* L. *J. Ecol.,* **59**, 887–905.

27. ELKINGTON, T. T. (1972). Variation in *Gentiana verna* L. *New Phytol.,* **71**, 1203–1211.

28. FEARN, G. M. (1971). Biosystematic studies of selected species in the Teesdale flora. Unpublished Ph.D. Thesis, University of Sheffield.

29. FEARN, G. M. (1972). The distribution of infraspecific chromosome races of *Hippocrepis comosa* L. and their phytogeographical significance. *New Phytol.,* **71**, 1221–1225.

30. FEARN, G. M. (1973). Biological Flora of the British Isles: *Hippocrepis comosa* L. *J. Ecol.,* **61**, 915–926.

31. FEARN, G. M. (1975). Variation of *Polygala amarella* Crantz in Britain. *Watsonia,* **10**, 371–383.

32. GODWIN, H. & WALTERS, S. M. (1967). The scientific importance of Upper Teesdale. *Proc. Bot. Soc. Brit. Is.,* **6**, 348–351.

33. HOLMES, N. T. H., LLOYD, E. J. H., POTTS, M. & WHITTON, B. A. (1972). Plants of the River Tyne and future water transfer scheme. *Vasculum,* **57** (3), 36–78.

34. HOLMES, N. T. H. & WHITTON, B. A. (1975a). Macrophytes of the River Tweed. *Trans. Bot. Soc. Edinb.,* **42**, 369–381.

35. HOLMES, N. T. H. & WHITTON, B. A. (1975b). Submerged bryophytes and angiosperms of the River Tweed and its tributaries. *Trans. Bot. Soc. Edinb.,* **42**, 383–395.

36. HOLMES, N. T. H. & WHITTON, B. A. (1975c). Notes on some macroscopic algae new or seldom recorded for Britain. *Vasculum*, **60** (3), 47–55.

37. HOLMES, N. T. H. (1976). The distribution and ecology of *Grimmia agassizii* (Sull. & Lesq.) Jaeg. in Teesdale. *J. Bryol.*, **9**, 275–278.

37a. HOLMES, N. T. H. (1976). The genus *Carex* from the River Tees, north-east England. *Vasculum*, **61** (3), 80–89.

37b. HOLMES, N. T. H. & WHITTON, B. A. (1977). The macrophytic vegetation of the River Tees in 1975: observed and predicted changes. *Freshwat. Biol.*, **7** (1), 43–70.

38. HORNUNG, M. (1969). Morphology, mineralogy and genesis of soils of the Moor House National Nature Reserve. Unpublished Ph.D. Thesis, University of Durham.

39. HORNUNG, M. & HATTON, A. A. (1974). Deep weathering in the Great Whin Sill, Northern England. *Proc. Yorks. Geol. Soc.*, **40**, 105–114.

40. HOUSTON, K. (1971). Carabidae (Col.) from two areas of the north Pennines. *Entom. Mon. Mag.*, **107**, 1–4.

41. HUGHES, M. K. & WHITTON, B. A. (1972). Algae of Slapestone Sike, Upper Teesdale. *Vasculum*, **57**, 35–41.

42. JEFFREY, D. W. & PIGOTT, C. D. (1973). The response of grasslands on sugar-limestone in Teesdale to applications of phosphorus and nitrogen. *J. Ecol.*, **61**, 85–92.

43. JOHNSON, G. A. L. & HICKLING, H. G. A. (1970). The Geology of Durham County. *Trans. Nat. Hist. Soc. Northumbr.*, **41**, 1–158.

44. JOHNSON, G. A. L., ROBINSON, D. & HORNUNG, M. (1971). Unique bedrock and soils associated with the Teesdale flora. *Nature, Lond.*, **232**, 453–456.

45. JONES, A. V. (1973). A phytosociological study of Widdybank Fell in Upper Teesdale. Unpublished Ph.D. Thesis, University of Durham.

46. LLOYD, N. D. H. (1974). Comparative eco-physiological studies on some species from the flora of Teesdale. Unpublished Ph.D. Thesis, University of Leeds.

47. MCCORD, N. (1971). *Durham History from the Air*. Newcastle-upon-Tyne.

48. MORRIS, R. M. & THOMAS, J. G. (1972). The seasonal pattern of dry-matter production of grasses in the north Pennines. *J. Br. Grassld. Soc.*, **27**, 163–172.

49. NELSON, J. M. (1971). The invertebrates of an area of Pennine moorland within the Moor House National Nature Reserve. *Trans. Soc. Brit. Ent.*, **19**, 173–235.

50. PETERS, J. C. (1972). The ecology of Tarn Dub. *Vasculum*, **57**, 42–50.

51. PIGOTT, C. D. (1970). The responses of plants to climate and climatic change. In *The Flora of a Changing Britain* (ed. Perring, F.), B.S.B.I. Conf. Rep. No. 11.

52. PRINCE, S. D. (1976). The effect of climate on grain development in barley at an upland site. *New Phytol.*, **76**, 377–389.

53. PROCTOR, H. G. (1971). Aquatic macrophytes in the Wheel of the Tees. *Vasculum*, **56** (3), 59–66.

54. PROCTOR, H. G. (1972). *Carex aquatilis* Wahlenb. in Upper Teesdale. *Vasculum*, **57** (3), 17–24.

55. RAWES, M. & WELCH, D. (1969). Upland productivity of vegetation and sheep at Moor House National Nature Reserve, Westmorland, England. *Oikos*, Suppl. II, 72 pp.

56. ROBINSON, D. (1971). The inhibiting effect of organic carbon on contact metamorphic recrystallization of limestones. *Contr. Mineral. & Petrol.*, **32**, 245–250.

57. SPRINGETT, J. A. (1968). A preliminary survey of the Enchytraeidae of Widdybank Fell, Upper Teesdale. Unpublished report; 12 duplicated pages.

58. SQUIRES, R. H. (1970). A contribution to the vegetational history of Upper Teesdale. Unpublished Ph.D. Thesis, University of Durham.

59. SQUIRES, R. H. (1971). Flandrian history of the Teesdale rarities. *Nature, Lond.*, **229**, 43–44.

60. THOMAS, J. G. & MORRIS, R. M. (1973). Seasonal patterns of digestible organic matter and protein production from grasses in the North Pennines. *J. Br. Grassld. Soc.*, **28**, 31–40.

61. TURNER, J. (1970). Vegetational History. In *Durham County and City with Teesside* (ed. Dewdney, J. C.), Brit. Ass. Adv. Sci., 123–133.

62. TURNER, J., HEWETSON, V. P., HIBBERT, F. A., LOWRY, K. H. & CHAMBERS C. (1973). The history of the vegetation and flora of Widdybank Fell and the Cow Green reservoir basin, Upper Teesdale. *Phil. Trans.*, **B 265**, 327–408.

63. WELCH, D. (1967). Communities containing *Juncus squarrosus* in Upper Teesdale, England. *Vegetatio,* **14**, 229–240.

64. WELCH, D. & RAWES, M. (1969). Moisture regime of soils on metamorphosed limestone in Upper Teesdale. *Trans. Nat. Hist. Soc. Northumbr.*, **17**, 57–67.

65. WHITTAKER, J. B. (1971). Population changes in *Neophilaenus lineatus* (L.) *(Homoptera: Cercopidae)* in different parts of its range. *J. anim. Ecol.*, **40**, 425–444.

66. WHITTON, B. A. & BUCKMASTER, R. C. (1970). Macrophytes of the River Wear. *Naturalist*, **914**, 97–116.

67. WOODWARD, F. I. & PIGOTT, C. D. (1976). The climatic control of the altitudinal distribution of *Sedum rosea* (L.) Scop. and *S. telephium* L. 1. Field observations. *New Phytol.*, **74**, 323–334.

68. WOODWARD, F. I. (1976). The climatic control of the altitudinal distribution of *Sedum rosea* (L.) Scop. and *S. telephium* L. 2. The analysis of plant growth in controlled environments. *New Phytol.*, **74**, 335–348.

II. Other publications to which reference is made.

Introduction

BACKHOUSE, JAMES, JR (1844). (Accounts of various botanical excursions). *The Phytologist*, **1**, *passim.*

BACKHOUSE, JAMES, JR (1884). Teesdale Botany: Historical and Personal Recollections. *The Naturalist*, 10–13.

BELL, J. (1844). New locality for *Saxifraga hirculus. The Phytologist*, **1**, 741.

BLACKBURN, K. B. (1931). The Late-Glacial and Post-Glacial periods in the north Pennines. II. Possible survivals in our flora. *Trans. North. Nat. Un.*, **1**, 30–36,

BRADSHAW, M. E. (1962). The distribution and status of five species of the *Alchemilla vulgaris* L. aggregate in Upper Teesdale. *J. Ecol.*, **50**, 681–706.

GODWIN, H. (1949). The spreading of the British flora considered in relation to conditions of the late-glacial period. *J. Ecol.*, **37**, 140–147.

KING, S. (1844). A botanical excursion in Teesdale. *The Phytologist*, **1**, 113–115.

MANLEY, G. (1952). *Climate and the British Scene.* New Naturalist Series. London.

SIMPSON, S. (1844). Botanical excursion in Teesdale. *The Phytologist*, **1**, 74–75.

WALTERS, S. M. (1949). *Alchemilla vulgaris* L. agg. in Britain. *Watsonia*, **1**, 6–18.
WILMOTT, A. J. (1930). Concerning the history of the British flora. In *Contributions à l'étude du peuplement des Iles Britanniques. Soc. de Biogéographie*, **3**, 163.
WINCH, N. J., THORNHILL, J. & WAUGH, R. (1805). *The Botanist's Guide through the Counties of Northumberland and Durham*. Newcastle-upon-Tyne.
WINCH, N. J. (1831). *Flora of Northumberland and Durham*. Newcastle.
WRIGHT, W. B. (1914). *The Quaternary Ice Age*. London.

Chapter 1

BLACKBURN, K. B. (1931). The Late-Glacial and Post-Glacial periods in the north Pennines. II. Possible survivals in our flora. *Trans. North. Nat. Un.*, **1**, 30–36.
BRADSHAW, M. E. (1963). Studies on *Alchemilla filicaulis* Bus., *sensu lato*, and *A. minima* Walters. I. Morphological variation in *A. filicaulis, sensu lato*. *Watsonia*, **5**, 304–320.
ELKINGTON, T. T. (1963). Biological Flora of the British Isles: *Gentiana verna* L. *J. Ecol.*, **51**, 755–767.
ELKINGTON, T. T. (1964). Biological Flora of the British Isles: *Myosotis alpestris* F. W. Schmidt. *J. Ecol.*, **52**, 709–722.
ELKINGTON, T. T. & WOODELL, S. R. J. (1963). Biological Flora of the British Isles: *Potentilla fruticosa* L. *J. Ecol.*, **51**, 769–781.
FEDOROV, A. (1969). *Chromosome Numbers of Flowering Plants*. Leningrad.
GODWIN, H. (1949). The spreading of the British flora considered in relation to conditions of the late-glacial period. *J. Ecol.*, **37**, 140–147.
HULTEN, E. (1950). *Atlas of the Distribution of Vascular Plants in N. W. Europe*. Stockholm.
IVIMEY-COOK, R. B. & PROCTOR, M. C. F. (1966). The plant communities of the Burren, Co. Clare. *Proc. Ir. Acad.*, **B 64**, 211–302.
MEUSEL, H. M., JAGER, E. & WEINERT, E. (1965). *Vergleichende Chorologie der zentraleuropäischen Flora*. Jena.
PERRING, F. H. & WALTERS, S. M. (Eds.) (1962). *Atlas of the British Flora*. London.
PIGOTT, C. D. (1956). The vegetation of Upper Teesdale in the North Pennines. *J. Ecol.*, **44**, 545–586.
PIGOTT, C. D. (1958). Biological Flora of the British Isles: *Polemonium caeruleum* L. *J. Ecol.*, **46**, 507–525.
PIGOTT, C. D. & WALTERS, S. M. (1954). On the interpretation of the discontinuous distributions shown by certain British species of open habitats. *J. Ecol.*, **42**, 95–116.
PROCTOR, M. C. F. (1957). Variation in *Helianthemum canum* Baumg. in Britain. *Watsonia*, **4**, 28–40.
RAVEN, J. & WALTERS, S. M. (1956). *Mountain Flowers*. New Naturalist Series. London.
RILEY, R. (1955). Genecological studies in *Thlaspi alpestre* L. Unpublished Ph.D. Thesis, University of Sheffield.
VALENTINE, D. H. & HARVEY, M. J. (1961). *Viola rupestris* Schmidt in Britain. *Proc. bot. Soc. Br. Isl.*, **4**, 129–135.
WILMOTT, A. J. (1930). Concerning the history of the British flora. In *Contributions à l'étude du peuplement des Iles Britanniques. Soc. de Biogéographie*, **3**, 163.

Reference is also made to the publications numbered 10, 14, 18, 22, 25, 26, 27, 28, 29, 30, 31, 42, 51 & 62 in the list on pp. 213–16.

Chapter 2

HARPER, J. L. (1967). A Darwinian approach to plant ecology. *J. Ecol.*, **55**, 247–270.

HARPER, J. L. & WHITE, J. (1974). The demography of plants. *Ann. Rev. Ecol. Syst.*, **5**, 419–463.

SHIMWELL, D. W. (1971). *Description and Classification of Vegetation*. London.

TANSLEY, A. G. (1946). *Introduction to Plant Ecology*. London.

Reference is also made to the publications numbered 23, 45 & 46 in the list on pp. 213–16.

Chapter 3

BAKER, J. G. (1863). *North Yorkshire: a study of its botany, geology and physical geography*. London.

BRADSHAW, M. E. & CLARK, W. A. (1965). Flora and Vegetation. Chapter 3 in *The Natural History of Upper Teesdale* (ed. Valentine, D. H.). Northumberland & Durham Naturalists' Trust.

PIGOTT, C. D. (1956). The vegetation of Upper Teesdale in the northern Pennines. *J. Ecol.*, **44**, 545–586.

RATCLIFFE, D. A. (1966). A botanical survey of the proposed Cow Green Reservoir site in Upper Teesdale. Unpublished report to the Nature Conservancy.

SHIMWELL, DAVID W. (1971). *Description & Classification of Vegetation*. London.

Reference is also made to the publications numbered 10, 11, 14 & 15 in the list on pp. 213–16.

Chapter 4

BAKER, J. G. (1863). *North Yorkshire: a study of its botany, geology and physical geography*. London.

GIBSON, E. (1722). Revision of Camden's *Britannia* (1586).

GODWIN, H. (1949). The spreading of the British flora considered in relation to conditions of the late-glacial period. *J. Ecol.*, **37**, 140–147.

HUTCHINSON, T. C. (1966). The occurrence of living and sub-fossil remains of *Betula nana* L. in Upper Teesdale. *New Phytol.*, **65**, 351-357.

JOHNSON, G. A. L. & DUNHAM, K. C. (1963). *The Geology of Moor House*. Nature Conservancy Monograph no. 2, H.M.S.O., London.

PIGOTT, C. D. (1956). The vegetation of Upper Teesdale in the north Pennines. *J. Ecol.*, **44**, 545–586.

RAISTRICK, A. & BLACKBURN, K. B. (1932). The Late-Glacial and Post-Glacial periods in the North Pennines. III. The Post-Glacial peats. *Trans. North. Nat. Un.*, **1**, 79–103.

Reference is also made to the publications numbered 12, 58, 59, 61 & 62 in the list on pp. 213–16.

Chapter 5

ALLEN, S. E. (1965). Chemical aspects of heather burning. *J. appl. Ecol.*, **1**, 347–367.

BELLAMY, D. J. & HOLLAND, P. J. (1966). Determination of net annual aerial production of *Calluna vulgaris* (L.) Hull in northern England. *Oikos*, **17**, 272–275.

BLACKMAN, G. E. (1936). The influence of temperature and available nitrogen supply on the growth of pasture in the spring. *J. agric. Sci.*, **26**, 620–647.

COOPER, J. P. (1964). Climatic variation in forage grasses. 1. Leaf development in climatic races of *Lolium* and *Dactylis*. *J. appl. Ecol.*, **1**, 45–61.

DAHL, E. (1951). On the relation between summer temperature and the distribution of alpine vascular plants in the lowlands of Fennoscandia. *Oikos*, **3**, 22–52.

GLASSPOOLE, J. (1932). The rainfall of the Tees valley. *Brit. Rainfall*, 289–291.

HOLLINGWORTH, S. E. (1934). Some solifluction phenomena in the northern Lake District. *Proc. Geol. Ass.*, **45**, 167–188.

JOHNSON, G. A. L. & DUNHAM, K. C. (1963). *The Geology of Moor House*. Nature Conservancy Monograph No. 2, H.M.S.O., London.

LEWIS, F. J. (1904). Geographical distribution of the vegetation of the basins of the rivers Eden, Tees, Wear and Tyne. *Geogrl. J.*, **23**, 313.

MANLEY, G. (1936). The climate of the northern Pennines. *Q. Jl. R. met. Soc.*, **62**, 103–113.

MANLEY, G. (1942). Meteorological observations on Dun Fell, a mountain station in northern England. *Q. Jl. R. met. Soc.*, **68**, 151–162.

MANLEY, G. (1943). Further meteorological averages for the northern Pennines, with a note on topographical effects. *Q. Jl. R. met. Soc.*, **69**, 251–261.

MANLEY, G. (1952). *Climate and the British Scene*. New Naturalist Series. London.

MILLAR, A. (1964). Notes on the climate near the upper forest limit in the northern Pennines. *Q. Jl. For.*, **58**, 239–246.

PENMAN, H. L. (1956). Estimating evaporation. *Trans. Amer. Geoph. U.*, **37**, 43–50.

Reference is also made to the publications numbered 8, 18, 48, 52, 67 & 68 in the list on pp. 213–16.

Chapter 6

BOTT, M. H. P. & MASSON-SMITH, D. (1953). Gravity measurements over the Northern Pennines. *Geol. Mag.*, **90**, 127–130.

CLYMO, R. S. (1962). An experimental approach to part of the calcicole problem. *J. Ecol.*, **50**, 701–731.

DUNHAM, K. C. (1948). Geology of the northern Pennines orefield. Vol. I. Tyne to Stainmore. *Mem. geol. Surv. U.K.*

DUNHAM, K. C., DUNHAM, A. C., HODGE, B. L. & JOHNSON, G. A. L. (1965). Granite beneath Visean sediments with mineralization at Rookhope, northern Pennines. *Q. Jl. geol. Soc. Lond.*, **121**, 383–417.

FORSTER, W. (1809, 1821). *A treatise on a section of strata from Newcastle-on-Tyne to the mountain of Cross Fell in Cumberland, with remarks on mineral veins in general*. First and second editions, Alston.

FORSTER, W. (1883). *A treatise on a section of strata from Newcastle-on-Tyne to the mountain of Cross Fell in Cumberland, with remarks on mineral veins in general*. Third edition, revised by Rev. W. Nall, Newcastle.

JOHNSON, G. A. L. & DUNHAM, K. C. (1963). *The Geology of Moor House*. Nature Conservancy Monograph no. 2. H.M.S.O., London.

PEARSALL, W. H. (1941). The 'mosses' of the Stainmore district. *J. Ecol.*, **29**, 161–175.

PHILLIPPS, J. (1836). *Illustrations of the Geology of Yorkshire.* Pt. II. *The Mountain Limestone District.* London.

PIGOTT, C. D. (1956). The vegetation of upper Teesdale in the north Pennines. *J. Ecol.*, **44**, 545–586.

WALLACE, W. (1861). *The laws which regulate the deposition of lead ore in veins; illustrated by an examination of the geological structure of the mining districts of Alston Moor.* London.

Reference is also made to the publications numbered 13, 43, 44 & 56 in the list on pp. 213–16.

Chapter 7

BAILEY, J. (1810). *General View of the Agriculture of the County of Durham.* London.

BARROW, G. W. (1973). *The Kingdom of the Scots.* London.

BRADSHAW, M. E. (1962). The distribution and status of five species of the *Alchemilla vulgaris* L. aggregate in Upper Teesdale. *J. Ecol.*, **50**, 681–706.

CHAPMAN, V. (19—). The Aukside Estate of Anthony Todd, Freeholder of Middleton-in-Teesdale. *Trans. Architect. & Archaeol. Soc. Durham & Northumberland*, **3**, 75–86.

DEWDNEY, J. (ed.) (1970). *Durham County and City with Teesside.* Brit. Ass. Adv. Sci., Durham.

DUNHAM, K. C. (1949). Geology of the Northern Pennine Orefield. *Mem. geol. Surv. U.K.* London.

EKWALL, E. (1960). *The Concise Oxford Dictionary of English Place-Names.* 4th edition. Oxford.

FRERE, S. (1967). *Britannia: A History of Roman Britain.* London.

HILDYARD, E. J. W. (1949–55). *The Archaeology of Weardale:* 3rd-5th Summary of Research 1947–52. Pickering (privately published).

JONES, G. R. J. (1971). The multiple estate as a model framework for tracing early stages in the evolution of settlement. In *L'Habitat et les Paysages Ruraux d'Europe*, ed. F. Dussart. Liège.

RAISTRICK, A. (1938). *Two Centuries of Industrial Welfare: The London (Quaker) Lead Company, 1692–1905.* London.

RAISTRICK, A. & JENNINGS, B. (1965). *A History of Lead Mining in the Pennines.* London.

SMAILES, A. (1960). *North England.* London & Edinburgh.

Reference is also to the publications numbered 1, 9, 47, 58 & 62 in the list on pp. 213–16.

Chapter 8

BANAGE, W. B. (1962). Some nematodes from the Moor House National Nature Reserve, Westmorland. *Nematologica*, **7**, 32–36.

BLOCK, W. C. (1965). Distribution of soil mites (Acarina) on the Moor House National Nature Reserve, Westmorland, with notes on their numerical abundance. *Pedobiologia*, **5**, 244–251.

CHERRETT, J. M. (1963). Notes on the seasonal occurrence of some Linyphidae (Araneida) on the Moor House National Nature Reserve, Westmorland, with some new county records. *Ent. Mon. Mag.,* **99**, 152–156.

COULSON, J. C. (1963). Mortality and egg production of the Meadow Pipit with special reference to altitude. *Bird Study,* **3**, 119–132.

CRAGG, J. B. (1958). The future of British uplands. In *The Biological Productivity of Britain.* Inst. Biol., 1–13.

CRAGG, J. B. (1961). Some aspects of the ecology of moorland animals. *J. anim. Ecol.,* **30**, 205–223.

CRISP, D. T. (1966). Input and output of minerals for an area of Pennine moorland; the importance of precipitation, drainage, erosion and animals. *J. appl. Ecol.,* **3**, 327–348.

HALE, W. G. (1966). A population study of moorland Collembola. *Pedobiologia,* **6**, 65–99.

HALE, W. G. (1966). The Collembola of the Moor House National Nature Reserve, Westmorland: a moorland habitat. *Rev. Ecol. Biol. Soc.,* **3**, 97–122.

JORDAN, A. M. (1962). *Coleophora alticolella* Zell. (Lepidoptera) and its food plant *Juncus squarrosus* L. in the northern Pennines *J. anim. Ecol.,* **31**, 293–304.

RAWES, M. & WELCH, D. (1964). Studies on sheep grazing in the northern Pennines. *J. Br. Grassld. Soc.,* **19**, 403–411.

REAY, R. C. (1964). The number of eggs and larvae of *Coleophora alticolella* Zell. (Lep.). *J. anim. Ecol.,* **33**, 117–127.

WELCH, D. (1965). A change in the upper altitudinal limit of *Coleophora alticolella* Zell. (Lep.). *J. anim. Ecol.,* **34**, 243–250.

WHITTAKER, J. B. (1964). Auchenorrhyncha (Homoptera) of the Moor House Nature Reserve, Westmorland, with notes on *Macrosteles alpinus* (Zett.), a species new to Britain. *Ent. Mon. Mag.,* **100**, 168–171.

Reference is also made to the publications numbered 19, 19a, 40, 49, 55 & 65 in the list on pp. 213–16.

Chapter 9

BUTCHER, R. W., LONGWELL, J. & PENTELOW, F. T. K. (1937). Survey of the River Tees. III. The non-tidal reaches – chemical and biological. *Tech. Pap. Wat. Pollut. Res. DSIR,* **6**, 1–189.

CAMPBELL, R. N. (1957). The effect of flooding on the growth rate of brown trout in Loch Tummel. *Sci. Invest. Freshwat. Fish. Scot.,* **14**, 1–7.

CAMPBELL, R. N. (1963). Some effects of impoundment on the environment and growth of brown trout (*Salmo trutta* L.) in Loch Garry (Inverness-shire). *Sci. Invest. Freshwat. Fish. Scot.,* **30**, 327–328.

CRISP, D. T. (1966). Input and output of minerals for an area of Pennine moorland: the importance of precipitation, drainage, peat erosion and animals. *J. appl. Ecol.,* **3**, 327–348.

ROOTS, B. I. (1956). The water relations of earthworms. II. Resistance to desiccation and immersion, and behaviour when submerged and when allowed a choice of environment. *J. exp. Biol.,* **33**, 29–44.

Reference is also made to the publications numbered 2, 3, 4, 5, 20 & 21 in the list on pp. 213–16.

Chapter 10

BIRKS, HILARY H. & BIRKS, H. J. B. (1966). *Grimmia agassizii* (Sull. & Lesq.) Jaeg. in Britain. *J. Bryol.,* **5**, 215–217.

BUTCHER, R. W. (1933). Studies on the ecology of rivers. I. On the distribution of macrophytic vegetation in the rivers of Britain. *J. Ecol.,* **21**, 58–91.

BUTCHER, R. W., LONGWELL, J. & PENTELOW, F. T. K. (1937). Survey of the River Tees. III. The non-tidal reaches – chemical and biological. *Tech. Pap. Wat. Pollut. Res. DSIR,* **6**, 1–189.

FRITSCH, F. E. (1929). The encrusting algal communities of certain fast-flowing streams. *New Phytol.,* **28**, 165–196.

MÅRTENSSON, O. (1956). Bryophytes of the Torneträsk Area, Northern Swedish Lappland. II. *Musci. K. Vetensk. Akad.,* Avh. no. 14.

NYHOLM, E. (1956). *Illustrated Moss Flora of Scandinavia.* II. *Musci.* Fasc. 2. Lund.

PEKKARI, S. (1965). Notes on aquatic vegetation. In *The Plant Cover of Sweden. Acta Phytogeogr. suec.,* **50**, 209–218.

TANSLEY, A. G. & CHIPP, T. F. (1826). *Aims and Methods in the Study of Vegetation.* Emp. Veg. Comm. London.

Reference is also made to the publications numbered 4, 33, 34, 35, 36, 53, 54 & 66 in the list on pp. 213–16.

Index

Index

Galium boreale 34, 36, 38, 75, 81, 83, 100; *cruciata* 81; *saxatile* 69; *sterneri* 73, 82; *verum* 81
galloways 157
Gammarus pulex 182, 206
garlic, wild, see *Allium ursinum*
Gaunless 156
geese in Upper Teesdale 149, 173, 193
gentian, field, see *Gentianella campestris*; spring, see *Gentiana verna*
Gentiana verna 17–18, 23, 27, 32, 34, 35, 36, 40–1, 47–52, 63, 74–6, 78, 81, 88, 99, 115, 137, 174, 197, 200, 202–3, Plate VI (p. 113)
Gentianella amarella 73, 84; *campestris* 81
geographic isolation, genetic effects of 35–9, 200–1
Geranium lucidum 67, 82; *robertianum* 67, 83; *sylvaticum* 67, 78, 80–1, 83, 138, 199, Plate VII (p. 128)
Geum rivale 67, 80, 83; *urbanum* 67
gill 147, 173
Gill Town 152, Plate 19 (p. 172)
Gilling 146, 148
glacial drift 125, 129, 130, 138
glacial plucking 128–9
glaciation of Upper Teesdale 22, 32, 128–9
gley, gleying 131–2, 135, 138
globe-flower, see *Trollius europaeus*
Glossiphonia complanata 182
Glyceria fluitans 193
Godwin, Sir Harry, 22, 24, 32–3, 89, 197
golden-rod, see *Solidago virgaurea*
graphite 157
graptolites 124
grass of Parnassus, see *Parnassia palustris*
grasses, growth of 108–110, 113–4; leaf-elongation 114
grasshoppers 161
grazing 33, 37, 39, 67, 76, 149, 159; by cattle 79, 95, 140, 173; by sheep 39, 40, 50, 82–3, 95, 113, 136, 171, 173–174; by rabbits 50, 173, 208; restrictions on 159
Great Whin Sill 16–17, 34, 72, 73, 122–3, 127–8, 133–4, 201

Grimmia agassizii 20, 195; *apocarpa* 82; *funalis* 83; *pulvinata* 82; *torquata* 83
gripping 208
grouse 159, 175–7; black 169–70; red 164, 169–71, 173
growing season, length of 106–111; onset of 108–110; and tree-growth 110–112
Gymnadenia conopsea 80
Gymnocarpium dryopteris 66; *robertianum* 82
Gymnostomum recurvirostrum 77, 139, Plate 16 (p. 161)

Hadrian's Wall 145
haggs 71, 91
hair-grass, crested, see *Koeleria cristata*; tufted, see *Deschampsia caespitosa*; wavy, see *D. flexuosa*
'half-life' of plants 49–50, 54–5, 58–9
Hammarbya paludosa 17–18
Haplodon wormskjöldii 132
harebell, see *Campanula rotundifolia*
hare's-tail, see *Eriophorum vaginatum*
Harriman, Rev. J. 17–19
hart's-tongue, see *Phyllitis scolopendrium*
harvest-spiders 161
Harwood, Harwood Valley 147, 152–3, 159, Plate 5 (p. 84)
hawkbit, autumnal, see *Leontodon autumnalis*; rough, see *L. hispidus*
hawk's-beard, marsh, see *Crepis paludosa*; soft, see *C. mollis*
hawkweed, see *Hieracium*; mouse-ear, see *H. pilosella*
hay, production of 79–80, 148, 152, 159
hay-meadows in Upper Teesdale 79–81, 138, 158–9, 171, 199, 208, Plates III (p. 48) and 4 (p. 81)
hazel, see *Corylus avellana*
head-dyke 142, 154, 156
heaf 174
heath, cross-leaved, see *Erica tetralix*
heath-grass, see *Sieglingia decumbens*
heather, see *Calluna vulgaris*
heather, bell, see *Erica cinerea*
heather-beetle, see *Lochmaea suturalis*
hedge-parsley, see *Anthriscus sylvestris*
heeler 157

Lemanea fluviatilis 194
Leontodon autumnalis 77, 79; hispidus
  80
Lepidoptera 161, 175–6
lettuce, wall, see Mycelis muralis
Leuctra inermis 182; moselyi 182
lily-of-the-valley, see Convallaria
  majalis
lime, for white-washing houses in Upper
  Teesdale 154
lime-kilns 158
Limestone, Great 126–7; Jew 126–7;
  Melmerby Scar 125–8; Peghorn 125–
  6; Robinson 125–6; Single Post
  126–7; Tyne Bottom 126–7
limestone heath 76
ling, see Calluna vulgaris
Linum catharticum 49, 73, 77, 82, 84, 137
Listera cordata 68; ovata 80
Little Fell 75, 82
livelong, see Sedum telephium
living museums 197
Lochmaea suturalis 164
Lolium perenne 80, 113, 119
London Lead Company 155–7
Longovicium 145
Lotus corniculatus 23, 81, 84
lousewort, marsh, see Pedicularis
  palustris
Luzula sylvatica 72
Lychnis flos-cuculi 81
Lycopodium alpinum 69; clavatum 69;
  selago 69
lynchets 150

Maglona 145
maidenhair fern, see Adiantum capillus-
  veneris
Malcolm, King 147
mammals in Upper Teesdale 161, 173–6
marble 125, 128, 134
marigold, marsh, see Caltha palustris
marjoram, see Origanum vulgare
Marsh Gill 152
marshes, 77–9, 202
mat-grass, see Nardus stricta
matric potential 136
mayflies 161, 171, 172, 179, 182
meadow-grass, alpine, see Poa alpina;
  Balfour's, see P. balfourii; rough-
  stalked, see P. trivialis

meadow-rue, alpine see Thalictrum
  alpinum
meadow-sweet, see Filipendula ulmaria
Meesia uliginosa 32, 77
Meldon Hill 93, 112
Melica nutans 67, 83
melick (grass), mountain (or wood), see
  Melica nutans
Menyanthes trifoliata 193
Mercurialis perennis 67, 82
mercury, dog's, see Mercurialis perennis
merlin 165
Mesolithic flints 142–3, 146; man 94–5,
  142–3, 146
metamorphic minerals 128
metamorphosed limestone in Upper
  Teesdale 17, 127–8, 203; sandstone
  128; shale 128
meteorological data from Widdybank
  Fell 107
Mickle Fell 15–16, 20, 34, 69, 70, 75, 91,
  93, 99
Mickleton 147, 150
Middleton-in-Teesdale 15, 18–19, 146,
  150, 156–7, 193, 199
migrating birds in Upper Teesdale 171
milfoil, water, see Myriophyllum
milkwort, bitter, see Polygala amara
mineral deficiencies in Upper Teesdale
  soils 35, 115, 136–7, 140, 205
mineral soils, fauna of 166–8, 175–6,
  206
mineral veins 123–4, 155–6
mining in Upper Teesdale 18, 141–2,
  152–3, 154–7, 193, 199
minnow 179, 185–6
Minuartia stricta 20, 22, 28–9, 34, 36,
  48, 77, 120, 139, Plate VI (p. 113);
  verna 34, 74–5, 77, 84, 137
mites 161, 175, 176, 206
Mnium marginatum 82;
  orthorrhynchum 83; pseudopunctatum 79; punctatum 79; seligeri
  79
Molinia caerulea 69, 78, 202
Molophilus ater 165
Montia fontana 72, 193
moonwort, see Botrychium lunaria
moor-grass, purple, see Molinia caerulea
Moor House National Reserve 15, 91,
  143, 179, 202, 204

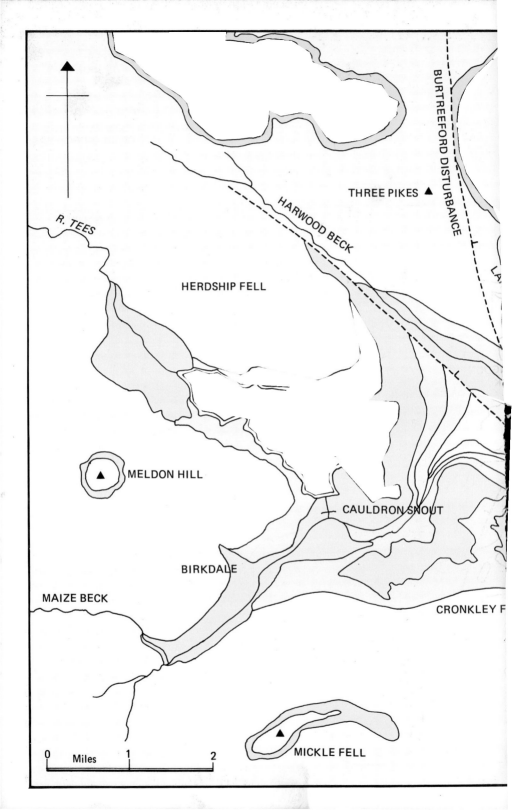